FUNDAMENTAL MATHEMATICS

for the

Social and Management Sciences

LLOYD S. EMERSON
Western New England College

LAURENCE R. PAQUETTE
Western New England College

FUNDAMENTAL MATHEMATICS
for the
Social and Management Sciences

Allyn and Bacon, Inc.
Boston • London • Sydney

Library of Congress Cataloging in Publication Data

Emerson, Lloyd S
   Fundamental mathematics for the social and management sciences.

   Edition for 1971 published under title: Linear algebra, calculus, and probability: fundamental mathematics for the social and management sciences.
   Includes bibliographical references.
   1. Algebras, Linear.   2. Calculus.   3. Probabilities.
I. Paquette, Laurence R., joint author.
II. Title.
QA184.E45   1975   510   74-16163
      ISBN: 0-205-04499-9
Second printing . . . August, 1975

To our wives,
    ELSIE AND BARBARA
And to our children,
    DOUGLAS, EDMOND, AND JONATHAN

Contents

Contents

Preface

Fundamental Mathematics for the Social and Management Sciences is an introductory text in mathematics for students of the social and management sciences. The selected topics from the broad field of mathematics are relevant to students in other fields as well. The aim of this text is to provide a good mathematical foundation as well as interesting examples of practical applications.

This book includes a systematic and logical presentation of topics from linear algebra, calculus, and probability. It is ideal for those schools that include a one-year mathematics course in their business administration curriculum.

Chapter 1 is introductory in nature, beginning with a brief reference to the real number system. The concepts of break-even analysis and fitting linear equations to data are presented. Topics selected from the field of linear algebra are covered in Chaps. 2, 3, and 4. Chapter 5, which treats linear programming, is designed to provide an application of the material covered in the three previous chapters. In addition to exponents and logarithms, some of the more important nonlinear functions are treated in Chap. 6. The concepts of a sequence and geometric progressions are applied to compound interest, present value, and annuities in Chap. 7.

Chapters 8, 9, 10, and 11 contain topics from the field of calculus dealing with the elementary functions in a single variable studied earlier in the text. The concepts selected from the field of probability are in Chaps. 12 and 13.

To the reader who is familiar with *Linear Algebra, Calculus, and Probability: Fundamental Mathematics for the Social and Man-*

agement Sciences, we would like to mention the following additions:

A chapter on the mathematics of finance (Chap. 7)
Many additional applied problems
A section on fitting straight lines to data (regression)
A section on input-output analysis
A section on probability as applied to decision making (expected value)
Computational problems based on formulas from statistics
Additional drill problems dealing with basic algebra throughout the text

The authors would like to thank the reviewers of the second edition: Professor Orlan Ohlausen of Mountain View College, Professor James E. Schaedel of Western Illinois University, Professor Kenneth L. Hankerson of the University of North Dakota, and Professor Robert L. Johnson of the University of Northern Colorado. We also wish to thank Professor Paul Banks of Boston College and Professor Alex Whitmore of McGill University for reviewing the first edition.

Finally, we wish to thank the many students and professors who used the first edition of this text for their valuable feedback, especially those at Western New England College. Special recognition is also in order for Barbara E. Paquette, who did most of the typing for the second edition.

Springfield, Massachusetts

L. S. Emerson
L. R. Paquette

ONE

Elementary algebra and break-even analysis

This chapter begins with a review of some of the concepts of elementary algebra, such as real numbers, functions, and systems of linear equations. An applied topic called break-even analysis is introduced. Break-even analysis is a technique for finding an operating point where cost equals revenue by solving linear systems. The problem of fitting a linear equation (a model) to raw data in the form of a scatter diagram is also discussed. Finally, the introduction of linear inequalities paves the way for the study of linear programming.

1-1 THE REAL NUMBER SYSTEM

In order to begin our discussion of the real number system, we must begin with a brief discussion of the notions of a *set* and *membership in a set*. The idea of a set is very important in mathematics. Other words that are synonymous with the word set are "collection" and "aggregate." The following are three examples of sets.

$$\{2, 4, 6, 8\}$$
$$\{1, 3, 5, 7, 9\}$$
$$\{a, b, c, \ldots, x, y, z\}$$

1

Braces, {. . .}, are used as the standard notation to indicate the members of a set; and the three dots, or ellipsis, indicate that some of the intermediate elements are not written.

The examples above can be described as follows: (1) the set of all even numbers between 1 and 9; (2) the set of all odd numbers between 0 and 10; and (3) the letters of the alphabet.

The particular objects that make up a set are said to be *members of the set, elements of the set,* or *in the set.* The number 4 is a member of the set in the first example, the number 5 is an element of the set in the second example, and k is in the set in the last example.

There are two ways of defining a particular set. One way is to make a list of all the elements (if possible) that belong to the set. The other method consists of specifying the distinctive property that is shared by each of the members in the set.

The notion of a set is not new and it is basic in our study of mathematics. As children we begin our study of mathematics by learning to count. The numbers $1, 2, 3, 4, \ldots$ used for counting are called the *natural numbers.* When these numbers are noted as $\{1, 2, 3, \ldots\}$, they constitute the set of natural numbers. The operations of addition and multiplication involve the assignment of a unique natural number to each pair of natural numbers. For example, the natural number 5 is assigned to the pair $(2, 3)$ under the operation of addition, i.e., $2 + 3 = 5$. In the case of multiplication, the natural number 6 is assigned to the pair $(2, 3)$. The fact that both the sum and the product of any pair of natural numbers are again natural numbers is expressed mathematically by the statement that the set of natural numbers is *closed* under addition and multiplication. The fact that the same numbers 5 and 6 are assigned to the pair $(3, 2)$ as to the pair $(2, 3)$ under addition and multiplication, respectively, is familiar to the reader. Therefore, for every pair of natural numbers a and b, $a + b = b + a$ and $ab = ba$. This is expressed mathematically by the statement that the familiar operations of addition and multiplication of natural numbers satisfy the *commutative law.*

As we progress in our mathematical training, we learn to work with negative numbers. The set of numbers $\{\ldots, -3, -2, -1, 0, 1, 2, 3, \ldots\}$ is called the set of all *integers.* It is always possible to subtract one integer from another and obtain an integer for the answer. Hence, the set of integers is closed under the operation of subtraction. However, division is not always possible in the integers. For example, 4 divided by 2 gives the integer 2, but 2 divided by 4 is not an integer. The more inclusive set of numbers consisting of the set of all possible ratios of integers provides a mathematical system in which division except by zero is always possible. These numbers are called *rational numbers.*

The numbers discussed so far can be represented geometrically as points on a line, as indicated in Fig. 1-1. Every rational number has a corresponding point on the line. It is natural to ask the following question: Does every point on the line correspond to some rational number? The answer to this question is "no." The point A in Fig. 1-1

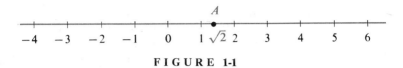

F I G U R E 1-1

is an example of such a point. It can be shown that $\sqrt{2}$ is not a rational number, i.e., it cannot be expressed as the ratio of two integers. We see then that the set of rational numbers has certain gaps. A still more inclusive set of numbers that does not have any such gaps is called the set of *real numbers*. In the set of real numbers, square roots of all non-negative numbers exist and every point on the line in Fig. 1-1 corresponds to some real number. Any real number that is not rational is called an *irrational number*.

A complete description of the real number system is well beyond the scope of this text.

The following eight properties provide a partial description of the real number system. Many of the familiar rules of elementary algebra can be derived from these eight properties, or axioms. The axioms are illustrated with examples, but no attempt is made to include proofs of the rules of algebra derived from these axioms. We have included this list of axioms to provide a basis for comparison of the algebra of square matrices with the algebra of real numbers. Matrices are taken up in Chap. 2.

A longer and very readable discussion of numbers and variables can be found in Chap. 1 of R. G. D. Allen. (See references at the end of this chapter.)

A-1   Every pair of real numbers a and b has a unique sum $a + b$ and a unique product ab which are real numbers.   *Law of Closure*

A-2 $a + b = b + a$, $ab = ba$ for all real numbers a and b.   *Commutative laws*

A-3 $a + (b + c) = (a + b) + c$, $a(bc) = (ab)c$ for all real numbers a, b, and c.   *Associative laws*

A-4 $a(b + c) = ab + ac$ for all real numbers a, b, and c.   *Distributive law*

A-5   There exists a unique real number 0, called the *additive identity* with the property that $a + 0 = 0 + a = a$ for every real number a. The additive identity is called zero.   *Additive identity*

3

A-6   For every real number a there exists a unique real number $-a$, called the *additive inverse* of a, with the property that $a + (-a) = 0$.   *Additive inverse*

A-7   There exists a unique real number 1, called the *multiplicative identity*, with the property that $a \cdot 1 = 1 \cdot a = a$ for every real number a. The multiplicative identity is called one.   *Multiplicative identity*

A-8   For every nonzero real number a there exists a unique real number a^{-1}, called the *multiplicative inverse* of a, with the property that $a^{-1}a = aa^{-1} = 1$.   *Multiplicative inverse*

The following examples illustrate some of the content of axioms A-1 through A-8.

Example 1. | Use the distributive law to rewrite $2x + 2y$.

Solution: This is a simple example of factoring. Therefore, by A-4,

$$2x + 2y = 2(x + y)$$

Example 2. | Verify the associative law for the numerical example

$$2 + (3 + 7) = (2 + 3) + 7$$

Solution:

$$2 + (3 + 7) = 2 + 10 \qquad (2 + 3) + 7 = 5 + 7$$
$$= 12 \qquad\qquad\qquad = 12$$

Example 3. | Find the multiplicative inverse of 3.

Solution: Recall that $3 \cdot \frac{1}{3} = 1$. Therefore, by A-8.
$3^{-1} = \frac{1}{3}$

Example 4. | Show that $(a + b)^2 = a^2 + 2ab + b^2$.

Solution: $(a + b)^2 = (a + b)(a + b)$.
Let $c = a + b$. Then

$$
\begin{aligned}
(a + b)(a + b) &= c(a + b) \\
&= ca + cb & \text{A-4} \\
&= ac + bc & \text{A-2} \\
&= a(a + b) + b(a + b) \\
&= a^2 + ab + ba + b^2 & \text{A-4} \\
&= a^2 + ab + ab + b^2 & \text{A-2} \\
&= a^2 + ab(1 + 1) + b^2 & \text{A-4} \\
&= a^2 + ab(2) + b^2 \\
&= a^2 + 2ab + b^2 & \text{A-2}
\end{aligned}
$$

The familiar operations of subtraction and division are defined as follows: $a - b = a + (-b)$, where $-b$ is the additive inverse of b; $a \div b = ab^{-1}$, $b \neq 0$, where b^{-1} is the multiplicative inverse of b.

The next example illustrates the fact that division is not associative.

Example 5. Compare $12 \div (6 \div 2)$ with $(12 \div 6) \div 2$.

Solution:

$$12 \div (6 \div 2) = 12 \div 3 = 4$$
$$(12 \div 6) \div 2 = 2 \div 2 = 1$$

Hence, $12 \div (6 \div 2) \neq (12 \div 6) \div 2$ and division is not associative.

We point out that in the more common notation for division, the result of Example 5 takes the form $\dfrac{12}{6/2} = \dfrac{12}{3} = 4$ and $\dfrac{12/6}{2} = \dfrac{2}{2} = 1$ as before. This means that we must be precise and distinguish between $\dfrac{a}{b/c}$ and $\dfrac{a/b}{c}$ because division is not an associative operation.

Example 6. Solve the equation $3x + 4 = 7$ for x.

Solution:

$$3x + 4 = 7$$
$$3x + 4 + (-4) = 7 + (-4)$$
$$3x + 0 = 3 \qquad\qquad A\text{-}6$$
$$3x = 3 \qquad\qquad A\text{-}5$$
$$3^{-1}(3x) = 3^{-1}(3)$$
$$1x = 1 \qquad\qquad A\text{-}8$$
$$x = 1 \qquad\qquad A\text{-}7$$

Note that multiplying both sides of an equation by a^{-1}, where $a \neq 0$, is the same as dividing both sides of the equation by a.

For the class of equations of the form $bx + c = 0$, $b \neq 0$, the solution is $x = -c/b$.

If we write $3x + 4 = 7$ from Example 6 in the form $3x - 3 = 0$, we find, as expected, that $x = 1$.

For the class of equations of the form $ax^2 + bx + c = 0$, where $b^2 - 4ac$ is nonnegative, the solutions are given by

$$x = \frac{-b \pm \sqrt{b^2 - 4ac}}{2a}$$

Equations of this form are called *quadratic equations*. The formula for finding the values of x that make $ax^2 + bx + c = 0$ a true statement is called the *quadratic formula*. The values are called *roots* of the equation, and they form the solution set for the given equation.

5

There are generally (but not always) two distinct roots of a quadratic equation. Sometimes both roots have meaning in an application; sometimes only one root has meaning. In the latter case, we simply ignore the root or solution that has no meaningful interpretation. The quadratic formula is very basic and should be committed to memory for later use.

Example 7. | Solve the equation $x^2 + 5x + 6 = 0$ for x using the quadratic formula.

Solution:

$$x^2 + 5x + 6 = 0$$

$$x = \frac{-b \pm \sqrt{b^2 - 4ac}}{2a}, \qquad a \neq 0$$

$$= \frac{-5 \pm \sqrt{25 - 4(1)(6)}}{2(1)}$$

$$= \frac{-5 \pm 1}{2}$$

$$x = -3, \; x = -2$$

Note that if one substitutes $x = -3$ or $x = -2$ in the expression $x^2 + 5x + 6$, the result will be zero.

PROBLEMS

1. Give the most specific description possible of the following sets of numbers using the words natural numbers, integers, rational numbers, and real numbers.
   (a) $\{-3, 5, -7, 12\}$ (d) $\{1, \sqrt{2}, 3, \frac{5}{7}\}$
   (b) $\{4, 3, 8, 27\}$ (e) $\{4, -3, \sqrt{25}, \frac{1}{3}\}$
   (c) $\{\frac{1}{2}, \frac{2}{3}, -\frac{5}{7}, 12\}$

2. List the additive inverse for each of the following real numbers:
   (a) $2, 5, -3$
   (b) $\frac{1}{2}, \frac{1}{4}, \frac{3}{4}$

3. Find the multiplicative inverse for each of the following real numbers:
   (a) $2, 5, -3$
   (b) $\frac{1}{2}, \frac{1}{4}, \frac{3}{4}$
   (c) $\frac{5}{3}, 10, 2$

4. Give three numerical examples of each of the following:
   (a) The commutative law of addition.
   (b) The associative law for multiplication.
   (c) The distributive law.

5. Illustrate how the axioms are used in solving the equation $2x + 3 = 7$.

6. Let $A = \dfrac{3/6}{2}$ and $B = \dfrac{3}{6/2}$.

(a) Rewrite both A and B using parentheses.
(b) Find the numerical values of A and B.
(c) Is the associative law valid for division?

7. Use the distributive law to factor the following expressions:
    (a) $2xy + 4xz$
    (b) $x^2y + xy^2$
    (c) $(a + b)x + (a + b)y$

8. Use the method of Example 4 to show that $(a - b)^2 = a^2 - 2ab + b^2$.

9. Solve the equation $2x + 3 = 17$ for x.

10. Use the appropriate axioms for the real number system to justify (prove) that $x = -c/b$ is the solution of $bx + c = 0$, $b \neq 0$. Verify this result by substitution.

11. Solve the following equations for x:
    (a) $2x - 6 = 0$ (d) $-3x - 12 = 0$
    (b) $3x + 12 = 0$ (e) $a + bx = 0$
    (c) $-2x + 10 = 0$ (f) $4x + 3 = -5$

12. Verify the quadratic formula by substitution.

13. Derive the quadratic formula by completing the square.

14. Use the quadratic formula to solve the following quadratic equations:
    (a) $x^2 - x - 6 = 0$ (e) $2x^2 + 6x = 0$
    (b) $x^2 + 4x + 4 = 0$ (f) $x^2 - 9 = 0$
    (c) $x^2 + 7x + 12 = 0$ (g) $x^2 + (2 - a)x - 2a = 0$
    (d) $2x^2 - 13x + 6 = 0$

15. Solve the quadratic equations in Prob. 14 by factoring. For example,
    $$x^2 + x - 6 = 0$$
    $$(x + 3)(x - 2) = 0$$
    $$x + 3 = 0 \text{ or } x - 2 = 0$$
    Solving these two equations for x gives $x = -3$ and $x = 2$ as the roots of the given quadratic equation.

1-2 FUNCTIONS

There are numerous situations in business and economics where changes in one quantity result in changes in some related quantity. For example, a decrease in price generally results in an increase in sales. It is also true that a decrease in consumer spending results from an increase in taxes. The mathematical concept of function is especially useful for studying such relationships.

DEFINITION 1.1.   *A symbol x, which can represent any number in a set of real numbers, is called a real variable.*

Other common symbols for a real variable are y, z, t, and w.

DEFINITION 1.2.   *A real variable y is said to be a function of the real variable x if one and only one value of y corresponds to each value of x.*

The set of all values that x may assume is called the *domain* of the function. The set of all corresponding y values is called the *range* of the function. The most common notation for a function is $y = f(x)$, where $f(a)$ denotes the value of y that corresponds to $x = a$. Given the function $y = f(x)$, x is called the independent variable, and y is called the dependent variable. Other common symbols for functions are $g(x)$, $F(x)$, and $h(x)$.

In the above definition, both the domain and range are sets of real numbers. This is by no means the most general definition of the function concept. For example, the domain might consist of ordered pairs of real numbers. In this case the function could be written in the form $z = f(x, y)$.

Example 1.

Discuss the function $y = f(x)$ defined as follows: $y = 2x - 10$ for each x between 5 and 10, inclusive.

Solution: The domain of $y = f(x)$ is the set of real numbers between $x = 5$ and $x = 10$, inclusive.

x	5	6	7.2	8.5	9	10
y	0	2	4.4	7	8	10

We see that $f(5) = 0, f(6) = 2, f(7.2) = 4.4$, and so on.

The range of this function is the set of real numbers between $y = 0$ and $y = 10$, inclusive.

A function $y = f(x)$, where x and y are real variables, can be represented graphically on a rectangular coordinate system.

Example 2.

Represent the function in Example 1 graphically.

Solution:

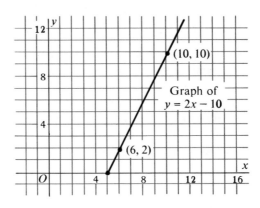

FIGURE 1-2

Example 3. Discuss and graph the function $y = x^2 - 2x + 1$ for x between -2 and 3, inclusive.

Solution: For convenience, we denote $x^2 - 2x + 1$ by $g(x)$. The domain of $y = g(x)$ is the set of x values between $x = -2$ and $x = 3$, inclusive. The range of $y = g(x)$ is the set of y values between $y = 0$ and $y = 9$, inclusive.

x	-2	-1	0	0.5	1	2	3
$g(x)$	9	4	1	0.25	0	1	4

$g(x) = x^2 - 2x + 1$

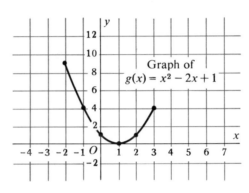

FIGURE 1-3

The function $y = x^2 - 2x + 1$ is an example of a nonlinear function.

PROBLEMS

1. Let $f(x) = x^2 + 2x + 1$. Calculate the following function values:
   (a) $f(0)$ (c) $f(3)$
   (b) $f(-2)$ (d) $f(2 + h)$
2. Graph the function: $y = 3x - 2$, x lies between 4 and 9, inclusive.
3. Determine the domain and range of the function given in Prob. 2.
4. Graph the function: $y = x^2 - 1$, x lies between -1 and 2, inclusive.
5. Determine the domain and range of the function given in Prob. 4.
6. Graph the functions $y = 5x + 1$ and $y = 3x + 2$ on the same coordinate system.
7. Restate Definition 1.2 for a real variable u as a function of the real variable t.

Graph the nonlinear functions given in Probs. 8 through 14.

8. $y = x^2 - 3x$

9. $y = x^2 + 3x + 4$

10. $y = x^3 + 2x^2$

11. $y = x^3 - 2x^2 + 2$

12. $y = x^3 + 6x$

13. $y = \dfrac{2}{x}$ [*Hint:* plot several points near $x = 0$.]

14. $y = \dfrac{2}{x - 3} + 4$ [*Hint:* plot some points near $x = 3$.]

15. The equations in Prob. 14 of Sec. 1-1 are of the form $f(x) = 0$. Graph the following functions, which are of the form $y = f(x)$, where $f(x)$ is the left-hand side of the equation $f(x) = 0$. Any value of x that makes $f(x) = 0$ a true statement is a root of the equation. Graphically, this is where the graph of $y = f(x)$ touches or crosses the x axis, i.e., where $y = 0$.

 (a) $y = x^2 - x - 6$ (d) $y = 2x^2 - 13x + 6$

 (b) $y = x^2 + 4x + 4$ (e) $y = 2x^2 + 6x$

 (c) $y = x^2 + 7x + 12$ (f) $y = x^2 - 9$

1-3 LINEAR FUNCTIONS

In this section we will examine some of the mathematical properties of functions of the form $y = mx + b$.

Since the graph of any function of the form $y = mx + b$ is a straight line, these functions are called linear functions. The reader should review the graph in Example 2 of Sec. 1-2 for an example of this statement.

The graph of any function of the form $y = mx + b$ crosses the y axis at the point $(0, b)$. For this reason, b is called the y intercept of $y = mx + b$. If m is not zero, then the x intercept is found by solving the equation $mx + b = 0$ for x.

Example 1.   Find the x and y intercepts of $2y = 6x + 8$. Draw the graph of this function.

Solution: First, we must divide both sides of the equation by 2 and put the equation in the form $y = mx + b$.

$$2y = 6x + 8$$
$$y = 3x + 4$$

The y intercept is 4.

$$3x + 4 = 0$$
$$3x = -4$$

Therefore, the x intercept is $-4/3$.

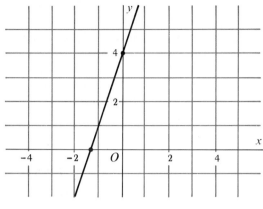

FIGURE 1-4

We have seen that b, in the function $y = mx + b$, can be given a simple geometric interpretation. Next we must try to find a geometric interpretation of m.

Let x_1 and x_2 be any pair of distinct values of x, and y_1 and y_2 be the corresponding y values.

Form the ratio $(y_2 - y_1)/(x_2 - x_1)$. Then

$$\frac{y_2 - y_1}{x_2 - x_1} = \frac{(mx_2 + b) - (mx_1 + b)}{x_2 - x_1}$$

$$\frac{y_2 - y_1}{x_2 - x_1} = \frac{mx_2 + b - mx_1 - b}{x_2 - x_1}$$

$$\frac{y_2 - y_1}{x_2 - x_1} = \frac{mx_2 - mx_1}{x_2 - x_1}$$

$$\frac{y_2 - y_1}{x_2 - x_1} = \frac{m(x_2 - x_1)}{x_2 - x_1} = m$$

The ratio $(y_2 - y_1)/(x_2 - x_1)$ is a measure of the "steepness" of the line in question. For example, the line $y = 3x + 2$ is "steeper" than the line $y = 2x + 2$, since $m = 3$ in the first case and $m = 2$ in the second case.

DEFINITION 1.3.   *Let L be any nonvertical straight line in the xy plane. Let $P_1(x_1, y_1)$ and $P_2(x_2, y_2)$ be any pair of distinct points on L. Then the ratio $\dfrac{y_2 - y_1}{x_2 - x_1}$ is called the slope of line L.*

The slope of a vertical line is not defined since this would give $x_1 = x_2$ and the ratio $(y_2 - y_1)/(x_2 - x_1)$ would involve division by zero. Recall from Sec. 1-1 that *division by zero is not defined.*

We conclude from the discussion preceding Definition 1.3 that if a line L has equation $y = mx + b$, then the slope of the line is equal to m.

Example 2.

Sketch the graphs of $y = 3x + 2$ and $y = 2x + 2$ on the same coordinate system.

Solution: Both lines have y intercept equal to 2. The slope of $y = 3x + 2$ is 3 and the slope of $y = 2x + 2$ is 2. This means that the first line will increase from 2 to 5 and the second line will increase from 2 to 4 if x is increased from 0 to 1. In other words, the first line passes through the points $(0, 2)$ and $(1, 5)$, and the second line passes through the points $(0, 2)$ and $(1, 4)$.

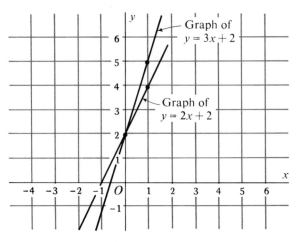

FIGURE 1-5

Example 3.

Graph the straight lines $y = 3$ and $x = 2$ on the same coordinate system.

Solution: The line $y = 3$ has zero slope and is a horizontal line. The line $x = 2$ is vertical and its slope is not defined.

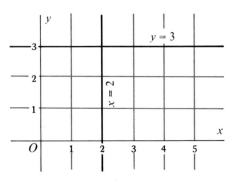

FIGURE 1-6

The next two examples illustrate the technique of finding an equation of a line from various kinds of geometric information.

Example 4.

Find an equation of the line whose slope is 5 and whose y intercept is -2.
Solution: Start with the form $y = mx + b$; this means we have $m = 5$ and $b = -2$. Therefore, $y = 5x - 2$ is an equation for this line.

Example 5. Find an equation of the straight line that passes through the points P_1 $(-2, -1)$ and P_2 $(3, -4)$.

Solution: The slope of a line is measured by the ratio $y_2 - y_1/x_2 - x_1$. Therefore, we have

$$m = \frac{-4 - (-1)}{3 - (-2)} = -\frac{3}{5}$$

This gives $y = -\frac{3}{5}x + b$.

Using P_1 to find the value of b, we have

$$-1 = -\frac{3}{5}(-2) + b$$

$$-1 = \frac{6}{5} + b$$

$$b = -\frac{11}{5}$$

Hence

$$y = -\frac{3}{5}x - \frac{11}{5}$$

This can be rewritten in the form

$$3x + 5y + 11 = 0$$

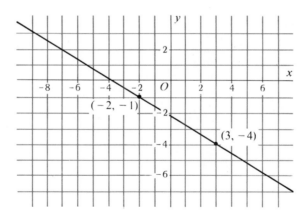

F I G U R E 1-7

PROBLEMS

1. Plot the points $A(0, 8)$, $B(1, 5)$, $C(2, 2)$, and $D(3, -1)$ and use the concept of slope to show that they lie on a straight line.

2. Draw the graph and use the formula $m = (y_2 - y_1/x_2 - x_1)$ to determine the slope of each of the following linear functions:

(a) $y = 2x + 3$ (c) $y = -2x + 5$ (e) $x - 2y - 3 = 0$
(b) $y = 3x - 3$ (d) $y - 2x - 6 = 0$

3. Find the x and y intercepts of the linear functions in Prob. 2.

4. Write the equation $9x + 3y + 15 = 0$ in the form $y = mx + b$.

5. Graph the straight lines $4x + 4.5y = P$ for $P = 900, 1600, 1800, 3600$, all on the same coordinate system.

6. After having worked with Prob. 5, describe the effect of changing the value of P in the equation $Ax + By = P$.

7. Find an equation for the line in Prob. 1.

8. Find an equation for each of the following straight lines:
    (a) The slope of the line is 3 and its y intercept is -5.
    (b) The line passes through the point (2, 5) and has slope 2.
    (c) The line passes through the point $(-2, 3)$ and has y intercept 2.
    (d) The line has slope 4 and x intercept 3.
    (e) The line passes through the two points (0, 3) and (1, -2).
    (f) The line passes through (10, -3) and (2, 5).

9. A certain research worker obtains the following data:

x	1	1	1	5	5	5
y	1.1	1.2	1.0	2.9	3.1	3.0

    (a) Plot these points.
    (b) Find an equation of the line passing through the points (1, 1) and (5, 3.1).
    (c) Find an equation of the line passing through the points (1, 1.2) and (5, 2.9).
    (d) Compare the slopes of the lines in (b) and (c).
    (e) Compare the y intercepts of the lines in (b) and (c).
    (f) Assume that y is a linear function of x. Can you think of any way to use these data to determine a better linear function than the two linear functions found in (b) and (c)? Explain your proposed method and obtain the resulting linear function.

10. Find an equation for each of the following straight lines:
    (a) The line has slope 5 and x intercept -2.
    (b) The line passes through the two points $(-3, 4)$ and (2, -6).

11. We know that two straight lines in a plane are parallel if their slopes are equal. It can also be shown that two straight lines in a plane are perpendicular (at right angles) if the product of their slopes is -1. Given this information, determine which of the following pairs of lines are (1) parallel; (2) perpendicular; or (3) neither:
    (a) $2x + 3y = 7$ (d) $2x + y = 4$
          $4x + 6y = 15$ $x + 3y = 6$
    (b) $x + 3y = 12$ (e) $2x + 6y = 4$
          $-3x + y = 4$ $-3x + y = -2$
    (c) $4x + 5y - 6 = 0$ (f) $-2x + 5y = 8$
          $3x + 2y + 4 = 0$ $y = 0.4x + 3$

12. Graph each pair of lines in Prob. 11 on a separate coordinate system.

13. The formula for the distance between two points in a plane. Let $A(x_2, y_2)$ and $B(x_1, y_1)$ be given. Form the supplementary point $D(x_2, y_1)$ as, for example, in Fig. 1-8. Applying the Pythagorean theorem of plane geometry to triangle ABD gives $d^2 = a^2 + b^2$, where $a = x_2 - x_1$ and $b =$

$y_2 - y_1$; therefore, $d = \sqrt{(x_2 - x_1)^2 + (y_2 - y_1)^2}$, where d is the distance between A and B. Use this *distance formula* to compute the distance between the following pairs of points:

(a) $(2, 1)$ and $(5, 5)$ (d) $(2, 0)$ and $(-4, 1)$
(b) $(-1, 2)$ and $(3, 5)$ (e) $(-1, -2)$ and $(3, 4)$
(c) $(0, 1)$ and $(4, -2)$ (f) $(0, 0)$ and (a, b)

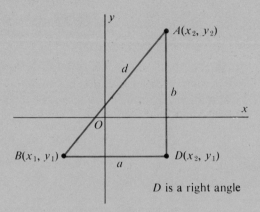

D is a right angle

FIGURE 1-8

14. Given the points $A(-1, 15)$, $B(1, 1)$, and $C(5, 3)$:
    (a) Plot the points and draw the triangle ABC.
    (b) Compute the slopes of BC and AC.
    (c) Is triangle ABC a right triangle?
    (d) Verify the Pythagorean theorem by applying the distance formula to the sides of this triangle.

15. Given the points $A(1, 2)$, $B(2, 3)$, and $C(3, 5)$:
    (a) Plot the points.
    (b) Use the results of Prob. 11 to determine if ABC is a right triangle.
    (c) Use the distance formula and the Pythagorean theorem to determine if ABC is a right triangle. [*Hint:* ABC is a right triangle if and only if $c^2 = a^2 + b^2$, where C is the right angle.]

1-4 SOLUTION OF SYSTEMS OF LINEAR EQUATIONS BY ELIMINATION

We begin this section by trying to determine the solutions of systems having two linear equations in two unknowns of the form

$$A_1x + B_1y + C_1 = 0$$
$$A_2x + B_2y + C_2 = 0$$

An equation of the form $Ax + By + C = 0$, $B \neq 0$, can be written in the form $y = mx + b$ as follows:

$$Ax + By + C = 0$$
$$By = -Ax - C$$
$$y = \frac{-Ax}{B} - \frac{C}{B}$$

$$y = mx + b$$

$$\text{where} \quad m = \frac{-A}{B}$$

$$b = \frac{-C}{B}$$

Since the graph of each equation in the above system is a straight line, we can interpret the solution of the system as the point at which these straight lines intersect.

Example 1.

The following system of equations has a solution of the form $x = a$, $y = b$, where both a and b are natural numbers. Find this solution by graphing each equation. Check your solution by substitution.

1. $2x - y + 6 = 0$
2. $4x + y - 12 = 0$

Solution:

1)	x	0	2		2)	x	0	2
	y	6	10			y	12	4

Since we are told that the coordinates of the point of intersection are both natural numbers, we see from the graph that the solution of the system is $x = 1$ and $y = 8$.

Checking $x = 1$, $y = 8$, we find

$$2(1) - 8 + 6 = 2 - 8 + 6 = 0$$

and

$$4(1) + 8 - 12 = 12 - 12 = 0$$

Hence $x = 1$, $y = 8$ is indeed the solution of the given system.

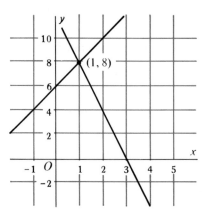

FIGURE 1-9

An algebraic method of finding the solution of such systems is based on the fact that at a point of intersection, the y value given by the first equation is the same as the y value given by the second equation. Hence, the x coordinate of a solution can be found by solving for y in terms of x in both equations, setting these two expressions equal, and solving the resulting equation for x. Then the y coordinate can be found by substitution into either equation.

Example 2. | Solve the system of Ex. 1 algebraically.

Solution:

$$2x - y + 6 = 0 \qquad 4x + y - 12 = 0$$
$$-y = -2x - 6 \qquad y = -4x + 12$$
$$y = 2x + 6$$

Equating these two expressions for y, we have

$$2x + 6 = -4x + 12$$
$$2x + 4x = 12 - 6$$
$$6x = 6$$
$$x = 1$$

Substitution of $x = 1$ into the first equation, $2x - y + 6 = 0$, gives

$$2(1) - y + 6 = 0$$
$$2 + 6 = y$$
$$y = 8$$

Hence the solution is $x = 1$, $y = 8$ as found in Example 1.

In the previous example, we eliminated the variable y by substitution. A variable can also be eliminated by adding or subtracting the two equations. In some instances, it is necessary to multiply the equations by constants and then proceed to add or subtract the equations.

Example 3. | Solve the previous system by addition of the two equations.

Solution:

$$2x - y + 6 = 0$$
$$\underline{4x + y - 12 = 0}$$
$$6x + 0 - 6 = 0$$
$$6x = 6$$
$$x = 1$$
$$y = 8$$

It is possible for a system of two linear equations in two unknowns to either fail to have a solution or to have an infinite number of solutions. These situations result if the graphs of the two equations are two different parallel lines, or if both equations represent the same straight line.

17

Example 4. Show that the system

$$2x + 3y - 6 = 0$$
$$4x + 6y - 10 = 0$$

has no solution, and the system

$$2x + 3y - 6 = 0$$
$$4x + 6y - 12 = 0$$

has an infinite number of solutions.

Solution: If we multiply the first equation by -2 and then add we have

$$-4x - 6y + 12 = 0$$
$$\underline{4x + 6y - 10 = 0}$$
$$0 + 0 + 2 = 0 \qquad \textit{this is a contradiction}$$

The *assumption* that the given system has a solution leads to the *contradictory statement* that $2 = 0$. Hence, this *assumption is incorrect* and the system has no solution.

Using the above method of multiplication on the second system,

$$2x + 3y - 6 = 0$$
$$4x + 6y - 12 = 0$$

leads to

$$-4x - 6y + 12 = 0$$
$$4x + 6y - 12 = 0$$

which gives, after addition, the true statement $0 = 0$. This is a reflection of the fact that both equations represent the same straight line. Any points whose coordinates satisfy the first equation also satisfy the second equation; hence the system has an infinite number of solutions.

The elimination method used here can also be used to solve systems of linear equations in more than two unknowns, as illustrated by the next example.

Example 5. Solve the following system by the method of elimination.

$$\begin{aligned} 1. \quad & x + 2y + 3z = 1 \\ 2. \quad & x + 3y + 5z = 2 \qquad (I) \\ 3. \quad & 2x + 5y + 9z = 3 \end{aligned}$$

Solution: If we subtract equation 2 from equation 1, we have

$$x + 2y + 3z = \ \ 1$$
$$\underline{x + 3y + 5z = \ \ 2}$$
$$-y - 2z = -1$$

Now, if we multiply equation 2 by two and subtract from equation 3, we have

$$2x + 5y + \ \ 9z = \ \ 3$$
$$\underline{2x + 6y + 10z = \ \ 4}$$
$$-y - \ \ z = -1$$

The resulting system, which does not involve x, is as follows.

$$\begin{aligned} 4. \quad & -y - 2z = -1 \\ 5. \quad & -y - \ \ z = -1 \qquad (II) \end{aligned}$$

If we subtract equation 5 from equation 4, we have

$$-z = 0$$
$$z = 0$$

The substitution of $z = 0$ in equation 5 gives $-y + 0 = -1$ and $y = 1$. The substitution of $y = 1$ and $z = 0$ into equation 1 gives $x + 2 + 0 = 1$, $x = 1 - 2 = -1$. Therefore, system I has the solution $x = -1$, $y = 1$, and $z = 0$.

PROBLEMS

1. (a) Write the equation $4x + 6y + 3 = 0$ in the form $y = mx + b$.
   (b) Write the equation $y = 6x - \frac{1}{2}$ in the form $Ax + By + C = 0$.

2. Solve the following systems of equations graphically.

   (a) $y = 2x - 3$ (c) $y = -x + 4$
        $y = 3x - 4$ $y = 3x - 2$

   (b) $2x + 3y - 4 = 0$ (d) $2x + 3y + 4 = 0$
        $x - 2y + 5 = 0$ $y = -\frac{4}{6}x - \frac{5}{6}$

3. Solve the systems in Prob. 2 by substitution.

4. Solve the systems in Prob. 2 by adding or subtracting the two equations after having multiplied each equation by appropriate constants.

5. Determine which of the following systems have solutions. Find the solutions if they exist.

   (a) $2x + 7y + 6 = 0$ (c) $2y = 4x + 2$
        $6x + 21y - 4 = 0$ $3y = 4x + 2$

   (b) $y = -2x + 3$ (d) $6y = -2x + 3$
        $-4y = 8x + 6$ $6y = x - 2$

6. Graph and find the solution for each of the following systems, if the solution exists.

   (a) $y = x + 3$ (b) $y = -x + 5$
        $y = 2x + 2$ $y = -\frac{1}{2}x + 4$
        $y = 3x + 1$ $y = 2x + 2$

7. Solve for x, y, and z.
   $$x + 2y + 3z = 3$$
   $$x + 3y + 5z = 4$$
   $$2x + 5y + 9z = 5$$

8. Solve for x, y, and z.
   $$x + y + z = 4$$
   $$2x + 2y + 2z = 7$$
   $$x - y + z = 2$$

9. Solve for x, y, and z.
   $$2x + 3y + 5z = 26$$
   $$4x + 6y + 6z = 32$$
   $$3x + y + 2z = 15$$

10. Which of the following systems has a solution?

    (a) $x + y + z = 20$
         $x + y + z = 10$
         $4x + 2y + z = 15$

    (b) $4x + y + 2z = 11$
         $2x + z = 4$
         $2x + y + z = 7$

11. Solve for x, y, and z.
$$2x - y + z = 0$$
$$3x - 2y - 4z = 16$$
$$4x - 3y + z = 2$$

12. Solve for z in terms of x, and graph z as a function of x.
$$x + y + z = 3$$
$$2x - y + z = 4$$

The concepts of supply and demand are fundamental principles in the study of economics. The following problems illustrate simple linear demand and supply functions.

13. Assume we are trying to use a straight line to model a relationship of price versus quantity demanded. If price is plotted on the y axis and quantity demanded is plotted on the x axis, would this straight line, i.e., the demand curve, be upsloping or downsloping?

14. Given the figures in Table 1-1.

TABLE 1-1

Total Quantity Demanded per Week	Price
2,000	$5
4,000	4
6,000	3
8,000	2
10,000	1

(a) Plot the above with price plotted on the y axis and quantity demanded plotted on the x axis.

(b) What is the equation of the demand curve?

15. Assume we are trying to use a straight line to model a price versus quantity supplied relationship. If price is plotted on the y axis and quantity supplied is plotted on the x axis, would this straight line, i.e., the supply curve, be upsloping or downsloping?

16. Given the figures in Table 1-2.

TABLE 1-2

Total Quantity Supplied per Week	Price
10,000	$5
8,000	4
6,000	3
4,000	2
2,000	1

(a) Plot the above with price plotted on the y axis and quantity supplied plotted on the x axis.

(b) What is the equation of this supply curve?

17. If equilibrium is where demand equals supply, what is the equilibrium price and the equilibrium quantity for the demand and supply curves presented in Probs. 14 and 16?

1-5 SUBSCRIPTS AND SUMMATION NOTATION

In the previous section, we used the symbols A_1, B_1, C_1, A_2, B_2, and C_2 to denote a typical system of two linear equations in two unknowns. You recall that the system was written in the form

$$A_1x + B_1y + C_1 = 0$$
$$A_2x + B_2y + C_2 = 0$$

The integer 1 in A_1, B_1, and C_1 and the integer 2 in A_2, B_2, and C_2 are called *subscripts*. In any symbol of the form x_i, where i is an integer, "i" is called a subscript of x.

Some examples of symbols with a subscript are x_1, a_0, A_3, Y_2, and $\mathbf{b}_i$.

Example 1.	Use subscript notation to denote a typical linear equation with 8 unknowns.

Solution: Denote the 8 unknowns by x_1, x_2, x_3, ..., x_7, x_8, where the three dots, or ellipsis points, indicate that some of the intermediate terms are not written.

Denoting the coefficients by a_1, a_2, ..., a_8 and the constant term by a_0, we have

$$a_0 + a_1x_1 + a_2x_2 + \cdots + a_8x_8 = 0$$

To illustrate the use of double subscripts we consider the system

$$A_1x_1 + B_1x_2 = k_1$$
$$A_2x_1 + B_2x_2 = k_2$$

This system can be written in the form

$$a_{11}x_1 + a_{12}x_2 = k_1$$
$$a_{21}x_1 + a_{22}x_2 = k_2$$

where $a_{11} = A_1$, $a_{12} = B_1$, $a_{21} = A_2$, and $a_{22} = B_2$. We have used the standard convention of indicating the number of the equation by the first subscript and the position of the term in the equation by the second subscript.

Example 2.	Use double subscripts to indicate a typical system of 3 linear equations in 3 unknowns.

Solution:

$$a_{11}x_1 + a_{12}x_2 + a_{13}x_3 = k_1$$
$$a_{21}x_1 + a_{22}x_2 + a_{23}x_3 = k_2$$
$$a_{31}x_1 + a_{32}x_2 + a_{33}x_3 = k_3$$

Next we introduce the summation notation. The symbol Σ, the Greek letter sigma, is used in mathematics to replace plus signs. Consider the expression $x_1 + x_2 + x_3 + \cdots + x_7$. This expression can be written as $\sum_{k=1}^{7} x_k$.

In general, $\sum_{k=1}^{N} x_k = x_1 + x_2 + \cdots + x_N$.

Example 3.

Use summation notation to rewrite the linear equation

$$a_1x_1 + \cdots + a_Nx_N = a_0$$

Solution: Using the summation symbol, we have

$$\sum_{k=1}^{N} a_k x_k = a_0$$

Example 4.

Write $\sum_{k=1}^{6} c_k x^k$ in expanded form.

Solution:

$$\sum_{k=1}^{6} c_k x^k = c_1 x + c_2 x^2 + c_3 x^3 + c_4 x^4 + c_5 x^5 + c_6 x^6$$

Example 5.

Compute $f(3)$ if $f(x) = \sum_{k=1}^{4} 2^k x^k$.

Solution:

$$f(x) = 2x + 4x^2 + 8x^3 + 16x^4$$
$$f(3) = 2(3) + 4(9) + 8(27) + 16(81)$$
$$= 6 + 36 + 216 + 1296$$
$$= 1554$$

The quantity $\bar{x} = (x_1 + x_2 + \cdots + x_n)/n$ is called the average or *arithmetic mean* of the set of data $\{x_1, x_2, \ldots, x_n\}$. In practice, this quantity is usually simply called the *mean*. Using summation notation, the mean can be expressed as

$$\bar{x} = \frac{1}{n} \sum_{i=1}^{n} x_i \qquad (mean)$$

Another important numerical description of a set of data is the *standard deviation*, s. The standard deviation is defined as follows:

$$s = \sqrt{\frac{\sum_{i=1}^{n} (x_i - \bar{x})^2}{n - 1}} \qquad (standard\ deviation)$$

Both of these quantities are basic to a study of statistics, and a knowledge of subscripts and summation notation is required for the calculation of these values.

PROBLEMS

1. Given $a_1 = 2$, $a_2 = 5$, $a_3 = 1$, and $a_4 = 6$, compute the following:
   (a) $\sum_{i=1}^{4} a_i$
   (b) $\sum_{i=1}^{4} a_i^2$

2. Use double subscript notation to indicate a typical system of three linear equations in four unknowns.

3. Write $\sum_{i=1}^{3} x_i f(x_i)$ in expanded form.

Prove the rules stated in Probs. 4 and 5 for summation of real numbers. Indicate the axioms (A-1 through A-8) that are used in your proofs.

4. $\sum_{i=1}^{n} (x_i + y_i) = \sum_{i=1}^{n} x_i + \sum_{i=1}^{n} y_i$

5. $\sum_{i=1}^{n} k x_i = k \sum_{i=1}^{n} x_i$ (k a constant)

6. Show that $\sum_{i=1}^{2} x_i y_i$ is *not equal* to $(\sum_{i=1}^{2} x_i)(\sum_{i=1}^{2} y_i)$ in general.

7. Let c_{ij} be defined as $c_{ij} = \sum_{k=1}^{3} a_{ik} b_{kj}$.
   (a) Express c_{13} in expanded form.
   (b) Express c_{31} in expanded form.

8. $f(x)$ is defined to be $f(x) = \sum_{k=1}^{3} 3^k x^{k+1}$.
   (a) Compute $f(2)$.
   (b) Compute $f(1)$.

Problems 9 through 18 are designed to illustrate the use of summation and subscript notation and to give the reader some computational experience with the mean and standard deviation, important statistical measures.

9. Compute the mean and standard deviation of the following test scores:

i	1	2	3	4	5	6	7	8
x_i	80	75	65	84	90	95	68	75

10. The sales figures for the Go Get Them Company for the past six years are listed below. Compute the six-year average sales, $\bar{x}$, for this company. Sales figures are given in thousands of dollars.

19X1	19X2	19X3	19X4	19X5	19X6
$1200	$1320	$1450	$1300	$1500	$1600

11. Your company employs five types of workers, each at a different wage rate. Assumptions: (1) All employees work 40 hours per week. (2) Each category has an equal number of workers. Compute the average wage rate for this company given the following data:

Type	1	2	3	4	5
Wage Rate	$2.25	$2.50	$3.00	$4.00	$5.00

12. Discuss the implications of relaxing the assumptions in Prob. 11.

13. For the data given below, where x_i denotes the number of lines in the ith invoice, calculate $\bar{x}$ and s.

i	1	2	3	4	5
x_i	6	4	3	1	11

14. Show that $\sum_{i=1}^{n} (x_i - \bar{x})^2 = \sum_{i=1}^{n} x_i^2 - n\bar{x}^2$. [*Hint:* $\sum_{i=1}^{n} x_i = n\bar{x}$.]

15. Show that $\sum_{i=1}^{n} (x_i - \bar{x})^2 = \sum_{i=1}^{n} x_i^2 - (\sum_{i=1}^{n} x_i)^2/n$.

16. Show that $s = \sqrt{\dfrac{\sum_{i=1}^{n} x_i^2 - (\sum_{i=1}^{n} x_i)^2/n}{n - 1}}$.

[*Hint:* Use the definition of s and the result of Prob. 14.]

Remark: This result provides a convenient alternative form for the computation of s.

17. Calculate s in Prob. 13 using the formula given in Prob. 16.

18. Calculate the mean and standard deviation for the following sets of data:

(a)

i	1	2	3	4	5	6	7
x_i	-3	-2	-1	0	1	2	3

(b)

i	1	2	3	4	5	6	7
x_i	\$5.00	10.00	20.00	25.00	30.00	40.00	45.00

19. The quantity $CS = \sum_{i=1}^{n} (o_i - t_i)^2/t_i$ is used frequently in marketing research and applied statistics. *CS* is an abbreviation for *chi square*, a technical term in statistics.

Computationally this value can be obtained quite easily. However, a detailed discussion of the statistical concept is beyond the scope of this text. Calculate chi square for the following set of data:

i	1	2	3	4
o_i	35	25	15	25
t_i	30	30	20	20

20. Calculate $\sum_{i=1}^{n} x_i$, $\sum_{i=1}^{n} y_i$, $\sum_{i=1}^{n} x_i^2$, $\sum_{i=1}^{n} x_i y_i$, and $(\sum_{i=1}^{n} x_i)^2$ for the following x_i and y_i values.

i	1	2	3	4	5
x_i	6	8	10	12	14
y_i	10	12	13	16	18

1-6 COST AND REVENUE FUNCTIONS

In this section we will discuss revenue and cost functions for both single product and multiple product firms.

Terminology: Costs that remain relatively constant regardless of the level of activity are called *fixed costs*. Costs that are proportional to output are called *variable costs*. The product of the number of units, x, sold at price, p, is called *total revenue*. The sum of the variable cost and the fixed cost that results from producing x units is called the *total cost*. As the reader no doubt expects, the *profit* is obtained by subtracting total cost from total revenue.

Assumptions: 1. Both total cost and total revenue can be represented by linear functions. 2. The future as it concerns the cost and revenue pattern of this company is treated as a known quantity, i.e., it is determinate.

Comments about these assumptions: The assumption of linearity leads to an extremely simple mathematical analysis that often gives an acceptable approximation of the real world situation for a limited range of production levels. To work without the assumption of certainty requires a knowledge of probability, a topic that is taken up in the final chapters of this text.

Example 1.   The total operating cost, C, of a certain firm is given as a function of the production level, x, by the linear function $C = 0.72x + 1000$. C is in dollars and x is in units produced. Discuss the variable cost and the fixed cost for this firm. Interpret this situation geometrically.

Solution: We see from the above definitions that the fixed cost is $1000. Also, the variable cost is $0.72x$. The variable cost per unit can be obtained by dividing the variable cost by the number of units produced. This involves dividing $0.72x$ by x; therefore, the variable cost per unit is 0.72. We note that the variable cost per unit is a constant in this case.

    This cost function is of the form $C = mx + b$, where $m = 0.72$ and $b = 1000$. This means that the variable cost per unit can be interpreted geometrically as the slope of the straight line and fixed cost can be interpreted as its C intercept.

Example 2.   Assume that you are in charge of a plant that has a fixed cost of $1000 and a cost of $3.10 is incurred for each additional unit of production. Express total cost, C, as a linear function of x, the number of units produced.

Solution: $C = cx + F$, where c is the cost per unit and F is fixed cost.

$$C = (3.10)x + 1000$$

    For a single product firm that is selling its product at a fixed price, p, we have $R = px$, where p = price per unit and R = total revenue. Next we illustrate a linear total revenue function for a firm that produces three products. If the number of units of the three products is denoted by x_1, x_2, and x_3, respectively, and the corresponding prices are denoted by p_1, p_2, and p_3, we have, for the total revenue function, $R = p_1x_1 + p_2x_2 + p_3x_3$. The function can be written with summation notation as $R = \sum_{i=1}^{3} p_ix_i$. More generally, for a firm that produces n products, we have $R = \sum_{i=1}^{n} p_ix_i$.

Example 3.   A certain firm produces tables, chairs, and desks. Find the total revenue function if tables, chairs, and desks are sold for $50, $25, and $40, respectively. Use this revenue function to compute the total revenue that results from the sale of 5 tables, 20 chairs, and 150 desks.

Solution: Let x_1, x_2, and x_3 denote the number of chairs, tables, and desks, respectively.

$$R = \sum_{i=1}^{3} p_i x_i$$

$R = p_1 x_1 + p_2 x_2 + p_3 x_3$, where $p_1 = 50$, $p_2 = 25$, and $p_3 = 40$ in this case. The total revenue function for this firm is $R = 50x_1 + 25x_2 + 40x_3$.

The revenue that results from the sale described above can be found by evaluating the revenue function at $x_1 = 5$, $x_2 = 20$, and $x_3 = 150$. This gives $R = 50(5) + 25(20) + 40(150)$. Hence, $R = \$6750$.

We switch now from revenue functions to a discussion of cost functions. The reader will recall that for a single product firm the linear total cost function has the form $C = cx + F$, where the various kinds of variable costs are grouped together in the single constant, c. Suppose now that costs are broken down further into material, labor, and variable overhead costs. If we use c_1 to denote material cost per unit of x, c_2 to denote the labor cost per unit of x, and c_3 to denote the variable overhead cost per unit of x, then the total cost function has the form

$$C = \sum_{i=1}^{3} c_i x + F$$

Finally, for a multiple product firm that produces n products and breaks down its variable costs into material, labor, and variable overhead costs, the total cost function has the form

$$C = \sum_{i=1}^{3} c_{i1} x_1 + \sum_{i=1}^{3} c_{i2} x_2 + \cdots + \sum_{i=1}^{3} c_{in} x_n + F$$

where c_{ij} is a variable cost for the product, which corresponds to x_j.

Example 4. Given the following variable costs:

	Tables (x_1)	Chairs (x_2)	Desks (x_3)
Materials	$15	$10	$12
Labor	5	6	7
Variable Overhead	3	2	2.50

and $F = \$2000$, find the cost function.

Solution: In this example, we have

$c_{11} = 15, c_{12} = 10, c_{13} = 12$

$c_{21} = 5, c_{22} = 6, c_{23} = 7$

$c_{31} = 3, c_{32} = 2, c_{33} = 2.50$

$C = \sum_{i=1}^{3} c_{i1} x_1 + \sum_{i=1}^{3} c_{i2} x_2 + \sum_{i=1}^{3} c_{i3} x_3 + F$

$$C = (15x_1 + 5x_1 + 3x_1) + (10x_2 + 6x_2 + 2x_2)$$
$$+ (12x_3 + 7x_3 + 2.50x_3) + 2000$$

$$C = 23x_1 + 18x_2 + 21.50x_3 + 2000$$

This gives the total cost as a function of x_1, x_2, and x_3.

PROBLEMS

1. Given that the cost-volume relationship is linear, the production cost for 100 units is $2550, and the production cost for 300 units is $2650.
   (a) Find the cost function.
   (b) Discuss the significance of the vertical intercept.
   (c) Discuss the significance of the slope.
   (d) Is the assumption of a linear relationship a good one?

2. If the total factory cost, C, of making x units of a product is given by $C = \$3.00x + \$200$ and if 50 units are made,
   (a) What is the variable cost?
   (b) What is the total cost?
   (c) What is the variable cost per unit?
   (d) What is the average cost per unit?

3. If we can sell the 50 units produced in Prob. 2 at a price of $8.00, what will the revenue be?

4. Using Probs. 2 and 3, calculate the profit resulting from the sale of 50 units.

5. A certain single product firm has a fixed cost of $300, a variable cost per unit of $2.00 and sells the product for $3.00 per unit. Find the total cost function and the total revenue function for this firm.

6. If you are a salesman and are paid a salary of $400 a month and a commission of 4% on your dollar sales for the month, how would you express your monthly pay as a linear function? What would your earnings be this month if you sold $5000 worth of merchandise?

7. Using Ex. 4 and an order for 5 tables, 20 chairs, and 150 desks, calculate the total cost.

8. Show that $\sum\limits_{j=1}^{n} \sum\limits_{i=1}^{3} c_{ij}x_j$ equals $\sum\limits_{i=1}^{3} c_{i1}x_1 + \sum\limits_{i=1}^{3} c_{i2}x_2 + \cdots + \sum\limits_{i=1}^{3} c_{in}x_n$.

9. Given the following information.

Variable Costs	Model 1	Model 2
Materials	$20	$10
Labor	15	5
Variable Overhead	10	3
Selling	5	2

The fixed costs are		
Administrative	$2000	
Fixed Overhead	$3000	

The selling price of Model 1 is $200 and the selling price of Model 2 is $150.

(a) What are the revenue and cost functions ?

(b) What is the profit if we receive an order for 20 units of Model 1 and 30 units of Model 2?

10. The water rates per quarter for the city of Nice and Green are:

For the first 5000 cubic feet or less, $0.34 per 100 cubic feet.
For the next 10,000 cubic feet or less, $0.28 per 100 cubic feet.
For the next 35,000 cubic feet or less, $0.22 per 100 cubic feet.
For the next 250,000 cubic feet or less, $0.13 per 100 cubic feet.
For use of over 300,000 cubic feet, the rate for the entire quantity used is $0.13 per 100 cubic feet.

Express this rate structure graphically using the vertical axis for total cost.

11. Discuss the implications of the rate structure in Prob. 10 for users near the 300,000 cubic foot level.

12. The electric rates for the city of Light and Cool are:

First   6,000 kwh, 0.12 per 100 kwh
Next   12,000 kwh, 0.10 per 100 kwh
Above 18,000 kwh, 0.08 per 100 kwh

Minimum billing per period is $3.00.
Express this rate structure graphically using the vertical axis for total cost.

13. Assume that Table 1-3 gives the minimum commission schedule on the New York Stock Exchange for single round lot orders.

TABLE 1-3 SINGLE ROUND LOT ORDERS

Money Involved in the Order	Minimum Commission
$100–$799.99	2.0% + $6.40
800–2499.99	1.3 + 12.00
2500 and over	0.9 + 22.00

Subject to the provision that the minimum commission on single round lot orders not exceed $65.00.

(a) Express the commission structure graphically using the vertical axis for commission.

(b) At what dollar sale is there no further increase in commission, i.e., at what point does the graph become horizontal?

14. Assume that Table 1-4 gives the minimum commission schedule on the New York Stock Exchange for multiple round lot orders.

TABLE 1-4 MULTIPLE ROUND LOT ORDERS

Money Involved in the Order	Minimum Commission
$100–$2,499.99	1.3% + $12.00
2,500–19,999.99	0.9 + 22.00
20,000–29,999.99	0.6 + 82.00
30,000–500,000	0.4 + 142.00

plus

First to tenth round lot, $6.00 per round lot
Eleventh round lot and over, $4.00 per round lot

An investor plans to buy 200 shares of stock at $100.00 per share. He can purchase these shares either (1) all on one day; or (2) 100 shares per day for two days. What would he save (if anything) in commission by buying two round lots of 100 shares each instead of buying a multiple round lot of 200 shares? Consult Prob. 13 for needed information. Assume no change in the stock price over the two days.

15. Repeat Prob. 14 with the price per share at $20.00.

16. A college contracts with a time-sharing company for computer time at a cost of $10.00 per hour. The minimum cost per month is $100.00, i.e., the first ten hours is applied to the minimum. Graph this cost function with the vertical axis as cost.

17. Repeat Prob. 16 if the maximum cost per month is $400.00.

18. A supplier agrees to furnish a certain item at the following prices:

$10.00 per unit for any order of 100 units or less
   9.00 per unit for any order from 101 to 200 units
   7.50 per unit for any order in excess of 200 units

(a) Graph this function with cost plotted on the vertical axis.
(b) Is it cheaper to buy 105 units than 98 units?

19. In shopping for your Thanksgiving turkey you find the following prices:

Under 10 pounds, $0.90 per pound
10 to 20 pounds,   0.80 per pound
Over 20 pounds,   0.60 per pound

(a) Graph your cost function with the vertical axis as cost.
(b) Is is true that you can buy a 24-pound turkey for the same price as an 18-pound turkey?

1-7 BREAK-EVEN ANALYSIS

Previously we found that the solution of a system of two linear equations in two unknowns gives the point of intersection of the graphs of the two equations involved. In particular, if one of the equations represents a linear cost function and the other a revenue function, then this point of intersection is called the break-even point.

Example 1. Given the following data, construct the cost and revenue functions and find the break-even point. Illustrate graphically.

Fixed cost = $1500
Variable cost per unit = $0.75
Selling price per unit = $1.50

Solution: Let x denote the number of units. Then Total Cost, C, equals $cx + F$.

$$C = (0.75)x + 1500$$
$$R = px \qquad \text{where } R \text{ is the revenue}$$
$$R = 1.50x$$

To find the break-even point, we set R equal to C and solve for x.

$$R = C$$
$$1.5x = 0.75x + 1500$$
$$0.75x = 1500$$
$$x = 2000$$

To find the other coordinate of the break-even point substitute $x = 2000$ into $R = 1.5x$. This gives $R = 1.5(2000) = \$3000$.

Since Profit, P, is defined as revenue minus total cost, we see that $P = R - C = 0$ at a break-even point.

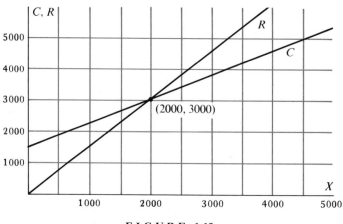

F I G U R E 1-10

Since the businessman is interested in making a profit and not just breaking even, the desired profit would normally be set equal to something other than zero.

Example 2.   Using the functions of Example 1, find the number of units that must be sold in order to make a profit of $500.

Solution:

$$P = R - C$$
$$500 = 1.5x - (0.75x + 1500)$$
$$500 = 0.75x - 1500$$
$$0.75x = 500 + 1500$$
$$0.75x = 2000$$
$$x = 2667 \text{ units}$$

The next example illustrates the use of break-even analysis and related ideas in a leasing situation.

Example 3.   The management of a certain firm is faced with the choice of leasing a machine from manufacturer A at an annual cost of $3000 plus $0.02 per unit produced on this machine or leasing from manufacturer B at an annual cost of $5250 plus $0.015 per unit produced. Calculate the number of units that must be sold to break even in each case. Each unit can be sold for $0.05.

Solution:

Manufacturer A	Manufacturer B
$R = C$	$R = C$
$0.05x = 3000 + 0.02x$	$0.05x = 5250 + 0.015x$
$0.03x = 3000$	$0.035x = 5250$
$x = 100{,}000$	$x = 150{,}000$

If the anticipated sales are 150,000 units, for example, the firm should lease from manufacturer A and make a profit. We note that leasing the machine from manufacturer B would result in a break-even situation.

Example 4.   What decision should be made if anticipated sales are (a) 300,000 units, and (b) 700,000?

Solution: In both cases we are past the break-even level. Since revenue is the same for both machines, the decision will be based on the total cost involved in leasing from either manufacturer A or manufacturer B.

If the anticipated sales are 300,000 units,

Manufacturer A	Manufacturer B
$C = 3000 + 300{,}000(0.02)$	$C = 5250 + 300{,}000(0.015)$
$= 3000 + 6000$	$= 5250 + 4500$
$C = 9000$	$C = 9750$

Hence, the machine should be leased from manufacturer A.

If the anticipated sales are 700,000 units,

Manufacturer A	Manufacturer B
$C = 17{,}000$	$C = 15{,}750$

Hence, the machine should be leased from manufacturer B.

PROBLEMS

1. Graph $y = 2x + 3$ and $y = 4x$ on the same coordinate system and find their point of intersection.
2. Given the cost and revenue functions $C = 1000 + 7x$, $R = 9x$.
   (a) Graph these straight lines on a break-even chart and identify the break-even point.
   (b) Find the break-even point algebraically.
3. Determine the production level necessary to give a profit of $500 for the cost and revenue functions in Prob. 2.
4. Plot the following data on a coordinate system. Take both C and R as the vertical axis.

x	R	C
0	0	2000
100	200	2150

5. Find the equations of the linear cost and revenue functions implied by the data in Prob. 4.

6. Find the break-even point for Prob. 5.

7. Determine a policy that your company would follow in renting a car from a concern that offers the following options:

   Plan 1: Eighty dollars a month and $0.08 per mile.
   Plan 2: A flat $0.12 per mile with a minimum of $40 per month.

   Note that neither plan includes the purchase of gasoline. Given that your company will be responsible for this cost ($0.05 per mile), what would be the point at which you would be indifferent to the choice of plan?

8. Suppose that you need to have 50 copies of a one-page table for your next business meeting. At the present time you have two options for reproducing this table:

   Option 1: Use a ZROZ-24 at a cost of $0.01 per page.
   Option 2: Prepare a spirit master at a cost of $0.30 for the master and a cost of $0.001 per sheet of duplicator paper.

   (a) Which option would you choose for this task?
   (b) In general, what sort of policy would you set up concerning the use of these two options?
   (c) How would your policy be affected if the ZROZ-24 rate changed to $0.0425 for the first four copies and $0.005 for every copy after the initial four?

9. The Good Product Company earns an after-tax profit of $2400 on sales of $88,000. The average tax rate of the company is 40%. The only product of the company sells for $20.00, of which $15.00 is variable cost. The firm has a capital structure as follows:

Debentures @ 8%	$62,500
Common Stock	85,000
Retained Earnings	6,600
	154,100

   (a) Fill in the following short-form income statement:

Sales	$88,000
Variable Costs	_____
Gross Profit	_____
Interest Expense	_____
Other Fixed Expenses	_____
Earnings before Taxes	_____
Taxes	_____
Net Income	2,400

   (b) What is the break-even point?

10. There are two alternative methods of acquiring a computer: rental from the manufacturer or outright purchase.

    The rental cost can be broken down into three components:

    1. Monthly rental payments.
    2. Overtime payments for use in excess of a stated amount. Assume these payments to be 10% of the cumulative rental cost.

3. Pre-tax investment credit, which is equal to $\frac{1}{3}(2)(0.07)(P)$ and is to be subtracted from the cumulative rental cost,

where C_r = cumulative cost of renting
   N = time in months
   R = monthly rental
   P = purchase cost

(a) Express C_r as a function of N, R, and P.
(b) Given that $P = \$150,000$ and $R = \$3000$, find C_r for $N = 12, 24, 36, 48,$ and 60 months.

Excluding a consideration of possible residual value, the cumulative purchase cost is made up of the following components:

1. The purchase cost.

2. Maintenance.

3. Insurance.

4. Cost of money for the purchase. Assume this to be $(N/12)(P)(S/2)$.

5. Investment tax credit, which is equal to $2(0.07)(P)$ and is to be subtracted from the cumulative purchase cost,

where C_p = cumulative cost of purchasing
   M = monthly maintenance
   S = an acceptable simple interest rate
   I = monthly insurance cost
   P = purchase cost
   N = time in months
   R = monthly rental

(c) Express C_p as a function of M, S, I, P, and N.
(d) Given that $P = \$150,000$, $R = \$3000$, $M = 10\%$ of the rental cost, $S = 0.08$, and $I = 1\%$ of the rental cost, find C_p for $N = 12, 24, 36, 48,$ and 60 months.
(e) Plot the results obtained in (b) and (d) with n on the horizontal axis.
(f) It appears that whether one should buy or lease a computer is determined by how long one is planning on keeping that particular machine. How long would you have to intend to keep your machine for C_p to be less than C_r?

1-8   FITTING STRAIGHT LINES TO DATA

In Sec. 1-6 we introduced the concept of a linear cost function and pointed out some of its limitations. Assumed linear cost and revenue functions were then used to determine break-even points. Rather than being given an assumed linear cost function for a company, suppose we are simply given some historical cost data for the company. In this section we discuss a procedure for fitting a straight line to a set of data.

The first step in this procedure consists of preparing a *scatter diagram* to display graphically a possible functional relationship between two sets of quantitative data. There are, roughly speaking, three possible outcomes of this first step:

1. The data points appear to lie or scatter around a straight line.
2. The data points appear to lie or scatter around the graph of an unknown nonlinear function.
3. The data points appear to be completely unrelated.

Example 1. | Prepare a scatter diagram for the following set of cost data. Use the vertical axis for cost.

	A	B	C	D	E	
x	100	200	300	400	500	(*output*)
y	50	75	80	85	110	(*cost in thousands of $*)

Solution:

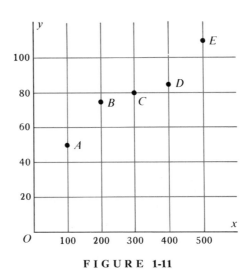

FIGURE 1-11

These points appear to lie along a straight line, and the assumption that cost can be expressed as a linear function of output seems reasonable.

Assuming that the scatter diagram for a given set of data supports the assumption that an approximate linear relationship exists, we then proceed to determine the appropriate linear function, $\hat{y} = a + bx$. Ultimately, we will use the *least-squares principle* as the criterion for fitting the *best* straight line to the data. Before introducing the least-squares criterion, we will look at another illustrative example.

Example 2. | Find the equation of the form $\hat{y} = a + bx$ that passes through the points A and E of Example 1.

Solution:

$$b = \frac{110 - 50}{500 - 100} = \frac{60}{400} = 0.15$$

$$a = 50 - 0.15(100) = 50 - 15 = 35$$

$$\therefore \hat{y} = 35 + 0.15x$$

Note that points B and D do not lie on the graph of $\hat{y} = 35 + 0.15x$ obtained in Example 2. In this case, we are using $\hat{y}$ to denote calculated or *predicted* values of y in contrast to *observed* values of y.

The least-squares criterion calls for minimization of the sum of the squares of the n differences, $y_i - \hat{y}_i$. In symbols, the values of a and b that minimize the quantity $\sum_{i=1}^{n} (y_i - \hat{y}_i)^2$ are used to form the best straight line. The sum of squares is illustrated below for the values of a and b derived in Example 2.

Example 3. Calculate $\hat{y}$ for each x value given in example 1 and find the sum of $(y_i - \hat{y}_i)$ and $(y_i - y_i)^2$.

Solution:

i	x_i	y_i	$\hat{y}_i$	$y_i - \hat{y}_i$	$(y_i - \hat{y}_i)^2$
1	100	50	50	0	0
2	200	75	65	10	100
3	300	80	80	0	0
4	400	85	95	-10	100
5	500	110	110	0	0
				0	200

We could, by a trial and error method, determine $\sum_{i=1}^{n} (y_i - \hat{y}_i)^2$ for several straight lines and choose the one for which this quantity is the smallest. This approach has two obvious disadvantages: (1) it would be tedious; and (2) it does not guarantee that we have the best of all possible straight lines. Fortunately, there is a simple systematic procedure for fitting a straight line to data to which it is reasonable to attempt such a fit.

Recall that the least-squares criterion calls for the minimization of $\sum_{i=1}^{n} r_i^2$, where $r_i = y_i - \hat{y}_i$. The difference, r_i, is called the ith *residual*. If we attempt to fit a linear function of the form $\hat{y} = a + bx$, we have $r_i = y_i - \hat{y}_i = y_i - (a + bx_i)$, and we must choose a and b to minimize $\sum_{i=1}^{n} [y_i - (a + bx_i)]^2$.

It can be shown, using differential calculus, that this minimization problem results in a system of two linear equations in a and b called *normal equations*. These equations are as follows:

35

$$na + \sum_{i=1}^{n} x_i b = \sum_{i=1}^{n} y_i$$

$$\sum_{i=1}^{n} x_i a + \sum_{i=1}^{n} x_i^2 b = \sum_{i=1}^{n} x_i y_i \qquad (\textit{normal equations for the two-variable case})$$

where n = number of observations.

Solving the above equations for a and b results in

$$b = \frac{n \sum_{i=1}^{n} x_i y_i - \sum_{i=1}^{n} x_i \sum_{i=1}^{n} y_i}{n \sum_{i=1}^{n} x_i^2 - (\sum_{i=1}^{n} x_i)^2}$$

and

$$a = \frac{\sum_{i=1}^{n} y_i}{n} - \frac{b \sum_{i=1}^{n} x_i}{n}$$

Example 4. Using the data given in Example 1, calculate the values of a and b that satisfy the least-squares criterion, and graph the fitted line.

Solution:

x_i	y_i	x_i^2	$x_i y_i$
100	50	10,000	5,000
200	75	40,000	15,000
300	80	90,000	24,000
400	85	160,000	34,000
500	110	250,000	55,000
1,500	400	550,000	133,000

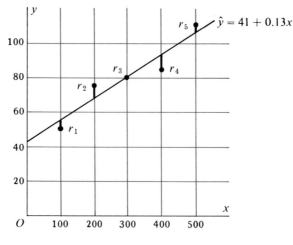

FIGURE 1-12

$$b = \frac{5(133{,}000) - 1500(400)}{5(550{,}000) - 1500^2} \qquad a = \frac{400}{5} - 0.13\frac{1500}{5}$$

$$= \frac{665{,}000 - 600{,}000}{2{,}750{,}000 - 2{,}250{,}000} \qquad\qquad = 80 - 39$$

$$= 0.13 \qquad\qquad\qquad\qquad = 41$$

Using the results of Example 4 we can form Table 1-5.

TABLE 1-5

i	y_i	$\hat{y}_i$	r_i	r_i^2
1	50	54	-4	16
2	75	67	8	64
3	80	80	0	0
4	85	93	-8	64
5	110	106	4	16
				160

Note that $\sum_{i=1}^{n} r_i^2 = 160$, which is less than the value of 200 obtained in Example 3.

PROCEDURE FOR FITTING STRAIGHT LINES TO DATA

1. Prepare a scatter diagram and ask yourself the following questions:
   (a) Do the data plotted appear to lie along a straight line?
   (b) Assuming the answer to (a) is yes, do the data appear to lie in a *band* or *strip*, i.e., between two parallel lines around the line you hope to fit?
2. If you have answered yes to both parts of Question 1, calculate a and b, and form the resulting linear function, $\hat{y} = a + bx$.
3. Plot $\hat{y} = a + bx$ on the scatter diagram, and reconsider questions (a) and (b). If your answers to (a) and (b) are still yes, retain $\hat{y} = a + bx$ as the best linear equation relating y to x.

A word of caution:

The above procedure for fitting straight lines to data is limited to the purely mathematical problem of determining the *best* straight line using the least-squares principle as the criterion for the meaning of the term *best*. This is not the whole story! These results do not give us a way of making any statements of *confidence* about the ability of the fitted line to predict additional observations. Such statements of confidence are important; however, they require knowledge of probability and statistics.

The study of fitting mathematical functions to data and the statistical evaluation of these fits is called *regression analysis*. The fitting of straight lines to data is an important special topic in regression analysis.

PROBLEMS

1. Find an equation of the line that passes through the points B and D in Example 1.
2. Using the equation obtained in Prob. 1 calculate $\sum_{i=1}^{n} (y_i - \hat{y}_i)^2$.
3. Calculate $\sum_{i=1}^{n} (y_i - \hat{y}_i)^2$ if $\hat{y} = 41 + 0.15x$. Is it smaller or larger than 160? In light of Example 4, would you expect this to happen? Why?
4. Calculate $\bar{x}$, the mean value of the x values, and $\bar{y}$, the mean value of the y values, for the data in Example 1. The point $(\bar{x}, \bar{y})$ should satisfy the equation $\hat{y} = 41 + 0.13x$. Does it?
5. Given Table 1-6.

TABLE 1-6

i	x_i	y_i	$x_i y_i$	x_i^2
1	2	8		
2	4	10		
3	6	11		
4	8	14		
5	10	15		

(a) Complete the table.
(b) Substitute the results of (a) in the following equations:

$$an + b \sum_{i=1}^{n} x_i = \sum_{i=1}^{n} y_i$$

$$a \sum_{i=1}^{n} x_i + b \sum_{i=1}^{n} x_i^2 = \sum_{i=1}^{n} x_i y_i$$

(c) Using the result of (b), solve the two equations for a and b.
(d) Calculate a and b using the formulas presented in this section, and compare these values with the result obtained in (c).

6. Given Table 1-7.

TABLE 1-7

x (direct labor in millions of dollars)	y (factory burden in millions of dollars)
1	2.75
2	3.00
3	3.75
4	3.90
5	4.40

(a) Prepare a scatter diagram.

(b) Is it reasonable to try to fit a straight line to these data?

(c) What is the equation of the straight line that best fits these data?

(d) What would you estimate factory burden to be if direct labor were $3.2 million?

7. You are trying to determine if there is a relationship between a diagnostic test given on the first day of class (x) and final average (y) when the course is completed. In a class of ten last semester the data in Table 1-8 were observed:

TABLE 1-8

Observation	x_i	y_i
A	10	30
B	20	40
C	35	90
D	40	90
E	20	55
F	30	50
G	45	90
H	15	50
I	25	80
J	35	75

(a) Plot the above observations on a scatter diagram.

(b) Pass a line through observations A and D. What is the equation of this line?

(c) Complete the following table using the line from (b):

i	x_i	y_i	$\hat{y}_i$	$(y_i - \hat{y}_i)$	$(y_i - \hat{y}_i)^2$
1 . . .					

(d) Calculate values for the *y* intercept *a* and slope *b* using the formulas given in this section.

(e) Redo (c) using the equation of the line obtained in (d).

(f) Does (c) or (e) yield the smallest sum of differences (i.e., residuals) squared?

8. Given the data in Table 1-9 on the cost of materials for constructing a 1400-square-foot house in A CITY and A STATE over the past six years.

TABLE 1-9

	x (year)	*y* (cost in thousands of $)
19XX	1	12.00
19XX	2	12.40
19XX	3	12.75
19XX	4	13.00
19XX	5	13.30
19XX	6	14.00

(a) Plot the data on a scatter diagram.

(b) What is the equation of the straight line that best fits these *x*, *y* values?

(c) What is your interpretation of the slope of the equation calculated in (b)?

(d) Assume you are planning to build a house three years from now (i.e., Year 9). Estimate what the cost of materials will be then.

1-9 INEQUALITIES

In Chap. 5, which deals with linear programming, the reader will encounter linear inequalities of the type $2x + 3y + 5z \leq 7$. In preparation for this, we must study the following relationships between real numbers.

$a < b$, this is read *a* is *less than b*
$a > b$, this is read *a* is *greater than b*
$a \leq b$, this is read *a* is *less than* or *equal to b*
$a \geq b$, this is read *a* is *greater than* or *equal to b*

If we represent the real numbers by the points on a straight line, then the relationship $a < b$ means that the point corresponding to *a* lies to the left of the point corresponding to *b*.

Example 1.　Let $a = 3$, $b = 7$, $c = -4$, $d = 0$, and $e = -6$. Represent these numbers as points on a line and discuss the relative position of these points.

Solution:　Denote the point corresponding to the real number a by A, and so forth.

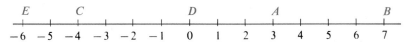

F I G U R E　1-13

A is to the left of B, ∴ $a < b$.
B is to the right of A, ∴ $b > a$.
E is to the left of C, ∴ $e < c$, that is, $-6 < -4$.
A is to the right of C, ∴ $a > c$, that is, $3 > -4$.
D is to the left of A, ∴ $d < a$, or $0 < 3$.
E is to the left of D, ∴ $e < d$, or $-6 < 0$.

DEFINITION 1.4.　*We say that $a < b$, a is less than b, if and only if there is a positive number h with the property that $a + h = b$. The notation $b > a$ has the same meaning as $a < b$.*

Example 2.　Find the numerical value of h for $3 < 8$ and $-6 < -4$.

Solution:

$$3 + 5 = 8, ∴ h = 5$$
$$-6 + 2 = -4, ∴ h = 2$$

The following rules for working with inequalities can be proven from this definition. The letters a, b, c, and d all denote real numbers.

Rule 1.　If $a < b$, then $a + c < b + c$.
Rule 2.　If $a < b$ and $b < c$, then $a < c$.
Rule 3.　If $a < b$ and $c < d$, then $a + c < b + d$.
Rule 4.　If $a < b$ and $0 < c$ (c is positive), then $ca < cb$.
Rule 5.　If $a < b$ and $c < 0$ (c is negative), then $ca > cb$.

Proof of Rule 2.　Assume $a < b$ and $b < c$. Then, by Definition 1.4, there are positive numbers h_1 and h_2 that give $a + h_1 = b$ and $b + h_2 = c$. By adding these two equations together, we have

$$a + h_1 + b + h_2 = b + c$$
$$a + h_1 + h_2 = c$$

Since h_1 and h_2 are positive, $h_1 + h_2$ is also positive. Let

$$h_3 = h_1 + h_2$$

41

Then $a + h_3 = c$. Therefore,

$a < c$ by Definition 1.4

Proof of Rule 4.   Assume $a < b$ and $0 < c$. There exists h such that $a + h = b$, and h is positive. If we multiply both sides by c, we have

$c(a + h_1) = cb$
$ca + ch_1 = cb$

If we define $h_2 = ch_1$, h_2 is positive since the product of two positive numbers is positive.

$ca + h_2 = cb$
$ca < cb$ by Definition 1.4

DEFINITION 1.5.   *The notation $a \leq b$ means $a < b$ or $a = b$. Similarly, $a \geq b$ means $a > b$ or $a = b$.*

Example 3.   Illustrate Definition 1.5 numerically.

Solution:

$3 \leq 4$ since $3 < 4$
$4 \leq 4$ since $4 = 4$
$-5 \geq -7$ since $-5 > -7$
$-5 \geq -5$ since $-5 = -5$

Example 4.   Solve the inequality $2x + 5 \leq 13$ for x. Illustrate the solution graphically.

Solution:

$2x + 5 \leq 13$
$2x + 5 + (-5) \leq 13 + (-5)$ *by Rule 1*
$2x + 0 \leq 8$ *by A-6*
$2x \leq 8$ *by A-5*
$\frac{1}{2}(2x) \leq \frac{1}{2}(8)$ *by Rule 4*
$x \leq 4$

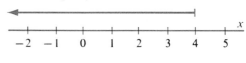

FIGURE 1-14

PROBLEMS

1.   Let $a = 2, b = -3, c = 6, d = -5$, and $e = 0$. Represent these numbers as points on a line and discuss the relative position of the following points:
(a) A and C
(b) D and B

    (c) A and B
    (d) D and E
    (e) C and E

2. Refer to Definition 1.4. Find the numerical value of h.
    (a) $6 < 7$
    (b) $-10 < -4$
    (c) $-3 < 0$
    (d) $10 > 7$ [*Hint:*   translate to less than symbol first.]

3. Use Definition 1.4 to prove the following: If $a < b$, then $a + c < b + c$.

4. Use $a = 2$, $b = 4$, $c = 3$, $d = 6$ to illustrate Rule 3.

5. Use Definition 1.4 to prove the following: If $a < b$ and $c < 0$ (c is negative), then $ca > cb$.   [*Hint*:   Modify the proof of Rule 4.]

6. Solve the following inequalities for x:
    (a) $3 - 2x \leq 9$
    (b) $2x + 3 \leq 5$
    (c) $2x + 7 \geq 13$

7. Graphically illustrate the solutions to Prob. 6.

8. Solve the following inequalities for x:
    (a) $4x + 3 \leq x - 2$
    (b) $3(x - 2) < 4$
    (c) $4 - 5x \geq 14$

9. Graph the following function:

$$f(x) = \begin{cases} 2x, & \text{if } 0 \leq x \leq 1 \\ x + 1, & \text{if } 1 \leq x \leq 2 \end{cases}$$

10. Express the function in Fig. 1-15 in the following form:

$$f(x) = \begin{cases} ax, & \text{if } 0 \leq x \leq 2 \\ bx + c, & \text{if } 2 \leq x \leq 4 \end{cases}$$

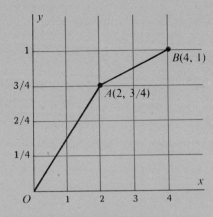

F I G U R E   1-15

11. Express the water rate structure for the city of Nice and Green (see Prob. 10, Sec. 1-6) as a function.

12. Express the electric rate structure for the city of Light and Cool (see Prob. 12, Sec. 1-6) as a function.

13. Express the commission schedule for the New York Stock Exchange (see Prob. 13, Sec. 1-6) as a function.

14. Express the cost structure of Prob. 18, Sec. 1-6 as a function.

15. Assume you are an office equipment manager interested in purchasing some optical mark document readers. In order to accelerate the popularity of his machine, a supplier has made you the offer in Table 1-10.

TABLE 1-10

Quantity (in units)	Price (per unit)	Discount
1	$2140	
2–10	1926	10%
11–20	1712	20%
21–30	1498	30%
31 or more	1284	40%

(a) Express this cost structure graphically using the vertical axis for cost.

(b) Express this cost structure functionally.

1–10 SYSTEMS OF LINEAR INEQUALITIES

After our introduction to inequalities in the previous section, we will begin this section with a study of inequalities of the type $y \leq mx + b$.

Example 1. Determine the points in the xy plane whose coordinates satisfy the inequality $y \leq 2x - 1$.

Solution:

x	-2	-1	0	1	2	3
y	$y \leq -5$	$y \leq -3$	$y \leq -1$	$y \leq 1$	$y \leq 3$	$y \leq 5$

Sample Calculation: Let $x = -2$.

$$y \leq 2(-2) - 1$$
$$y \leq -4 - 1$$
$$y \leq -5$$

This table suggests that we draw the graph of $y = 2x - 1$ and illustrate graphically the above information.

It should be clear from the graph that the inequality $y \leq 2x - 1$ is satisfied by the coordinates of any point that lies on the graph of $y = 2x - 1$ or below it.

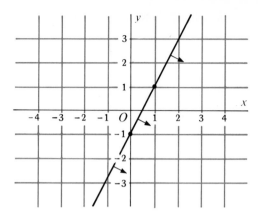

F I G U R E 1-16

Example 2. Find the points whose coordinates satisfy the inequality $2x + 3y \leq 12$.

Solution:

$$2x + 3y \leq 12$$
$$3y \leq 12 - 2x \qquad \textit{by Rule 1}$$
$$y \leq 4 - \tfrac{2}{3}x \qquad \textit{by Rule 4}$$

The solution consists of the points on or below the line $y = 4 - \tfrac{2}{3}x$.

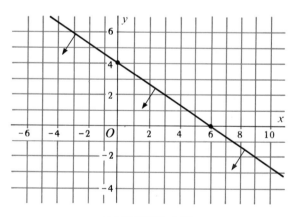

F I G U R E 1-17

DEFINITION 1.6

$$a_{11}x_1 + a_{12}x_2 + \cdots + a_{1n}x_n \leq b_1$$
$$a_{12}x_1 + a_{22}x_2 + \cdots + a_{2n}x_n \leq b_2$$
$$\begin{array}{ccccc} \cdot & & \cdot & & \cdot \\ \cdot & & \cdot & & \cdot \\ \cdot & & \cdot & & \cdot \end{array}$$
$$a_{m1}x_1 + a_{m2}x_2 + \cdots + a_{mn}x_n \leq b_m$$

is called a system of m linear inequalities in n unknowns.

45

DEFINITION 1.7.   *We now adopt the term solution space of an inequality or of a system of inequalities to mean the set of points whose coordinates satisfy the given inequality or system of inequalities.*

An examination of the graphs for Examples 1 and 2 illustrates the fact that the solution space for a linear inequality of the form $Ax + By < C$ consists of all the points on one side of the line $Ax + By = C$. The following procedure is based on this fact.

PROCEDURE

Step 1:   Draw the graph of the straight line $Ax + By = C$.

Step 2:   Test one point that is not on this line to see if its coordinates satisfy the inequality $Ax + By < C$. If the coordinates of this point satisfy the inequality, then all points on the same side of the line $Ax + By = C$ are in the solution space. If the coordinates of the point fail to satisfy the given inequality, then the solution space consists of the points on the opposite side of the line, in addition to the points on the line.

Example 3.   Find the solution space for the inequality $2x + 3y \leq 6$.

Solution:

$$2x + 3y = 6$$

Step 1

x	0	3
y	2	0

Step 2

$$2(0) + 3(0) = 0, \qquad \textit{using the convenient point } (0, 0)$$
$$0 < 6$$

Therefore, the origin is in the solution space.

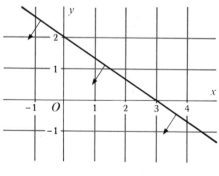

F I G U R E 1-18

The solution space for a system of inequalities can be found as follows:

Indicate the solution space of each inequality in the system with an arrow. Next, determine the points that belong to the solution space of all of the inequalities in the system. This set of points is the solution space for the whole system.

Example 4. | Find the solution space for the system.

$$2x + 3y \le 6$$
$$x \ge 0$$

Solution:

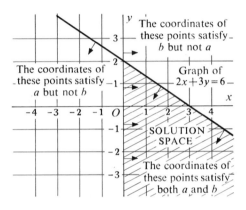

F I G U R E 1-19

Example 5. | Find the solution space for the system.

$$2x + 3y \ge 6$$
$$y - x \ge 1$$
$$x \ge 0$$

Solution:

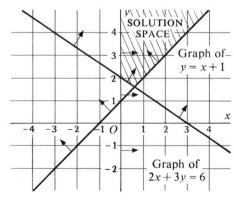

F I G U R E 1-20

47

Example 6.

Find the solution space for the system.

$$2x + y \leq 3$$
$$3x + y \leq 4$$
$$x \geq 0$$
$$y \geq 0$$

Solution: If we solve the equations $2x + y = 3$ and $3x + y = 4$ simultaneously, we have

$$(y = 4 - 3x) - (y = 3 - 2x)$$

After subtraction we have

$$0 = 1 - x$$

Therefore,

$$x = 1$$

and

$$y = 4 - 3$$
$$y = 1$$

The coordinates of the point B are $x = 1$ and $y = 1$.

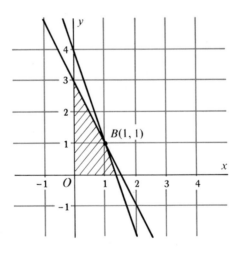

F I G U R E 1-21

PROBLEMS

In Probs. 1 through 4, shade the points in the xy plane whose coordinates satisfy the given inequalities.

1. $y \leq 4$

2. $y \leq 4 - 2x$

3. $x + y \geq 4$

4. $4y \geq 6x + 24$

Find the solution space for the systems of inequalities given in Probs. 5 through 8.

5. $x \geq 0$
$y \geq 0$

6. $2x + y \leq 8$
$x + 2y \leq 8$

7. $3x + 4y \geq 0$
$x + 3y \leq 6$
$3x + 2y \leq 6$

8. $x + y \leq 4$
$x + 2y \leq 6$
$x \geq 0$
$y \geq 0$

9. Find the coordinates of each of the corners of the solution space in Probs. 5 through 8.

10. You are about to buy a kayak and have the following desires and constraints:

You would like to take a companion with you on your trip.

You are going to be flown to your departure point and cannot carry a kayak that is longer than 16 feet aboard the aircraft.

Because you will be making frequent portages, you would like the weight to be less than 80 pounds.

The trip will take a month, requiring you to bring quite a few supplies. It is therefore desirable to have a load capacity of between 700 and 750 pounds.

Your budget allows $350 for the purchase of the kayak. Express these specifications mathematically using the following variables:

z = weight q = load capacity
x = number of seats w = dollar cost
y = length

11. Express the following company objectives symbolically:

Sales of $1,000,000 or more
Cost of goods sold not to exceed $650,000
Net income to exceed $100,000
Rate of return of at least 11%

where S = sales
CGS = cost of goods sold
NI = net income
RR = rate of return

12. You are planning to buy a corporate aircraft and want to meet the following specifications:

Altitude	(ALT)	in excess of 18,000 feet
Airspeed	(AS)	in excess of 330 m.p.h.
Number of passengers	(NP)	minimum of 6
Useful load	(UL)	minimum of 2 tons
Landing run	(LR)	within 3000 feet
Willing to pay	(S)	up to $800,000

Express the above symbolically using inequalities.

13. In accepting employment with a company you have the following objectives:

> Starting salary of at least $10,000
> Two-week vacation, minimum
> Location within 20 miles of your present home

Express the above mathematically using the following variable names:

> D = distance from home
> S = starting salary
> V = weeks of vacation

REFERENCES

Books

Acton, Forman S. *Analysis of Straight Line Data.* New York: Dover Publications, Inc., 1959.

Allen, R. G. D. *Mathematical Analysis for Economists.* New York: St. Martin's Press, Inc., 1967.

Allendoerfer, Carl B., and Oakley, Cletus O. *Principles of Mathematics.* New York: McGraw-Hill Book Co., Inc., 1969.

Bardell, Ross H., and Spitzbart, Abraham. *College Algebra.* Reading, Mass.: Addison-Wesley, Inc., 1966.

Bowen, Earl K. *Mathematics with Applications in Management and Economics.* Homewood, Ill.: Richard D. Irwin, Inc., 1967.

Daus, Paul H., and Whyburn, William M. *Algebra with Applications to Business and Economics.* Reading, Mass.: Addison-Wesley, Inc., 1961.

Draper, N. R., and Smith, H. *Applied Regression Analysis.* New York: John Wiley & Sons, Inc., 1966.

Hamburg, Morris. *Statistical Analysis for Decision Making.* New York: Harcourt Brace Jovanovich, Inc., 1970.

Keedy, Mervin L. *Number Systems: A Modern Introduction.* Reading, Mass.: Addison-Wesley, Inc., 1965.

Macduffee, Cyrus C. *Theory of Equations.* New York: John Wiley & Sons, Inc., 1954.

May, W. Graham. *Foundations in Modern Mathematics.* Waltham, Mass.: Blaisdell Publishing Co. Inc., 1967.

Article

Brandon, Dick H. "Computer Acquisition Method Analysis." *Datamation:* Sept. 1972, pp. 76–79.

TWO

Introduction to vectors and matrices

Chapters 2 and 3 deal mainly with matrices. A *matrix* is a doubly sub-scripted set of objects, normally arranged in *rows* and *columns*. The mathematical operations of addition and multiplication can be defined in a meaningful way for certain classes of matrices. These definitions and associated theorems result in a rich and useful mathematical structure.

The following examples of matrix application are developed in this text:

coefficient matrix	(systems of linear algebraic equations)
parts explosion matrix	(inventory analysis)
technological matrix	(Leontief input-output model)
payoff matrix	(financial decision-making)
transition matrix	(Markov chains)

2-1 DEFINITION, EQUALITY, AND ADDITION OF VECTORS

In this section and in the next section we will introduce the concept of a vector. First we must define what is meant by a vector, then we will describe certain algebraic manipulations that can be carried out with vectors. Finally, we will point out how this new mathematical concept can be used to express systems of linear equations in a new way.

DEFINITION 2.1. *A vector is an ordered n-tuple $(x_1, x_2, \ldots, x_n)$ of numbers arranged in a row or in a column.*

If the numbers, which are called components, are arranged in a row, the vector is called a *row vector*, and if the components are arranged in a column, the vector is called a *column vector*. The following are examples of row vectors:

$$(3, 6, 1) \qquad (9, 2) \qquad (4, 6, 1, 8) \qquad (x_1, x_2, x_3, x_4)$$

The following are examples of column vectors:

$$\begin{pmatrix} 4 \\ 3 \\ 2 \\ 1 \end{pmatrix} \qquad \begin{pmatrix} 6 \\ 2 \end{pmatrix} \qquad \begin{pmatrix} 1 \\ 9 \\ 8 \end{pmatrix} \qquad \begin{pmatrix} b_1 \\ b_2 \\ b_3 \end{pmatrix}$$

Even though a vector consists of n distinct components, the entire vector should be considered as a single entity. In keeping with this consideration, vectors, in this text, are denoted by single letters set in boldface print. The following examples illustrate this point.

$$\mathbf{a} = (1, 3, 8) \qquad \mathbf{b} = \begin{pmatrix} 2 \\ 6 \\ 1 \end{pmatrix} \qquad \mathbf{c} = (c_1, c_2, c_3, c_4)$$

DEFINITION 2.2. *Two row vectors are said to be equal if they have the same number of components and their corresponding components are equal. Similarly, two column vectors are said to be equal if they have the same number of components and their corresponding components are equal.*

A *row vector* is never equal to a *column vector*. Equality of vectors $\mathbf{a}$ and $\mathbf{b}$ is denoted by $\mathbf{a} = \mathbf{b}$. This definition is illustrated by the following examples:

1. $(2, 3, 6) = (2, 3, 6)$

2. $(4, 7, 2)$ does not equal $(4, 8, 2)$ since the middle components are not equal.

3. $\begin{pmatrix} 2 \\ 3 \\ 8 \end{pmatrix}$ does not equal $(2, 3, 8)$ since one is a column vector and the other is a row vector.

4. $\begin{pmatrix} 2 \\ 6 \\ 7 \end{pmatrix}$ and $\begin{pmatrix} 2 \\ 6 \\ 7 \\ 8 \end{pmatrix}$ are not equal since the second vector has more components than the first.

Definition 2.3. *The sum of two row vectors or two column vectors (with the same number of components) is formed by adding the corresponding components of the given row vectors or column vectors.*

Addition of a row vector and a column vector is not defined. The sum of vectors **a** and **b** is denoted by **a** + **b**.

The following examples illustrate this definition:

1. $(1, 4, 2) + (4, 2, 1) = (5, 6, 3)$

2. $\begin{pmatrix} 9 \\ 2 \\ 4 \end{pmatrix} + \begin{pmatrix} 8 \\ 5 \\ 2 \end{pmatrix} = \begin{pmatrix} 17 \\ 7 \\ 6 \end{pmatrix}$

3. The sum of **a** $= (2, 1, 9)$ and **b** $= \begin{pmatrix} 30 \\ 1 \\ 4 \end{pmatrix}$ is not defined since **a** is a row vector and **b** is a column vector.

4. The sum of **c** $= (3, 5, 9, 4)$ and **d** $= (1, 5, 2)$ is not defined since **c** and **d** do not have the same number of components.

PROBLEMS

1. Test the following pairs of vectors for equality. If the pairs are not equal, give the reason for the inequality.
    (a) $(2, 3, 4); (2, 3, 4)$
    (c) $(2, 1, 2); (2, 1, 2, 5)$
    (b) $(1, 3, 5); \begin{pmatrix} 1 \\ 3 \\ 5 \end{pmatrix}$
    (d) $(1, 2, 3); (3, 2, 1)$

2. Add each of the pairs of vectors for which the sum is defined. If the sum is not defined, give the reason.
    (a) $(2, 3, 7); (1, 4, 2)$
    (c) $(4, 3, 7); (1, 0, 2, 4)$
    (b) $(1, 4, 1); \begin{pmatrix} 2 \\ 3 \\ 5 \end{pmatrix}$
    (d) $(a, b, c); (0, 0, 0)$

3. Let **x** be a row vector with 5 components and let **y** be a row vector with 6 components.
    (a) Write out **x** and **y** using subscript notation.
    (b) Is it possible for **x** to equal **y**? Why?
    (c) Is is possible to add **x** and **y** together? Why?

4. Vectors with only two components can be represented geometrically as follows. Take the first component of the given vector as the x coordinate of a point in the xy plane and take the second component of the vector as the y coordinate of the point. Plot the point that corresponds to each of the vectors given below.
    (a) **a** $= (2, 3)$
    (c) **c** $= \begin{pmatrix} -1 \\ -2 \end{pmatrix}$
    (b) **b** $= (-3, 6)$
    (d) **d** $= \begin{pmatrix} 3 \\ -5 \end{pmatrix}$

5. Calculate and illustrate geometrically the sum of the following pairs of vectors:

(a) (2, 3); (1, 5)   (c) $\begin{pmatrix} 1 \\ 2 \end{pmatrix}$; $\begin{pmatrix} -1 \\ 1 \end{pmatrix}$

(b) (-1, -2); (3, 0)   (d) $\begin{pmatrix} -1 \\ 4 \end{pmatrix}$; $\begin{pmatrix} 3 \\ 1 \end{pmatrix}$

6. Given that you have a column vector called **x**, which has five components, write out this vector in component form.

7. Give an example of a row vector that has four components and a column vector that has five components.

8. Add the following vectors:

(a) $\begin{pmatrix} x_1 \\ x_2 \\ x_3 \end{pmatrix} + \begin{pmatrix} y_1 \\ y_2 \\ y_3 \end{pmatrix}$ (b) $(a, b, c) + (3, 2, 1)$

9. In order to manufacture a certain product, three raw materials are needed. Assume the product is cement, which requires the following:

2 units of sand d_1
1 unit of Portland cement d_2
1 unit of water d_3

Express these ingredients as a row vector.

10. The demand in units for three types of goods is as follows:

$$g_1 = 100,000, \ g_2 = 150,000, \ g_3 = 125,000$$

Express the above demand as a column vector.

11. The total output of goods from three industries in millions of dollars is as follows:

$$i_1 = 1200, \ i_2 = 1000, \ i_3 = 800$$

Express the above production data as a column vector.

12. There are three other suppliers of a certain product besides your own company. Each supplier has the following market share in percents:

$$s_1 = 30, \ s_2 = 15, \ s_3 = 25, \ s_4 = 30$$

Express the above market shares as a column vector.

2-2 MULTIPLICATION OF A VECTOR BY A SCALAR AND BY A VECTOR

DEFINITION 2.4. *Let* **a** *be a row or column vector and let k be a real number. Then the product k**a** is defined to be the vector whose components are given by k times the corresponding components of* **a**.

This type of multiplication is called *multiplication by a scalar*, where the number k is called a *scalar*.

The following examples illustrate Definition 2.4.

1. $\frac{1}{2}(4, 8, 2) = (2, 4, 1)$

2. $0.2 \begin{pmatrix} 2 \\ 6 \\ 5 \end{pmatrix} = \begin{pmatrix} 0.4 \\ 1.2 \\ 1 \end{pmatrix}$

3. $4(2, 1, 3, 5) = (8, 4, 12, 20)$

DEFINITION 2.5.   *Let* **a** *be a row vector and* **b** *be a column vector, both with n components. Then the product of* **a** *times* **b** *is defined to be the scalar* $a_1b_1 + a_2b_2 + \cdots + a_nb_n$. *This product is denoted by* **ab**. *This product can also be written*

$$\mathbf{ab} = \sum_{k=1}^{n} a_k b_k$$

It is called the inner product.

The following examples illustrate the above definition.

1. $(1, 4, 2) \begin{pmatrix} 3 \\ 4 \\ 2 \end{pmatrix} = (1)(3) + (4)(4) + (2)(2) = 23$

2. $\begin{pmatrix} 3 \\ 4 \\ 2 \end{pmatrix}$ times $(1, 4, 2)$ does not exist according to the above definition.

Remark: Definition 2.5 only admits multiplication of a column vector by a row vector and always leads to a scalar quantity as an answer. Later in the chapter the concept of a matrix will be introduced and a definition of matrix multiplication will be given at that time. In the more general matrix setting, a row vector with n components can be multiplied by a column vector with m components, but the answer will be a matrix instead of a scalar.

3. $(2, 8, 6, 5) \begin{pmatrix} 7 \\ 8 \end{pmatrix}$ is not defined because the row vector has four components and the column vector has only two components.

Next we give an example to illustrate how these definitions can be used to express *a system of linear equations* as a *single vector equation*.

Example 1.   Write the system

$$2x + 3y + 5z = 4$$
$$3x + 5y + 6z = 2$$
$$x + 2y + 5z = 3$$

as a single vector equation.

Solution: Form the four column vectors

$$\mathbf{a} = \begin{pmatrix} 2 \\ 3 \\ 1 \end{pmatrix}, \qquad \mathbf{b} = \begin{pmatrix} 3 \\ 5 \\ 2 \end{pmatrix}, \qquad \mathbf{c} = \begin{pmatrix} 5 \\ 6 \\ 5 \end{pmatrix}, \qquad \mathbf{d} = \begin{pmatrix} 4 \\ 2 \\ 3 \end{pmatrix}$$

Then the given system can be written in the form

$$x \begin{pmatrix} 2 \\ 3 \\ 1 \end{pmatrix} + y \begin{pmatrix} 3 \\ 5 \\ 2 \end{pmatrix} + z \begin{pmatrix} 5 \\ 6 \\ 5 \end{pmatrix} = \begin{pmatrix} 4 \\ 2 \\ 3 \end{pmatrix}$$

55

where x, y, and z are treated as unknown scalars. The system can be written even more simply as $x\mathbf{a} + y\mathbf{b} + z\mathbf{c} = \mathbf{d}$.

This can be checked as follows:

$$x\begin{pmatrix} 2 \\ 3 \\ 1 \end{pmatrix} + y\begin{pmatrix} 3 \\ 5 \\ 2 \end{pmatrix} + z\begin{pmatrix} 5 \\ 6 \\ 5 \end{pmatrix} = \begin{pmatrix} 4 \\ 2 \\ 3 \end{pmatrix}$$

$$\begin{pmatrix} 2x \\ 3x \\ 1x \end{pmatrix} + \begin{pmatrix} 3y \\ 5y \\ 2y \end{pmatrix} + \begin{pmatrix} 5z \\ 6z \\ 5z \end{pmatrix} = \begin{pmatrix} 4 \\ 2 \\ 3 \end{pmatrix} \qquad \textit{by Definition 2.4}$$

$$\begin{pmatrix} 2x + 3y + 5z \\ 3x + 5y + 6z \\ 1x + 2y + 5z \end{pmatrix} = \begin{pmatrix} 4 \\ 2 \\ 3 \end{pmatrix} \qquad \textit{by Definition 2.3}$$

$$\begin{aligned} 2x + 3y + 5z &= 4 \\ 3x + 5y + 6z &= 2 \qquad \textit{by Definition 2.2} \\ x + 2y + 5z &= 3 \end{aligned}$$

PROBLEMS

1. Perform the following multiplications:

(a) $0.5\begin{pmatrix} 4 \\ 6 \\ 2 \end{pmatrix}$

(c) $x\begin{pmatrix} 1 \\ 4 \\ 2 \end{pmatrix}$

(b) $3(4, 8, 7)$

(d) $5\begin{pmatrix} 4 \\ 2 \\ 1 \end{pmatrix}$

2. Perform the following multiplications:

(a) $(2, 3)\begin{pmatrix} 7 \\ 1 \end{pmatrix}$

(c) $(7, 8, 2, 1)\begin{pmatrix} 4 \\ 3 \\ 2 \\ 1 \end{pmatrix}$

(b) $(2, 8, 4)\begin{pmatrix} 3 \\ 6 \\ 1 \end{pmatrix}$

(d) $(9, 1, 2, 8)\begin{pmatrix} 4 \\ 3 \\ 6 \\ 7 \end{pmatrix}$

3. Perform the following if they are defined. If they are not, explain why.

(a) $(6, 7, 2)\begin{pmatrix} 8 \\ 4 \end{pmatrix}$

(c) $(2, 7, 6)\begin{pmatrix} 8 \\ 4 \\ 2 \end{pmatrix}$

(b) $x\begin{pmatrix} 5 \\ 2 \end{pmatrix}$

(d) $\begin{pmatrix} 8 \\ 3 \\ 2 \end{pmatrix}\begin{pmatrix} 6 \\ 7 \\ 5 \end{pmatrix}$

4. Why are the following not defined?

(a) $(3, 6, 2)\begin{pmatrix} 4 \\ 8 \end{pmatrix}$

(c) $\begin{pmatrix} 2 \\ 1 \end{pmatrix}\begin{pmatrix} 6 \\ 4 \\ 7 \end{pmatrix}$

(b) $(2, 4, 1)(8, 3, 6)$ **(d)** $\begin{pmatrix} 2 \\ 2 \\ 1 \end{pmatrix}(4, 8, 3, 6)$

5. Show that multiplying $3\begin{pmatrix} 6 \\ 4 \\ 2 \end{pmatrix}$ gives the same result as

$$\begin{pmatrix} 6 \\ 4 \\ 2 \end{pmatrix} + \begin{pmatrix} 6 \\ 4 \\ 2 \end{pmatrix} + \begin{pmatrix} 6 \\ 4 \\ 2 \end{pmatrix}$$

6. Write the following system as a vector equation:

$$4x + 6y + 3z = 2$$

$$5x + 4y + z = 1$$

$$5x + 6y = 4$$

7. Perform the scalar multiplications and write as a system of equations.

$$w\begin{pmatrix} 4 \\ 9 \\ 3 \end{pmatrix} + x\begin{pmatrix} 2 \\ 1 \\ 2 \end{pmatrix} + y\begin{pmatrix} 3 \\ 2 \\ 4 \end{pmatrix} = \begin{pmatrix} 4 \\ 9 \\ 3 \end{pmatrix}$$

8. A certain single product firm has variable costs per unit:

Labor	$0.50
Material	0.30
Variable overhead	0.20

   (a)   Express these variable costs as a column vector.
   (b)   Express the variable costs of producing 200 units as a column vector.
   (c)   Multiply the column vector in (b) by a row vector to determine the total variable cost of producing 200 units of this product.

9. A company buys 3 machines at a cost of $20,000, $15,000, and $13,000, respectively. The salvage value after 4 years is 10% of the original cost.
   (a)   Express machine costs as a row vector.
   (b)   Use the row vector in (a) to find the machine costs that are to be depreciated (i.e., the depreciable base).

Problems 10 through 17 are designed to acquaint the reader with the concept of *n*-space. The set of all *n*-tuples of real numbers is called *n*-space, which we denote by the symbol R^n. One usually speaks of a particular *n*-tuple in *n*-space as a *vector* or *point* in R^n.

10. Give three numerical examples of a point in 5-space, R^5.

11. Let k be a real number and let **a** be a point in R^n. Show that $k\mathbf{a}$ is also a point in R^n.

12. Let **a** and **b** be points in R^n. Show that $\mathbf{a} + \mathbf{b}$ is also a point in R^n.

13. Let **a** and **b** be points in R^n, and define $-\mathbf{a}$ to be $-1\mathbf{a}$ and $\mathbf{a} - \mathbf{b}$ to be $\mathbf{a} + (-\mathbf{b})$. Calculate $3\mathbf{a}$, $-\mathbf{b}$, $\mathbf{a} + \mathbf{b}$, and $\mathbf{a} - \mathbf{b}$ for the following pairs of points:
   (a) $\mathbf{a} = (2, -3)$, $\mathbf{b} = (-1, 4)$
   (b) $\mathbf{a} = (2, 1, -6)$, $\mathbf{b} = (1, 3, 4)$
   (c) $\mathbf{a} = (-1, 2, -3, 4, -3)$, $\mathbf{b} = (2, 4, 3, 6, 1)$

14. The *distance* between two points **a** and **b** in R^n is defined by

$$d(\mathbf{a}, \mathbf{b}) = \sqrt{(a_1 - b_1)^2 + (a_2 - b_2)^2 + \cdots + (a_n - b_n)^2}$$

where $d(\mathbf{a}, \mathbf{b})$ denotes the distance between $\mathbf{a}$ and $\mathbf{b}$.
  (a) Compute the distance between the pairs of points in Prob. 13.
  (b) Write the expression for $d(\mathbf{a}, \mathbf{b})$ using summation notation.

15. Let $\mathbf{a}, \mathbf{b}$, and $\mathbf{c}$ be points in R^n and let k and 1 be real numbers. Show that
  (a) $(\mathbf{a} + \mathbf{b}) + \mathbf{c} = \mathbf{a} + (\mathbf{b} + \mathbf{c})$
  (b) $\mathbf{a} + 0 = 0 + \mathbf{a} = \mathbf{a}$, where $0 = (0, 0, \ldots, 0)$
  (c) $\mathbf{a} + (-\mathbf{a}) = 0$, where $-\mathbf{a} = (-a_1, -a_2, \ldots, -a_n)$
  (d) $\mathbf{a} + \mathbf{b} = \mathbf{b} + \mathbf{a}$
  (e) $k(\mathbf{a} + \mathbf{b}) = k\mathbf{a} + k\mathbf{b}$
  (f) $(k + 1)\mathbf{a} = k\mathbf{a} + 1\mathbf{a}$
  (g) $(k1)\mathbf{a} = k(1\mathbf{a})$
  (h) $1\mathbf{a} = \mathbf{a}$
  These eight properties are used in the definition of an important mathematical structure called a *vector space*.

16. An experimenter makes n observations, $x_1, x_2, \ldots, x_n$, on a certain process and computes the mean, $\bar{x} = (1/n) \sum_{i=1}^n x_i$. Think of $\mathbf{x} = (x_1, x_2, \ldots, x_n)$ and $\mathbf{y} = (\bar{x}, \bar{x}, \ldots, \bar{x})$ as points in n-space. Give a formula for s, the standard deviation of the observations, in terms of $d(\mathbf{x}, \mathbf{y})$. See Prob. 14 for the definition of $d(\mathbf{x}, \mathbf{y})$.

17. Apply the ideas of Prob. 16 to the two observations $x_1 = 2$ and $x_2 = 4$, and illustrate the situation graphically.

2-3 DEFINITION, EQUALITY, AND ADDITION OF MATRICES

In this section we will introduce the concept of a matrix and some of the standard notation that is used in the study of matrices.

DEFINITION 2.6. *An m by n matrix is a rectangular array of numbers consisting of m rows and n columns. The expression m by n or m × n is called the size of the matrix. The numbers a_{ij} are called elements of the matrix.*

$$\begin{pmatrix} a_{11} & a_{12} & \cdots & a_{1n} \\ a_{21} & a_{22} & \cdots & a_{2n} \\ \cdot & \cdot & \cdot & \cdot \\ \cdot & \cdot & \cdot & \cdot \\ \cdot & \cdot & \cdot & \cdot \\ a_{m1} & a_{m2} & \cdots & a_{mn} \end{pmatrix}$$

As with vectors, the reader should adopt the point of view that even though an m by n matrix contains m times n elements, the entire matrix should be considered as a single entity. In keeping with this point of view, matrices are denoted by single capital letters. Definition 2.6 is illustrated below.

1. $\begin{pmatrix} 2 & 3 \\ 4 & 2 \\ 1 & 7 \end{pmatrix}$ *is a 3 by 2 matrix*

2. $\begin{pmatrix} 3 & -2 & 4 & 7 \\ 5 & 6 & -8 & 2 \end{pmatrix}$ *is a 2 by 4 matrix*

When a matrix is denoted by a capital letter, as A, it is customary to write $A = (a_{ij})$, where i stands for the row and j for the column in which the element a_{ij} is found. This double subscript notation is illustrated in the next two examples.

1. $A = \begin{pmatrix} a_{11} & a_{12} & a_{13} \\ a_{21} & a_{22} & a_{23} \end{pmatrix}$ *could be written as* (a_{ij}), *where* $i = 1, 2$ *and* $j = 1, 2, 3$

2. If $B = \begin{pmatrix} 2 & 3 & 5 \\ 1 & 0 & 4 \end{pmatrix}$,   *then* $b_{11} = 2$, $b_{12} = 3$, $b_{21} = 1$, *and so on*

Next we define equality and addition for matrices.

DEFINITION 2.7.   *Two matrices A and B are said to be equal, written $A = B$, if the following two conditions are met:*

    a.   *A and B have the same number of rows and columns (i.e., A and B are the same size).*

    b.   *Each element of A equals the corresponding element of B (i.e., $a_{ij} = b_{ij}$ for each i and j involved).*

This definition is illustrated below.

1. $\begin{pmatrix} 2 & 1 & 3 \\ 4 & 2 & 1 \end{pmatrix} = \begin{pmatrix} 2 & 1 & 3 \\ 4 & 2 & 1 \end{pmatrix}$ *since both matrices are the same size and their corresponding elements are equal*

2. $\begin{pmatrix} 2 & 3 \\ 4 & 7 \end{pmatrix}$ and $\begin{pmatrix} 2 & 3 & 1 \\ 4 & 7 & 2 \end{pmatrix}$ *are not equal since they are not the same size*

3. $\begin{pmatrix} 3 & 1 & 7 \\ 4 & 2 & 4 \end{pmatrix}$ and $\begin{pmatrix} 3 & 1 & 7 \\ 4 & 2 & 8 \end{pmatrix}$ *are not equal since the elements in the second row and third column are not equal*

Example 1.   Given the matrix equation

$$\begin{pmatrix} x + y & 4 \\ x - y & 6 \end{pmatrix} = \begin{pmatrix} 3 & 4 \\ 5 & 6 \end{pmatrix}$$

solve for x and y.

Solution:

$$x + y = 3$$
$$x - y = 5$$

by the definition of equality of matrices

First eliminate y by adding the two equations together.

$$
\begin{aligned}
x + y &= 3 \\
\underline{x - y} &= \underline{5} \\
2x + 0 &= 8 \\
x &= 4
\end{aligned}
$$

Substituting $x = 4$ into $x + y = 3$ gives $4 + y = 3$ or $y = -1$. Hence, the solution is $x = 4$ and $y = -1$.

Example 2.   Given that $a_{11} = 2$, $a_{12} = 3a_{11}$, $a_{13} = 5a_{12}$, $a_{21} = a_{13}$, $a_{22} = a_{12}$, and $a_{23} = 8$, write out the matrix A.

Solution:

$$a_{12} = (3)(2) = 6$$
$$a_{13} = (5)(6) = 30$$
$$a_{21} = a_{13} = 30$$
$$a_{22} = a_{12} = 6$$
$$a_{23} = 8$$

Recall that a_{ij} is in the ith row and jth column of A; therefore, we have

$$A = \begin{pmatrix} 2 & 6 & 30 \\ 30 & 6 & 8 \end{pmatrix}$$

DEFINITION 2.8.   *Let A and B be two matrices with the same number of rows and of columns. Then the sum of A and B, written A + B, is the matrix obtained by adding corresponding elements from A and B. Symbolically, A + B = C, if $c_{ij} = a_{ij} + b_{ij}$ for each i and j involved.*

1. $\begin{pmatrix} 2 & 3 & 4 \\ 1 & 7 & 2 \end{pmatrix} + \begin{pmatrix} 3 & 4 & 1 \\ 2 & 8 & 4 \end{pmatrix} = \begin{pmatrix} 5 & 7 & 5 \\ 3 & 15 & 6 \end{pmatrix}$

2. The sum of $\begin{pmatrix} 2 & 3 & 4 \\ 1 & 7 & 2 \end{pmatrix}$ and $\begin{pmatrix} 2 & 1 \\ 8 & 4 \end{pmatrix}$ is not defined since the two matrices are not the same size.

Example 3.   Given the matrix equation

$$\begin{pmatrix} x^2 & 2 \\ 1 & 4 \end{pmatrix} + \begin{pmatrix} 3x & 2 \\ 2 & 5 \end{pmatrix} = \begin{pmatrix} -2 & 4 \\ 3 & 9 \end{pmatrix}$$

solve for x.

Solution: From the definition of equality and addition for matrices, we have the quadratic equation $x^2 + 3x = -2$. This can be written as

$$x^2 + 3x + 2 = 0$$
$$(x + 2)(x + 1) = 0$$

By equating each factor to zero, we have $x + 2 = 0$ or $x + 1 = 0$. This gives

$$x = -2, \qquad x = -1$$

Before proceeding to the next section, we must point out that a *vector* is a special case of a *matrix*. For example, a row vector with 5 components is a 1 by 5 matrix, and a column vector with 3 components is a 3 by 1 matrix.

1. The row vector (2, 3, 4, 5) can be viewed as a 1 by 4 matrix.

2. The column vector $\begin{pmatrix} 2 \\ 4 \\ 7 \\ 9 \end{pmatrix}$ can be viewed as a 4 by 1 matrix.

PROBLEMS

1. Test the following pairs of matrices for equality. If they are not equal, give the reason.

   (a) $\begin{pmatrix} 4 & 2 & 1 \\ 3 & 6 & 2 \end{pmatrix}, \begin{pmatrix} 4 & 2 & 2 \\ 3 & 6 & 2 \end{pmatrix}$

   (b) $\begin{pmatrix} 4 & 3 \\ 2 & 6 \\ 1 & 2 \end{pmatrix}, \begin{pmatrix} 4 & 2 & 1 \\ 3 & 6 & 2 \end{pmatrix}$

2. Give an example of a pair of 3 by 4 matrices that are equal.

3. Perform the indicated matrix additions.

   (a) $\begin{pmatrix} 1 & 2 \\ 3 & 4 \end{pmatrix} + \begin{pmatrix} 8 & 7 \\ 6 & 2 \end{pmatrix}$

   (b) $\begin{pmatrix} 4 & 6 & 8 \\ 9 & 3 & 2 \end{pmatrix} + \begin{pmatrix} 2 & -1 & 3 \\ -4 & 2 & 5 \end{pmatrix}$

   (c) $\begin{pmatrix} 8 & 9 & 10 \\ 6 & 3 & 4 \\ 5 & 2 & 1 \end{pmatrix} + \begin{pmatrix} 8 & 3 & 2 \\ 4 & 7 & 1 \\ 2 & 1 & 4 \end{pmatrix}$

4. Which of the following pairs of matrices can be added? If addition is not defined, give the reason.

   (a) $\begin{pmatrix} 2 & 3 & 1 \\ 4 & 5 & 7 \end{pmatrix}, \begin{pmatrix} 1 & 4 \\ 2 & -2 \\ 1 & -3 \end{pmatrix}$

   (b) $\begin{pmatrix} 1 & 4 \\ 2 & 3 \\ 3 & 2 \end{pmatrix}, \begin{pmatrix} -2 & 5 \\ 4 & 6 \\ 8 & 7 \end{pmatrix}$

   (c) $\begin{pmatrix} 2 \\ 1 \\ 3 \end{pmatrix}, (4, 5, 7)$

5. Given

   $$\begin{pmatrix} 2 & 3 & 4 \\ 1 & 2 & 3 \end{pmatrix} + \begin{pmatrix} a & b & 2 \\ 3 & 1 & 4 \end{pmatrix} = \begin{pmatrix} 5 & 8 & 6 \\ 4 & 3 & 7 \end{pmatrix}$$

   Find a and b.

6. The entries a_{i3} ($i = 1, 2, 3, 4$) make up the _____ row or column of the matrix A.

7. Given that you have a 6×5 matrix called B. Write the elements (i.e., $b_{11}, \ldots$) in matrix form.

8. A company produces potatoes in three different agricultural regions. These potatoes are then shipped to four warehouses from which they are distributed to retailers. Any region can ship to any warehouse. The available shipping routes are shown in Fig. 2-1. The shipping costs for the various routes are shown in Table 2-1.

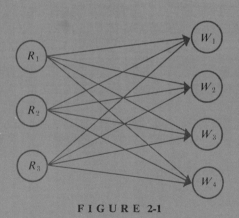

FIGURE 2-1

TABLE 2-1

From	To	Cost per bushel (in cents)
R_1	W_1	5
R_1	W_2	7
R_1	W_3	9
R_1	W_4	16
R_2	W_1	10
R_2	W_2	5
R_2	W_3	11
R_2	W_4	10
R_3	W_1	8
R_3	W_2	7
R_3	W_3	4
R_3	W_4	8

Express the cost schedule in tabular form using regions as row headings and warehouses as column headings.

9. (a) Express the cost information in Prob. 8 as a 3 by 4 matrix. Call this matrix C.
    (b) Give the numerical value of c_{11}.
    (c) What route is associated with the element c_{21}? c_{12}?

10. (a) Construct a 4 by 2 variable cost matrix from the cost information of Prob. 9 in Sec. 1-6. Use the same order of labeling for rows and columns. Call this matrix V.
    (b) Describe v_{11} and v_{32} in words.
    (c) Describe $\sum_{i=1}^{4} v_{i1}$ in words.

11. Assume that one can either buy or lease a machine and that demand will be either high or low. Set up a table that illustrates the possible situations that can occur, given the following:

    If demand is low and you purchase the machine, a net profit of $10,000 will result. If demand is low and you lease the machine, a net profit of $12,000 will result. If demand is high and you purchase the machine, a net profit of $20,000 will result. Otherwise the net profit is $5000.

12. Express the payoffs in Prob. 11 as a payoff matrix.

13. Given the matrix equation

$$\begin{pmatrix} 2x + y & 4 \\ 3 & x + 3y \end{pmatrix} = \begin{pmatrix} 1 & 4 \\ 3 & 2 \end{pmatrix}$$

Solve for x and y.

2-4 MULTIPLICATION OF A MATRIX BY A SCALAR AND BY A MATRIX

To distinguish them from vectors or matrices, real numbers are commonly called *scalars* when dealing with real numbers and vectors or real numbers and matrices. Next we define multiplication of a matrix of any size by a scalar.

DEFINITION 2.9. *Let $A = (a_{ij})$ be an m by n matrix and k be a real number (i.e., a scalar). Then the product of A by k denoted by kA is the m by n matrix (ka_{ij}). In words, the product of a matrix by a scalar is found by multiplying each element of the given matrix by the given scalar.*

Example 1. | Multiply $A = \begin{pmatrix} 1 & 3 & 6 \\ 2 & 5 & 3 \end{pmatrix}$ by $k = 0.3$.

Solution:

$$0.3A = \begin{pmatrix} (0.3)(1) & (0.3)(3) & (0.3)(6) \\ (0.3)(2) & (0.3)(5) & (0.3)(3) \end{pmatrix}$$

$$0.3A = \begin{pmatrix} 0.3 & 0.9 & 1.8 \\ 0.6 & 1.5 & 0.9 \end{pmatrix}$$

Example 2. | Let $A = \begin{pmatrix} 1 & 6 & 2 \\ 2 & 5 & 3 \end{pmatrix}$. Calculate $3A$ and $A + A + A$.

Solution:

$$3A = \begin{pmatrix} 3 & 18 & 6 \\ 6 & 15 & 9 \end{pmatrix} \qquad \text{by Definition 2.9}$$

$$A + A + A = \begin{pmatrix} 1+1+1 & 6+6+6 & 2+2+2 \\ 2+2+2 & 5+5+5 & 3+3+3 \end{pmatrix}$$

$$= \begin{pmatrix} 3 & 18 & 6 \\ 6 & 15 & 9 \end{pmatrix} \qquad \text{by definition of addition of matrices}$$

$$= 3A$$

The previous example illustrates the fact that multiplication of a matrix by a positive integer k is equivalent to adding the matrix together k times.

63

The multiplication of a matrix by a matrix is the most complicated operation with matrices that we have had so far. Before giving the definition, we point out that multiplication of a matrix by a matrix actually involves a sequence of multiplications of a column vector by a row vector. Recall that this type of multiplication was taken up in Sec. 2-2.

DEFINITION 2.10.   *Let A and B be two matrices such that the number of columns of A equals the number of rows of B. Call this number N. Then the product A times B denoted by AB is defined as follows: The elements of C = AB are defined to be $c_{ij} = a_{i1}b_{1j} + a_{i2}b_{2j} + a_{i3}b_{3j} + \cdots + a_{iN}b_{Nj}$. Using summation notation,*

$$c_{ij} = \sum_{k=1}^{N} a_{ik}b_{kj}$$

Example 3.   Determine $C = AB$ if $A = \begin{pmatrix} 1 & 2 \\ 3 & 4 \end{pmatrix}$ and $B = \begin{pmatrix} 5 & 6 \\ 7 & 8 \end{pmatrix}$.

Solution:

$$\begin{aligned} c_{11} &= a_{11}b_{11} + a_{12}b_{21} \\ &= (1)(5) + (2)(7) \\ &= 5 + 14 \\ &= 19 \end{aligned} \qquad \begin{aligned} c_{12} &= a_{11}b_{12} + a_{12}b_{22} \\ &= (1)(6) + (2)(8) \\ &= 6 + 16 \\ &= 22 \end{aligned}$$

$$\begin{aligned} c_{21} &= a_{21}b_{11} + a_{22}b_{21} \\ &= (3)(5) + (4)(7) \\ &= 15 + 28 \\ &= 43 \end{aligned} \qquad \begin{aligned} c_{22} &= a_{21}b_{12} + a_{22}b_{22} \\ &= (3)(6) + (4)(8) \\ &= 18 + 32 \\ &= 50 \end{aligned}$$

Therefore,

$$\begin{pmatrix} 1 & 2 \\ 3 & 4 \end{pmatrix}\begin{pmatrix} 5 & 6 \\ 7 & 8 \end{pmatrix} = \begin{pmatrix} 19 & 22 \\ 43 & 50 \end{pmatrix}$$

A careful reading of Definition 2.10 and the above example will show that the calculation of c_{11} involves the multiplication of the first column, interpreted as a column vector, of the second matrix by the first row, interpreted as a row vector, of the matrix on the left. In general,

$$c_{ij} = (i\text{th } row \text{ of } A). \begin{pmatrix} j\text{th} \\ c \\ o \\ l \\ u \\ m \\ n \\ \text{of } B \end{pmatrix}$$

Example 4. | Perform the matrix multiplication

$$C = \begin{pmatrix} 1 & 2 & 3 \\ 4 & 5 & 6 \end{pmatrix} \begin{pmatrix} 2 & 4 \\ 1 & 2 \\ 4 & 7 \end{pmatrix}$$

Solution:

$$c_{11} = (1, 2, 3) \begin{pmatrix} 2 \\ 1 \\ 4 \end{pmatrix} \qquad c_{12} = (1, 2, 3) \begin{pmatrix} 4 \\ 2 \\ 7 \end{pmatrix}$$

$$= 2 + 2 + 12 \qquad\qquad = 4 + 4 + 21$$
$$= 16 \qquad\qquad\qquad = 29$$

$$c_{21} = (4, 5, 6) \begin{pmatrix} 2 \\ 1 \\ 4 \end{pmatrix} \qquad c_{22} = (4, 5, 6) \begin{pmatrix} 4 \\ 2 \\ 7 \end{pmatrix}$$

$$= 8 + 5 + 24 \qquad\qquad = 16 + 10 + 42$$
$$= 37 \qquad\qquad\qquad = 68$$

Therefore,

$$C = \begin{pmatrix} 16 & 29 \\ 37 & 68 \end{pmatrix}$$

Recall from Definition 2.10 that *the product* of two matrices *is not defined unless* the *number of columns* of the matrix written on the left *equals* the *number of rows* of the matrix written on the right. The following examples illustrate this point:

1. The product of $\begin{pmatrix} 2 & 3 & 4 \\ 1 & 2 & 1 \end{pmatrix}$ times $\begin{pmatrix} 2 & 4 & 7 \\ 4 & 8 & 3 \end{pmatrix}$ is not defined since the left factor has *three columns,* but the right-hand factor has only *two rows.*

2. The product $\begin{pmatrix} 1 & 2 \\ 4 & 3 \end{pmatrix} \begin{pmatrix} 2 \\ 4 \end{pmatrix}$ is defined, but the product $\begin{pmatrix} 2 \\ 4 \end{pmatrix} \begin{pmatrix} 1 & 2 \\ 4 & 3 \end{pmatrix}$ is not defined. Note that the *order* of the factors *does* make a difference. More will be said about this later in the text.

It was pointed out in Sec. 2-2 that Definition 2.5 only admits multiplication of a column vector by a row vector and that this always leads to a scalar. The next example illustrates the fact that when we are dealing with matrices, a *row vector* interpreted as a 1 by n matrix can be multiplied by a *column vector* interpreted as an m by 1 matrix. Furthermore, the result is no longer a scalar, but an m by n matrix.

Example 5.   Perform the matrix multiplication

$$\begin{pmatrix} 2 \\ 3 \end{pmatrix} (4 \quad 5) = C$$

Solution:

$$c_{11} = (2)(4) = 8$$
$$c_{12} = (2)(5) = 10$$
$$c_{21} = (3)(4) = 12$$
$$c_{22} = (3)(5) = 15$$

65

Therefore,

$$\binom{2}{3}(4 \quad 5) = \begin{pmatrix} 8 & 10 \\ 12 & 15 \end{pmatrix}$$

Finally, we include some simple rules to determine when two matrices can be multiplied and to calculate the size of the product involved. Let A be an m by n matrix and B be a p by q matrix.

I.   *The product AB is defined if and only if $n = p$.*
II. *If $n = p$, then the product AB exists and is an m by q matrix.*

The following illustrate these rules.

1. The product of a 2 by 3 matrix times a 4 by 2 matrix is not defined.
2. The product of a 2 by 3 matrix times a 3 by 7 matrix is defined and is a 2 by 7 matrix.

PROBLEMS

1. Perform the following scalar multiplications:

    (a) $8 \begin{pmatrix} 6 & 9 \\ 2 & 1 \end{pmatrix}$

    (c) $0.3 \, (4, 8)$

    (b) $3 \begin{pmatrix} 2 & 1 & 4 \\ 5 & 6 & 8 \\ 7 & 3 & 2 \end{pmatrix}$

    (d) $1.4 \begin{pmatrix} 9 \\ 2 \\ 1 \end{pmatrix}$

2. Perform the following matrix multiplications:

    (a) $\begin{pmatrix} 1 & 2 \\ 3 & 4 \end{pmatrix} \begin{pmatrix} 8 & 7 \\ 6 & 2 \end{pmatrix}$

    (c) $(3, 2, 1) \begin{pmatrix} 6 \\ 8 \\ 9 \end{pmatrix}$

    (b) $\begin{pmatrix} 1 & 2 & 3 \\ 4 & 5 & 6 \end{pmatrix} \begin{pmatrix} 2 & 1 \\ 4 & 8 \\ 7 & 2 \end{pmatrix}$

    (d) $\begin{pmatrix} 6 & 8 & 2 \\ 1 & 4 & 3 \\ 6 & 2 & 1 \end{pmatrix} \begin{pmatrix} 4 & 8 & 2 \\ 3 & 2 & 1 \\ 4 & 2 & 8 \end{pmatrix}$

3. Explain why none of the following pairs of matrices can be multiplied.

    (a) $\begin{pmatrix} 2 & 1 \\ 4 & 8 \\ 7 & 2 \end{pmatrix}, \begin{pmatrix} 1 & 2 & 3 \\ 4 & 5 & 6 \\ 7 & 2 & 1 \end{pmatrix}$

    (c) $\begin{pmatrix} 2 \\ 4 \end{pmatrix}, \begin{pmatrix} 2 & 6 \\ 7 & 3 \end{pmatrix}$

    (b) $\begin{pmatrix} 6 & 3 \\ 2 & 9 \end{pmatrix}, (1, 3)$

    (d) $\begin{pmatrix} 1 & 2 & 3 \\ 4 & 5 & 6 \end{pmatrix}, \begin{pmatrix} 7 & 4 & 9 \\ 8 & 2 & 1 \end{pmatrix}$

4. Perform the following matrix multiplications:

    (a) $\begin{pmatrix} 1 & 0 & 0 \\ 0 & 1 & 0 \\ 0 & 0 & 1 \end{pmatrix} \begin{pmatrix} 2 & 3 & 8 \\ 4 & 1 & 2 \\ 3 & 7 & 5 \end{pmatrix}$

    (b) $\begin{pmatrix} a_{11} & a_{12} & a_{13} \\ a_{21} & a_{22} & a_{23} \\ a_{31} & a_{32} & a_{33} \end{pmatrix} \begin{pmatrix} 1 & 0 & 0 \\ 0 & 1 & 0 \\ 0 & 0 & 1 \end{pmatrix}$

5. Multiply the following if multiplication is defined.

(a) $\begin{pmatrix} 1 & 2 \\ 3 & 4 \end{pmatrix} \begin{pmatrix} 8 & -7 \\ -6 & 2 \end{pmatrix}$

(d) $\begin{pmatrix} 6 & 8 & 3 & 1 \\ 4 & 9 & 2 & 3 \\ 7 & 1 & 4 & 2 \end{pmatrix} \begin{pmatrix} 7 & 2 & 3 \\ 8 & 4 & 1 \\ 6 & 5 & 2 \\ 2 & 9 & 8 \end{pmatrix}$

(b) $\begin{pmatrix} 4 & 6 & 8 \\ 9 & 3 & 2 \end{pmatrix} \begin{pmatrix} 6 & 7 \\ 2 & 1 \\ 3 & 2 \end{pmatrix}$

(e) $\begin{pmatrix} 2 & 1 \\ 4 & 3 \end{pmatrix} \begin{pmatrix} 2 & 9 & 8 & 6 & 4 \\ 3 & 2 & 2 & 1 & 4 \end{pmatrix}$

(c) $\begin{pmatrix} 4 & 9 & 6 \\ 8 & 7 & 2 \end{pmatrix} \begin{pmatrix} 4 & 8 & 2 \\ 9 & 1 & 4 \end{pmatrix}$

(f) $\begin{pmatrix} 3 \\ 2 \\ 4 \end{pmatrix} (1, \quad 6, \quad 7)$

6. Consider pairs of matrices with sizes given below. Determine which pairs of matrices can be multiplied and indicate the size of the product if multiplication is defined.

(a) $3 \times 2, 2 \times 4$ **(d)** $3 \times 3, 3 \times 3$

(b) $1 \times 3, 1 \times 3$ **(e)** $3 \times 1, 1 \times 3$

(c) $2 \times 2, 2 \times 3$ **(f)** $6 \times 8, 8 \times 7$

7. Let $A = \begin{pmatrix} a_{11} & a_{12} & \cdots & a_{18} \\ a_{21} & a_{22} & \cdots & a_{28} \end{pmatrix}$, $B = \begin{pmatrix} b_{11} & b_{12} \\ b_{21} & b_{22} \\ \cdot & \cdot \\ \cdot & \cdot \\ \cdot & \cdot \\ b_{81} & b_{82} \end{pmatrix}$, and $C = AB$.

Use summation notation to express the four elements of C.

8. A company employs three different types of workers: skilled, semi-skilled, and laborers. Of the skilled workers, 10 have been with the company less than a year, 20 from 1 to 4 years, 50 from 5 to 19 years, and 60 for 20 years or more. Of the semi-skilled employees, 50 have been with the company less than a year, 150 from 1 to 4 years, 250 from 5 to 19 years, and 200 for 20 years or more. Of the laborers, 90 have been with the company less than 1 year, 30 from 1 to 4 years, 50 from 5 to 19 years, and 40 for 20 years or more.

(a) Express the above in tabular form with type of worker as the row heading.

(b) Express the above as a matrix W with type of worker as the row heading.

(c) Using subscript notation, how would you make reference to the number of skilled workers who have been with the company for over 20 years?

(d) Using summation notation, how would you express the total number of laborers?

9. Given Table 2-2.

TABLE 2-2

Length of Time, t, with Company in Years	Vacation Days
$t < 1$	5
$1 \leq t \leq 4$	10
$5 \leq t \leq 19$	15
$20 \leq t$	20

> **(a)** Express the number of vacation days as a column vector.
> **(b)** Using the matrix developed in Prob. 8 and the column vector from (a), calculate, by type of worker, the number of days of work that will be lost because of vacation.
> **10.** Given Table 2-3.
>
>   TABLE 2-3
>
> | Type of Worker | Average Pay per Day |
> | --- | --- |
> | skilled | $40.00 |
> | semi-skilled | 30.00 |
> | laborer | 25.00 |
>
> **(a)** Express the data as a row vector.
> **(b)** Using matrix multiplication and the result of $9 - b$, find the cost of providing vacations to employees this year.

2-5 SYSTEMS OF EQUATIONS AS SINGLE MATRIX EQUATIONS

The definitions of equality and multiplication of matrices make it possible to write a system of linear equations in n unknowns as a single matrix equation. The next two examples illustrate this point.

Example 1.

Write the matrix equation

$$\begin{pmatrix} 2 & 3 & 1 \\ 4 & 2 & 3 \\ 1 & 1 & 6 \end{pmatrix} \begin{pmatrix} x \\ y \\ z \end{pmatrix} = \begin{pmatrix} 2 \\ 1 \\ 3 \end{pmatrix}$$

as a system of equations.

Solution: If we perform the indicated multiplication we arrive at the vector equation

$$\begin{pmatrix} 2x + 3y + z \\ 4x + 2y + 3z \\ x + y + 6z \end{pmatrix} = \begin{pmatrix} 2 \\ 1 \\ 3 \end{pmatrix}$$

This gives the system of equations

$$2x + 3y + z = 2$$
$$4x + 2y + 3z = 1$$
$$x + y + 6z = 3$$

by definition of equality of vectors.

Example 2.

Write the system of equations

$$x + 2y + 3z = 1$$
$$x + 3y + 5z = 2$$

$$2x + 5y + 9z = 3$$

as a single matrix equation.

Solution: Form the three matrices

$$\begin{pmatrix} 1 & 2 & 3 \\ 1 & 3 & 5 \\ 2 & 5 & 9 \end{pmatrix}, \qquad \begin{pmatrix} x \\ y \\ z \end{pmatrix}, \text{ and } \begin{pmatrix} 1 \\ 2 \\ 3 \end{pmatrix}$$

This system can be written as the single matrix equation

$$\begin{pmatrix} 1 & 2 & 3 \\ 1 & 3 & 5 \\ 2 & 5 & 9 \end{pmatrix}\begin{pmatrix} x \\ y \\ z \end{pmatrix} = \begin{pmatrix} 1 \\ 2 \\ 3 \end{pmatrix}$$

as can be verified by the method of Example 1.

In general, a system of equations of the form *I*,

$$\begin{array}{c} a_{11}x_1 + a_{12}x_2 + \cdots + a_{1n}x_n = b_1 \\ a_{21}x_1 + a_{22}x_2 + \cdots + a_{2n}x_n = b_2 \\ \vdots \qquad\qquad\qquad\qquad\qquad \vdots \\ a_{m1}x_1 + a_{m2}x_2 + \cdots + a_{mn}x_n = b_m \end{array} \qquad (I)$$

where x_1, x_2, ... are used instead of x, y, ..., can be written as a single matrix equation of form *II* .

$$\begin{pmatrix} a_{11} & a_{12} & \cdots & a_{1n} \\ a_{21} & a_{22} & \cdots & a_{2n} \\ \vdots & \vdots & & \vdots \\ a_{m1} & a_{m2} & \cdots & a_{mn} \end{pmatrix}\begin{pmatrix} x_1 \\ x_2 \\ \vdots \\ x_n \end{pmatrix} = \begin{pmatrix} b_1 \\ b_2 \\ \vdots \\ b_m \end{pmatrix} \qquad (II)$$

The matrix equation *II* can be abbreviated further to read

$$A\mathbf{x} = \mathbf{b}, \text{ where } A = (a_{ij}), \mathbf{x} = \begin{pmatrix} x_1 \\ x_2 \\ \vdots \\ x_n \end{pmatrix}, \text{and } \mathbf{b} = \begin{pmatrix} b_1 \\ b_2 \\ \vdots \\ b_m \end{pmatrix}$$

and A is called the matrix of coefficients.

A procedure for fitting straight lines to data was discussed in Sec. 1-8. The normal equations are repeated below for convenience:

$$na + \sum_{i=1}^{n} x_i b = \sum_{i=1}^{n} y_i$$

$$\sum_{i=1}^{n} x_i a + \sum_{i=1}^{n} x_i^2 b = \sum_{i=1}^{n} x_i y_i$$

(normal equations for the two-variable case)

Example 3. | Write the normal equations in matrix form.

Solution:

$$\begin{pmatrix} n & \sum_{i=1}^{n} x_i \\ \sum_{i=1}^{n} x_i & \sum_{i=1}^{n} x_i{}^2 \end{pmatrix} \begin{pmatrix} a \\ b \end{pmatrix} = \begin{pmatrix} \sum_{i=1}^{n} y_i \\ \sum_{i=1}^{n} x_i y_i \end{pmatrix}$$

PROBLEMS

1. Write the system

$$\begin{aligned} x - 2y + z &= 9 \\ 2x + y - 2z &= -1 \\ x + y + 3z &= 2 \end{aligned}$$

in matrix form.

2. Given the system of equations

$$\begin{aligned} x + 2y + 3z &= 1 \\ x + 3y + 5z &= 2 \\ 2x + 5y + 9z &= 3 \end{aligned}$$

Write the above as a matrix equation.

3. Write the system of equations

$$\begin{aligned} 4x + 6y + 3z &= 2 \\ 5x + 4y + z &= 1 \\ 5x + 6y &= 4 \end{aligned}$$

as a single matrix equation.

4. Write the matrix equation

$$\begin{pmatrix} 4 & 2 & 6 \\ 9 & 1 & 0 \\ 3 & 2 & 4 \end{pmatrix} \begin{pmatrix} x_1 \\ x_2 \\ x_3 \end{pmatrix} = \begin{pmatrix} 4 \\ 9 \\ 3 \end{pmatrix}$$

as a system of equations.

5. Given the following system:

$$\begin{aligned} x_1 + 2x_2 + 3x_3 &= 2 \\ 2x_1 + 3x_2 + 4x_3 &= -5 \\ 2x_1 - x_2 &= 3 \end{aligned}$$

Write the above as a matrix equation.

6. Write the following vector equation as a matrix equation.

$$x \begin{pmatrix} 2 \\ 1 \\ 3 \end{pmatrix} + y \begin{pmatrix} 4 \\ 1 \\ 2 \end{pmatrix} + z \begin{pmatrix} 5 \\ 8 \\ 4 \end{pmatrix} = \begin{pmatrix} 2 \\ 1 \\ 3 \end{pmatrix}$$

7. Substitute the following values, $\sum_{i=1}^{n} x_i = 1500$, $\sum_{i=1}^{n} y_i = 400$, $\sum_{i=1}^{n} x_i{}^2 = 550{,}000$, $\sum_{i=1}^{n} x_i y_i = 133{,}000$, and $n = 5$, in the normal equations in matrix form of Example 3 of this section.

8. Verify that $a = 41$ and $b = 0.13$ is the solution to the system in Prob. 7.

Problems 9 and 10 are designed to give computational experience in fitting a function of the form $y = b_0 + b_1 x_1 + b_2 x_2$ to data. In this case y is a *linear* function of the two independent variables x_1 and x_2. It can be shown that the resulting normal equations for this three-variable model are:

$$\Sigma\, y = b_0 n + b_1 \Sigma\, x_1 + b_2 \Sigma\, x_2$$

$$\Sigma\, x_1 y = b_0 \Sigma\, x_1 + b_1 \Sigma\, x_1{}^2 + b_2 \Sigma\, x_1 x_2$$

$$\Sigma\, x_2 y = b_0 \Sigma\, x_2 + b_1 \Sigma\, x_1 x_2 + b_2 \Sigma\, x_2{}^2$$

(normal equations for the three-variable case)

The summations are all from 1 to n, where n is the number of observations of y.

9. Set up the normal equations for the three-variable case above in matrix form.

10. (a) Set up the normal equations for fitting the function $\hat{y} = b_0 + b_1 x_1 + b_2 x_2$ to the data from Table 2-4.

TABLE 2-4

x_1	x_2	y
1	1	8.9
1	1	9.1
−1	1	2.8
−1	1	3.2
−1	−1	−5.3
−1	−1	−4.7
1	−1	0.9
1	−1	1.1

(b) Determine b_0, b_1, and b_2.

2-6 BUSINESS APPLICATIONS OF VECTOR AND MATRIX MULTIPLICATION

We will begin this section with an example that involves multiplication of a *vector* by a *scalar*.

Example 1.   The material needed to build one wall of a building is known to be five pounds of nails, twenty two-by-fours, four two-by-sixes, and five sheets of plywood. This information can be expressed as the row vector $\mathbf{m} = (5, 20, 4, 5)$. How much material will be needed to construct four walls of this type?

Solution: The amount of material needed can be found by performing the multiplication $4\mathbf{m} = (20, 80, 16, 20)$. Note that the first component of $4\mathbf{m}$ equals 20; this means that 20 pounds of nails are needed to make the four walls.

The next example involves multiplication of a *column vector* by a *row vector* to determine a total material cost.

Example 2. In addition to the information given in Example 1, it is known that nails cost $0.20/pound, two-by-fours cost $0.60 each, two-by-sixes cost $3.00 each, and plywood costs $6.00/sheet. This information can be expressed by the column vector $\mathbf{c} = \begin{pmatrix} 0.20 \\ 0.60 \\ 3.00 \\ 6.00 \end{pmatrix}$. Find the total cost of material.

Solution: The scalar quantity $\mathbf{mc} = (5, 20, 4, 5) \begin{pmatrix} 0.20 \\ 0.60 \\ 3.00 \\ 6.00 \end{pmatrix} = \$55.00$ is the cost of the material needed to produce one wall.

The next example involves multiplication of a *matrix* by a *vector*.

Example 3. Consider a manufacturer who can produce two different products, P_1 and P_2. One unit of P_1 requires 3 parts of type a and 2 parts of type b. Also, one unit of P_2 requires 2 parts of type a, 6 parts of type b, and 2 parts of type c. This information can be displayed in matrix form as follows.

$$
\begin{array}{c}
\\
Products
\end{array}
\begin{array}{c|ccc}
 & \multicolumn{3}{c}{Parts} \\
 & a & b & c \\
\hline
1 & 3 & 2 & 0 \\
2 & 2 & 6 & 2
\end{array}
$$

Note: one unit of product 1 requires 3 parts of type a, 2 parts of type b, and no parts of type c, and so forth.

Call the matrix $\begin{pmatrix} 3 & 2 & 0 \\ 2 & 6 & 2 \end{pmatrix}$ the parts matrix P. Let us suppose that the company has been requested to fill an order for 300 units of P_1 and 150 units of P_2. Adopting the convention of *representing orders by row vectors*, we have $\mathbf{o} = (300, 150)$. Find the number of parts of each type required to fill the order.

Solution: Multiply the parts matrix P by the order vector $\mathbf{o}$. This gives $(300, 150) \begin{pmatrix} 3 & 2 & 0 \\ 2 & 6 & 2 \end{pmatrix} = (1200, 1500, 300)$. Interpreting this answer, we see that 1200 parts of type a, 1500 parts of type b, and 300 parts of type c are needed to fill the order.

The following type of problem can be handled conveniently by using matrix multiplication.

A manufacturer can produce four products, A, B, C, and D. Each of these products requires sub-assemblies I, II, III, IV, and V. Each sub-assembly requires parts a, b, c, d, e, f, and g. Given an order for four products, determine the number of each part that is required in order to fill the order. To solve such a problem, form the sub-assembly matrix S.

Sub-Assembly

I II III IV V

Product $\begin{matrix} A \\ B \\ C \\ D \end{matrix}$

Next form the parts matrix P.

Parts

a   b   c   d   e   f   g

Sub-Assembly $\begin{matrix} I \\ II \\ III \\ IV \\ V \end{matrix}$

The matrix obtained by multiplying the *sub-assembly matrix* times the *parts matrix* gives a matrix SP, which expresses the number of parts needed for each product. Finally, the solution is obtained by multiplying the order size expressed as a row vector **o** times the matrix, SP. This is an example of a *parts explosion* problem.

Notice that in setting up these matrices, we placed the highest order of production (i.e., a product is of higher order than a sub-assembly and a sub-assembly is of higher order than a part) as *row headings*. This insures that the matrix multiplications will always be possible and that we are always adding like units. In the previous example, the use of this convention leads to the multiplication of a (4×5) matrix times a (5×7) matrix. Without this convention the second factor could have been a (7×5) matrix, in which case multiplication would be undefined. The product **o** (SP) is a (1×7) vector and gives the amount of each part required to fill the order.

Example 4.   Given the sub-assembly matrix

Sub-Assembly

$$S = \begin{matrix} & \begin{matrix} I & II & III & IV & V \end{matrix} \\ \begin{matrix} A \\ B \\ C \\ D \end{matrix} & \begin{pmatrix} 4 & 2 & 1 & 6 & 7 \\ 3 & 1 & 2 & 4 & 4 \\ 2 & 3 & 5 & 2 & 1 \\ 1 & 2 & 4 & 1 & 2 \end{pmatrix} \end{matrix}$$

and the parts matrix

Part

$$P = \begin{matrix} & \begin{matrix} a & b & c & d & e & f & g \end{matrix} \\ \begin{matrix} I \\ II \\ III \\ IV \\ V \end{matrix} & \begin{pmatrix} 2 & 3 & 5 & 7 & 8 & 2 & 1 \\ 1 & 4 & 3 & 6 & 2 & 1 & 5 \\ 5 & 2 & 4 & 6 & 1 & 8 & 4 \\ 1 & 2 & 2 & 1 & 3 & 4 & 6 \\ 8 & 1 & 6 & 7 & 2 & 4 & 2 \end{pmatrix} \end{matrix}$$

and the order size vector $\mathbf{o} = (20, 10, 10, 5)$. Find the total number of each kind of part needed.

Solution: The solution is simply $\mathbf{o}(SP)$. The element in the upper left hand corner of SP is given by $4(2) + 2(1) + (1)(5) + (6)(1) + (7)(8) = 8 + 2 + 5 + 6 + 56 = 77$.

Continuing in this manner, we have

$$
\begin{array}{c}
\quad\quad\quad\quad\quad Part \\
\quad\quad a \quad b \quad c \quad d \quad e \quad f \quad g \\
SP = \begin{array}{c} A \\ B \\ C \\ D \end{array}
\begin{pmatrix}
77 & 41 & 84 & 101 & 69 & 70 & 68 \\
53 & 29 & 58 & 71 & 48 & 55 & 48 \\
42 & 33 & 49 & 71 & 35 & 59 & 51 \\
41 & 23 & 41 & 58 & 23 & 48 & 37
\end{pmatrix}
\end{array}
$$

To produce a unit of product A, one needs 77 of part a, 41 of part b, and so forth. If we multiply $\mathbf{o}$ times SP, we get the number of each part required to fill the order.

$\mathbf{o}(SP) = (20, 10, 10, 5)(SP)$
$\mathbf{o}(SP) = (2695, 1555, 2955, 3730, 2325, 2780, 2535)$

The first component of this vector is given by

$$
\begin{aligned}
&= 20(77) + 10(53) + 10(42) + 5(41) \\
&= 1540 + 530 + 420 + 205 \\
&= 2695
\end{aligned}
$$

We now know that 2695 units of part a, 1555 units of part b, and so forth are required in order to fill the order.

Let us carry this one step further. If we know the cost of each part, we can compute the total material cost of the order.

The product $\mathbf{o}(SP)$ is a (1×7) vector that gives the amount of each part required to fill the order. If we write the cost per part as a column vector, we have

$$
\mathbf{c} = \begin{pmatrix} \$1 \\ 0.5 \\ 2 \\ 1 \\ 3 \\ 2 \\ 1 \end{pmatrix}
$$

where $1.00 is the cost of part a
$0.50 is the cost of part b

The result gives a Total Cost equal to $[\mathbf{o}(SP)]\mathbf{c}$, where

$$
[\mathbf{o}(SP)]\mathbf{c} = (2695, 1555, 2955, 3730, 2325, 2780, 2535) \begin{pmatrix} \$1 \\ 0.5 \\ 2 \\ 1 \\ 3 \\ 1 \end{pmatrix}
$$

$$
= \$28,182.50
$$

Therefore, the total material cost of the order is \$28,182.50.

PROBLEMS

1. Given that a person purchases the following items: 1 stepladder, 4 gallons of red paint, 1 gallon of white paint, 2 paint brushes, and 1 five-quart pail, express these quantities as a row vector.

2. Given that the items in Prob. 1 cost $24.00, $5.00, $4.50, $4.00, and $0.25, respectively, express these costs as a column vector.

3. Obtain the total cost of the purchase using Probs. 1 and 2 and vector multiplication.

4. Consider a manufacturer who can produce YIPS, YAPS, and ZAPS. Assume that in order to produce one YIP, two units of A and six units of B are required. To produce one YAP, 3 units of A and 1 unit of B are required. One ZAP requires 1 unit of A and 2 units of B. Construct a parts matrix. Use parts as the column headings.

5. If you received an order for 6 YIPS, 2 YAPS, and 7 ZAPS, would you use a row or column vector to represent the order, assuming that the formula to compute the total number of parts required is determined by multiplying the order vector times the parts matrix?

6. Multiply the order vector of Prob. 5 times the parts matrix of Prob. 4. Determine the total number of units required.

7. Given that the cost of one unit of A is $2.00 and the cost of one unit of B is $3.00, express the cost as a vector.

8. Obtain the total cost of the order using the results of Probs. 6 and 7.

9. We can produce two products P_1 and P_2. To produce a P_1 requires four of sub-assembly I, two of sub-assembly II, and three of sub-assembly III. To produce a P_2 requires two of sub-assembly I and one of sub-assembly III. Form the sub-assembly matrix. [*Note:* Place the highest order of production as row headings.]

10. Each sub-assembly in Prob. 9 requires the following parts: Sub-assembly I requires two units of part number 061 and three units of part number 072; sub-assembly II requires one of part number 061 and two of part number 072; sub-assembly III requires four units of part number 061 and five units of part number 072. Form the parts matrix. [*Note:* Place the highest order of production as row headings.]

11. Using Probs. 9 and 10, determine how many of each part is required to produce each product.

12. Given an order for sixteen P_1's and ten P_2's, write this order as a row vector and find out how many of each part is required in inventory to fill the order. Use the result of Prob. 11.

13. If the cost per unit of part number 061 is $0.50 and the cost per unit of part number 072 is $1.00, compute the total material cost of the order. Use the result of Prob. 12.

14. Given the following information:

$$\text{Product} \begin{array}{c} A \\ B \end{array} \begin{array}{cc} \overset{\text{\small Sub-Assembly}}{\overset{\text{I} \quad \text{II}}{}} \\ \begin{pmatrix} 5 & 4 \\ 6 & 1 \end{pmatrix} \end{array} \qquad \text{Sub-Assembly} \begin{array}{c} \text{I} \\ \text{II} \end{array} \begin{array}{ccc} \overset{\text{\small Part}}{\overset{a \quad b \quad c}{}} \\ \begin{pmatrix} 5 & 4 & 2 \\ 3 & 1 & 0 \end{pmatrix} \end{array}$$

(a) What is the significance of the figures in these matrices?

(b) Given the order vector (100, 200), how many parts are required to fill the order?

(c) Given that the cost of part a is \$0.25, part b is \$0.30, and part c is \$0.10, express cost as a column vector.

(d) What is the material cost of the order?

15. If at present we have 10,000 units of part a on hand, 7500 units of part b, and 4000 units of part c, can we fill the order in Prob. 14? If not, what part, or parts, are needed?

16. Let the following variable cost information be given for a firm making tables, chairs, and desks.

	Tables (x_1)	Chairs (x_2)	Desks (x_3)
Material	\$14	\$11	\$10
Labor	5	4	8
Variable overhead	3	1	2

(a) Express the above information in matrix form. Call this matrix A.

(b) Given an order for 5 tables, 20 chairs, and 100 desks, use the matrix A in (a) to compute the total variable cost.

17. Find the total variable cost function for the firm described in Prob. 16.

18. A firm purchases two machines at a cost of \$10,000 and \$20,000, respectively. Both machines have a lifetime of four years and have zero salvage values at the end of the four years. The two machines are depreciated using the "straight line method" (i.e., equal amounts each year). Express the costs as a row vector and the percentages as a column vector. By matrix multiplication, find the depreciation schedule.

THREE

Algebra of square matrices

3-1   INTRODUCTION TO THE ALGEBRA OF SQUARE MATRICES

In Chap. 2 we discussed the addition and multiplication of matrices. The reader will recall that two matrices cannot be *added* unless they are both the *same size*. In the case of *multiplication*, the left factor must have the *same number of columns* as the right factor has *rows* in order for the product to be defined. In this chapter we will restrict our attention to the class of n by n matrices (i.e., square matrices). For a fixed value of n, both the sum and the product of any pair of n by n matrices are defined.

We restrict our attention for the moment to the class of 3 by 3 matrices as a typical class of n by n matrices. Consider the 3 by 3 matrix

$$Z = \begin{pmatrix} 0 & 0 & 0 \\ 0 & 0 & 0 \\ 0 & 0 & 0 \end{pmatrix}$$

If we compute the sum $A + Z$, where $A = (a_{ij})$, $i, j = 1, 2, 3$, we have

$$\begin{pmatrix} a_{11} & a_{12} & a_{13} \\ a_{21} & a_{22} & a_{23} \\ a_{31} & a_{32} & a_{33} \end{pmatrix} + \begin{pmatrix} 0 & 0 & 0 \\ 0 & 0 & 0 \\ 0 & 0 & 0 \end{pmatrix} = \begin{pmatrix} a_{11} & a_{12} & a_{13} \\ a_{21} & a_{22} & a_{23} \\ a_{31} & a_{32} & a_{33} \end{pmatrix} \quad \begin{array}{l} \textit{by definition} \\ \textit{of addition} \\ \textit{of matrices} \end{array}$$

Briefly, $A + Z = A$. In other words, the matrix Z behaves in the class of 3 by 3 matrices like the additive identity 0 of the real number system.

Assisted by the fact that there is a 3 by 3 matrix which behaves like a *zero*, it seems natural to seek a matrix which behaves like a *one* in the sense that $AI = IA = A$. We might test the 3 by 3 matrix with all ones as its elements for this property. A quick check will reveal that the matrix just described does not have the desired property. However, if we retain three of the ones and consider the matrix

$$I = \begin{pmatrix} 1 & 0 & 0 \\ 0 & 1 & 0 \\ 0 & 0 & 1 \end{pmatrix}$$

we find that $AI = A$.

Example 1.   Show that $AI = A$, where $A = (a_{ij})$, $i,j = 1, 2, 3,$ and

$$I = \begin{pmatrix} 1 & 0 & 0 \\ 0 & 1 & 0 \\ 0 & 0 & 1 \end{pmatrix}$$

Solution:

$$AI = \begin{pmatrix} a_{11} & a_{12} & a_{13} \\ a_{21} & a_{22} & a_{23} \\ a_{31} & a_{32} & a_{33} \end{pmatrix} \begin{pmatrix} 1 & 0 & 0 \\ 0 & 1 & 0 \\ 0 & 0 & 1 \end{pmatrix}$$

$$= \begin{pmatrix} a_{11} + 0 + 0 & 0 + a_{12} + 0 & 0 + 0 + a_{13} \\ a_{21} + 0 + 0 & 0 + a_{22} + 0 & 0 + 0 + a_{23} \\ a_{31} + 0 + 0 & 0 + a_{32} + 0 & 0 + 0 + a_{33} \end{pmatrix} \quad \begin{array}{l} \textit{by definition} \\ \textit{of matrix} \\ \textit{multiplication} \end{array}$$

$$= \begin{pmatrix} a_{11} & a_{12} & a_{13} \\ a_{21} & a_{22} & a_{23} \\ a_{31} & a_{32} & a_{33} \end{pmatrix}$$

$$= A$$

DEFINITION 3.1.   *The elements a_{11}, a_{22}, a_{33}, . . . , a_{nn} of the n by n matrix A constitute what is called the principal diagonal of A.*

DEFINITION 3.2.   *The n by n matrix Z, all of whose elements equal zero, is called the additive identity for the class of n by n matrices.*

DEFINITION 3.3.   *The n by n matrix I, with ones on the principal diagonal and zeros elsewhere, is called the multiplicative identity for the class of n by n matrices.*

Example 2.   Write the additive and multiplicative identities for the class of 4 by 4 matrices.

Solution:

$$Z = \begin{pmatrix} 0 & 0 & 0 & 0 \\ 0 & 0 & 0 & 0 \\ 0 & 0 & 0 & 0 \\ 0 & 0 & 0 & 0 \end{pmatrix} \quad \text{and} \quad I = \begin{pmatrix} 1 & 0 & 0 & 0 \\ 0 & 1 & 0 & 0 \\ 0 & 0 & 1 & 0 \\ 0 & 0 & 0 & 1 \end{pmatrix}$$

The multiplicative identity I for a given value of n is often called simply the *identity matrix* or just the *identity*.

PROBLEMS

1. Write the additive and multiplicative identities for the class of two by two matrices.
2. Show that the matrix B is *not* the multiplicative identity of A where

$$A = \begin{pmatrix} 4 & 2 & 1 \\ 6 & 3 & 4 \\ 8 & 7 & 1 \end{pmatrix} \quad \text{and} \quad B = \begin{pmatrix} 1 & 1 & 1 \\ 1 & 1 & 1 \\ 1 & 1 & 1 \end{pmatrix}$$

3. Given the matrix $A = \begin{pmatrix} 2 & 1 & 3 \\ 4 & 5 & 6 \\ 2 & 1 & 2 \end{pmatrix}$ and the matrix $Z = \begin{pmatrix} 0 & 0 & 0 \\ 0 & 0 & 0 \\ 0 & 0 & 0 \end{pmatrix}$, verify that the matrix Z behaves like a *zero* (i.e., compute $A + Z$).

4. Given that $A = \begin{pmatrix} 2 & 6 \\ 1 & 4 \end{pmatrix}$ and that $I = \begin{pmatrix} 1 & 0 \\ 0 & 1 \end{pmatrix}$, verify that I behaves like a *one* (i.e., compute AI).

5. What is the appropriate additive identity for the following matrices?

   (a) $\begin{pmatrix} 2 & 4 & 1 & 6 \\ 8 & 3 & 2 & 4 \\ 5 & 9 & 6 & 2 \\ 1 & 8 & 3 & 4 \end{pmatrix}$ (b) $\begin{pmatrix} 2 & 1 \\ 3 & 8 \end{pmatrix}$

6. What is the appropriate multiplicative identity for the matrices in Prob. 5?

7. Show that $AI = IA$ for the class of 3 by 3 matrices.

8. Compute $\begin{pmatrix} 0 & 0 \\ 0 & 0 \end{pmatrix}\begin{pmatrix} 2 & 3 \\ 4 & 7 \end{pmatrix}$.

9. Show that $ZA = Z$ for the class of 3 by 3 matrices.

A solid waste manager is in charge of the collection system described below. The system consists of three trucks (with crew), three garages, three collection zones, and one land fill site. The garages are built at various places throughout the collection region other than the land fill site. Problems 10 through 13 relate to this system.

10. Let L denote the land fill site, g_i ($i = 1, 2, 3$) denote the garages, and z_i ($i = 1, 2, 3$) denote the collection zones. Draw a schematic diagram for the system using the suggested notation.

11. If

    a_{ij} = distance from g_i to z_j
    x_j = distance from z_j to L
    b_i = distance from L to g_i
    y_j = distance through z_j
    d_{ij} = total distance from garage i to zone j, through zone j to the land fill site, and back to garage i

    show that $d_{ij} = a_{ij} + y_j + x_j + b_i$.

12. Use the result of Prob. 11 to determine the total distance matrix, $D = (d_{ij})$, for the waste collection system in Fig. 3-1.

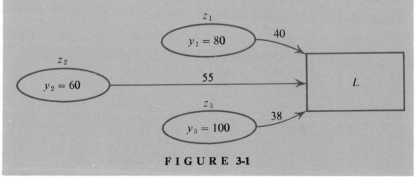

z_1 $y_1 = 80$ 40

z_2 $y_2 = 60$ 55 L

z_3 $y_3 = 100$ 38

FIGURE 3-1

$$\mathbf{b} = (b_1, b_2, b_3) = (110, 170, 38) \qquad A = (a_{ij}) = \begin{pmatrix} 12 & 18 & 14 \\ 6 & 10 & 12 \\ 45 & 12 & 25 \end{pmatrix}$$

13. An assignment problem.
   (a) Use the total distance matrix D from Prob. 12 with garages as row headings and zones as column headings to determine the sum of the distances of all three trucks if the manager assigns zone 1 to garage 1, zone 2 to garage 2, and zone 3 to garage 3.
   (b) How many different ways can the manager assign zones to garages?
   (c) What is the best assignment in the sense of minimum combined distance?

14. The *trace* of a square matrix A is defined to be the sum of the elements in the principal diagonal and is denoted by tr A.
   (a) Observe that $\operatorname{tr} A = \sum_{i=1}^{n} a_{ii}$.

   (b) Compute the trace of $A = \begin{pmatrix} 2 & 1 & 3 \\ 4 & 1 & 2 \\ 1 & 8 & 3 \end{pmatrix}$.

   (c) Show that $\operatorname{tr}(kA) = k \operatorname{tr} A$, where k is a real number.
   (d) Show that $\operatorname{tr}(A + B) = \operatorname{tr} A + \operatorname{tr} B$.

3-2 SOME ALGEBRAIC LAWS FOR SQUARE MATRICES

In addition to possessing both an additive and a multiplicative identity, square matrices also satisfy the following important *theorems* where A, B, and C are n by n matrices.

1. $A + B = B + A$ Commutative Law for Addition
2. $(A + B) + C = A + (B + C)$ Associative Law for Addition
3. $(AB)C = A(BC)$ Associative Law for Multiplication
4. $A(B + C) = AB + AC$ Left-hand Distributive Law
5. $(A + B)C = AC + BC$ Right-hand Distributive Law

It should be pointed out that even though we are restricting our discussion to square matrices, these theorems are also true for non-square matrices as well, providing the sizes are such that the operations are defined.

Proofs of some of these theorems are beyond the scope of this text, so we limit our treatment of them to some illustrative numerical examples.

Example 1.   Let $A = \begin{pmatrix} 1 & 3 \\ 2 & 4 \end{pmatrix}$, $B = \begin{pmatrix} 3 & 5 \\ 6 & 7 \end{pmatrix}$, and $C = \begin{pmatrix} 4 & 8 \\ 4 & 9 \end{pmatrix}$. Verify the associative law for addition (i.e., calculate $(A + B) + C$ and $A + (B + C)$ and compare the resulting matrices for equality).

Solution:

$$(A + B) + C = \left[\begin{pmatrix} 1 & 3 \\ 2 & 4 \end{pmatrix} + \begin{pmatrix} 3 & 5 \\ 6 & 7 \end{pmatrix} \right] + \begin{pmatrix} 4 & 8 \\ 4 & 9 \end{pmatrix}$$

$$= \begin{pmatrix} 4 & 8 \\ 8 & 11 \end{pmatrix} + \begin{pmatrix} 4 & 8 \\ 4 & 9 \end{pmatrix}$$

$$= \begin{pmatrix} 8 & 16 \\ 12 & 20 \end{pmatrix}$$

$$A + (B + C) = \begin{pmatrix} 1 & 3 \\ 2 & 4 \end{pmatrix} + \left[\begin{pmatrix} 3 & 5 \\ 6 & 7 \end{pmatrix} + \begin{pmatrix} 4 & 8 \\ 4 & 9 \end{pmatrix} \right]$$

$$= \begin{pmatrix} 1 & 3 \\ 2 & 4 \end{pmatrix} + \begin{pmatrix} 7 & 13 \\ 10 & 16 \end{pmatrix}$$

$$= \begin{pmatrix} 8 & 16 \\ 12 & 20 \end{pmatrix}$$

Therefore, $(A + B) + C = A + (B + C)$.

Example 2.   Use the matrices A, B, and C given in Example 1 to verify the left-hand distributive law for square matrices.

Solution: Show that $A(B + C) = AB + AC$.

$$A(B + C) = \begin{pmatrix} 1 & 3 \\ 2 & 4 \end{pmatrix} \left[\begin{pmatrix} 3 & 5 \\ 6 & 7 \end{pmatrix} + \begin{pmatrix} 4 & 8 \\ 4 & 9 \end{pmatrix} \right]$$

$$= \begin{pmatrix} 1 & 3 \\ 2 & 4 \end{pmatrix} \begin{pmatrix} 7 & 13 \\ 10 & 16 \end{pmatrix}$$

$$= \begin{pmatrix} 37 & 61 \\ 54 & 90 \end{pmatrix}$$

$$AB + AC = \begin{pmatrix} 1 & 3 \\ 2 & 4 \end{pmatrix} \begin{pmatrix} 3 & 5 \\ 6 & 7 \end{pmatrix} + \begin{pmatrix} 1 & 3 \\ 2 & 4 \end{pmatrix} \begin{pmatrix} 4 & 8 \\ 4 & 9 \end{pmatrix}$$

$$= \begin{pmatrix} 21 & 26 \\ 30 & 38 \end{pmatrix} + \begin{pmatrix} 16 & 35 \\ 24 & 52 \end{pmatrix}$$

$$= \begin{pmatrix} 37 & 61 \\ 54 & 90 \end{pmatrix}$$

Therefore, $A(B + C) = AB + AC$, as expected.

PROBLEMS

Use the matrices $A = \begin{pmatrix} 2 & 4 \\ 6 & 3 \end{pmatrix}$, $B = \begin{pmatrix} 8 & 7 \\ 2 & 1 \end{pmatrix}$, and $C = \begin{pmatrix} 4 & 9 \\ 2 & 3 \end{pmatrix}$ in Probs. 1 through 5.

1. State and verify the associative law for addition.

2. State and verify the associative law for multiplication.

3. State and verify the left-hand distributive law.

4. State and verify the right-hand distributive law.

5. State and verify the commutative law for addition.

6. Let $A = \begin{pmatrix} a_{11} & a_{12} \\ a_{21} & a_{22} \end{pmatrix}$ and $B = \begin{pmatrix} b_{11} & b_{12} \\ b_{21} & b_{22} \end{pmatrix}$. Show that $A + B = B + A$.

   [*Hint:* Use Axiom A-2 from Sec. 1-1.]

7. Compute $\begin{pmatrix} 2 & 1 & 3 \\ 3 & 1 & 2 \\ 1 & 1 & 4 \end{pmatrix} \begin{pmatrix} 4 & 1 & 2 \\ 1 & 3 & 2 \\ 2 & 1 & 1 \end{pmatrix}$.

8. Compute $\begin{pmatrix} 4 & 1 & 2 \\ 1 & 3 & 2 \\ 2 & 1 & 1 \end{pmatrix} \begin{pmatrix} 2 & 1 & 3 \\ 3 & 1 & 2 \\ 1 & 1 & 4 \end{pmatrix}$.

9. Are the results in Probs. 7 and 8 equal? Can you see any implications of this situation for the existence of a commutative law for multiplication of 3 by 3 matrices?

10. Show that $A + B = B + A$, where A and B are both m by n matrices with real elements. [*Hint:* Let $X = A + B$ and $Y = B + A$. Then show that $X = Y$ by using appropriate matrix definitions and properties of real numbers.]

11. Show that $(A + B) + C = A + (B + C)$, where A, B, and C are all m by n matrices with real elements.

3-3 FAILURE OF THE COMMUTATIVE LAW FOR MATRIX MULTIPLICATION

Conspicuously absent from the list of theorems in the previous section is the commutative law for multiplication. To see that this law does not hold in general even for square matrices, we will cite the following examples involving

$$A = \begin{pmatrix} 1 & 2 & 1 \\ 3 & 1 & 2 \\ 4 & 2 & 1 \end{pmatrix} \quad \text{and} \quad B = \begin{pmatrix} 2 & 1 & 2 \\ 1 & 2 & 3 \\ 2 & 1 & 3 \end{pmatrix}$$

Example 1. Compute AB.

Solution:

$$\begin{pmatrix} 1 & 2 & 1 \\ 3 & 1 & 2 \\ 4 & 2 & 1 \end{pmatrix} \begin{pmatrix} 2 & 1 & 2 \\ 1 & 2 & 3 \\ 2 & 1 & 3 \end{pmatrix} = \begin{pmatrix} 6 & 6 & 11 \\ 11 & 7 & 15 \\ 12 & 9 & 17 \end{pmatrix}$$

Example 2. Compute BA.

Solution:

$$\begin{pmatrix} 2 & 1 & 2 \\ 1 & 2 & 3 \\ 2 & 1 & 3 \end{pmatrix} \begin{pmatrix} 1 & 2 & 1 \\ 3 & 1 & 2 \\ 4 & 2 & 1 \end{pmatrix} = \begin{pmatrix} 13 & 9 & 6 \\ 19 & 10 & 8 \\ 17 & 11 & 7 \end{pmatrix}$$

These two examples taken together constitute a counterexample for a commutative law for multiplication of square matrices.

Now, since the *commutative law* for multiplication is included as an axiom for the real number system and since *it does not hold for square matrices*, we would expect to find significant differences between the familiar algebra of the real number system and the algebra of square matrices. The following two examples provide a somewhat dramatic, it seems to us, manifestation of these differences. Both examples involve the matrices $A = \begin{pmatrix} 1 & -2 \\ 3 & 1 \end{pmatrix}$ and $B = \begin{pmatrix} 3 & 2 \\ 4 & 1 \end{pmatrix}$.

Example 3.

Compute $(A + B)^2$ where $(A + B)^2$ has the usual meaning $(A + B)(A + B)$.

Solution:

$$\left[\begin{pmatrix} 1 & -2 \\ 3 & 1 \end{pmatrix} + \begin{pmatrix} 3 & 2 \\ 4 & 1 \end{pmatrix} \right]^2 = \begin{pmatrix} 4 & 0 \\ 7 & 2 \end{pmatrix} \begin{pmatrix} 4 & 0 \\ 7 & 2 \end{pmatrix}$$

Therefore, $(A + B)^2 = \begin{pmatrix} 16 & 0 \\ 42 & 4 \end{pmatrix}$

Example 4.

Compute $A^2 + 2AB + B^2$

Solution:

$$A^2 = \begin{pmatrix} 1 & -2 \\ 3 & 1 \end{pmatrix} \begin{pmatrix} 1 & -2 \\ 3 & 1 \end{pmatrix} \qquad B^2 = \begin{pmatrix} 3 & 2 \\ 4 & 1 \end{pmatrix} \begin{pmatrix} 3 & 2 \\ 4 & 1 \end{pmatrix}$$

$$A^2 = \begin{pmatrix} -5 & -4 \\ 6 & -5 \end{pmatrix} \qquad B^2 = \begin{pmatrix} 17 & 8 \\ 16 & 9 \end{pmatrix}$$

$$AB = \begin{pmatrix} 1 & -2 \\ 3 & 1 \end{pmatrix} \begin{pmatrix} 3 & 2 \\ 4 & 1 \end{pmatrix} \qquad 2AB = AB + AB$$

$$= \begin{pmatrix} -5 & 0 \\ 13 & 7 \end{pmatrix} \qquad\qquad = \begin{pmatrix} -5 & 0 \\ 13 & 7 \end{pmatrix} + \begin{pmatrix} -5 & 0 \\ 13 & 7 \end{pmatrix}$$

$$= \begin{pmatrix} -10 & 0 \\ 26 & 14 \end{pmatrix}$$

Therefore,

$$A^2 + 2AB + B^2 = \begin{pmatrix} -5 & -4 \\ 6 & -5 \end{pmatrix} + \begin{pmatrix} -10 & 0 \\ 26 & 14 \end{pmatrix} + \begin{pmatrix} 17 & 8 \\ 16 & 9 \end{pmatrix}$$

$$= \begin{pmatrix} 2 & 4 \\ 48 & 18 \end{pmatrix}$$

The fact that the results of Examples 3 and 4 are not equal shows that the very familiar identity from high school algebra, $(a + b)^2 = a^2 + 2ab + b^2$, does not hold for square matrices. To see why this formula is not valid for matrices, we expand $(A + B)^2$ as far as possible using the theorems of Sec. 3-2.

$$(A + B)^2 = (A + B)(A + B)$$
$$= (A + B)A + (A + B)B \qquad \textit{Left-hand Distributive Law}$$
$$= AA + BA + AB + BB \qquad \textit{Right-hand Distributive Law}$$
$$= A^2 + BA + AB + B^2$$

Therefore, $(A + B)^2 = A^2 + BA + AB + B^2$.

It is now clear why the familiar identity fails. Namely, to obtain $2AB$ from $BA + AB$ would require the use of the *commutative law*. The commutative law *does not hold* for matrices.

PROBLEMS

Use the matrices $A = \begin{pmatrix} 1 & 4 \\ 2 & 6 \end{pmatrix}$ and $B = \begin{pmatrix} 3 & 5 \\ 4 & 2 \end{pmatrix}$ in Probs. 1 through 4.

1. Illustrate the *failure* of the commutative law for matrix multiplication.
2. Compute $(A - B)(A - B)$.
3. Compute $A^2 - 2AB + B^2$.
4. Are the results of Prob. 2 and Prob. 3 equal? Why?
5. Find the value of x for which

$$\begin{pmatrix} 1 & 0 \\ 0 & x \end{pmatrix} \begin{pmatrix} 2 & 1 \\ 1 & 4 \end{pmatrix} = \begin{pmatrix} 2 & 1 \\ 1 & 4 \end{pmatrix} \begin{pmatrix} 1 & 0 \\ 0 & x \end{pmatrix}$$

6. Find all values of x and y for which the matrix $\begin{pmatrix} x & 1 \\ 2 & 3 \end{pmatrix}$ commutes with the matrix $\begin{pmatrix} 2 & 1 \\ 2 & y \end{pmatrix}$.

7. Consider the matrix equation $A\mathbf{x} + \mathbf{a} = B\mathbf{x} + \mathbf{b}$, where A and B are n by n, and $\mathbf{a}$, $\mathbf{b}$, and $\mathbf{x}$ are n-component column vectors. Rewrite $A\mathbf{x} + \mathbf{a} = B\mathbf{x} + \mathbf{b}$ in the form $C\mathbf{x} = \mathbf{c}$, showing and giving a reason for each step.

8. Consider the matrix equation $A\mathbf{x} = \mathbf{b}$, where A is n by n. Show that if there exists an n by n matrix B with the property that $BA = I$, then $\mathbf{x} = B\mathbf{b}$. Give reasons.

9. Consider the matrix equation $XA = B$, where X is n by m, A is m by m, and B is n by m. Show that if there exists an m by m matrix C with the property that $AC = I$, then $X = BC$. Give reasons.

3-4   THE INVERSE OF A SQUARE MATRIX

The expressions $a + (-a) = 0$ and $aa^{-1} = 1$ are included in the list of axioms for the real numbers in Sec. 1-1. In the list of axioms A-1–A-8, we find the statements that every real number has an additive inverse and every nonzero real number has a multiplicative inverse. We are now ready to study additive and multiplicative inverses for square matrices.

DEFINITION 3.4.   *Let A be an n by n matrix. Then the matrix $-A$ with the property that $A + (-A) = Z$, where Z is the n by n matrix with all elements equal to zero, is called the additive inverse of A.*

DEFINITION 3.5.   *Let A be an n by n matrix. Then the matrix A^{-1} with the property that $AA^{-1} = I$, where I is the n by n matrix with ones on the principal diagonal and zeros elsewhere, is called the multiplicative inverse of A.*

As can be seen from the following examples, it is easy to obtain the additive inverse of a matrix.

Example 1.   Find the additive inverse of $A = \begin{pmatrix} a & b \\ c & d \end{pmatrix}$.

Solution:

$$\begin{pmatrix} a & b \\ c & d \end{pmatrix} + \begin{pmatrix} x & y \\ z & w \end{pmatrix} = \begin{pmatrix} 0 & 0 \\ 0 & 0 \end{pmatrix}$$

$a + x = 0, b + y = 0, c + z = 0,$ and $d + w = 0$

$x = -a, y = -b, z = -c,$ and $w = -d$

Therefore, the additive inverse of A is $-A = \begin{pmatrix} -a & -b \\ -c & -d \end{pmatrix}.$

Example 2.

$$\begin{pmatrix} a_{11} & a_{12} & a_{13} \\ a_{21} & a_{22} & a_{23} \\ a_{31} & a_{32} & a_{33} \end{pmatrix} + \begin{pmatrix} -a_{11} & -a_{12} & -a_{13} \\ -a_{21} & -a_{22} & -a_{23} \\ -a_{31} & -a_{32} & -a_{33} \end{pmatrix} = \begin{pmatrix} 0 & 0 & 0 \\ 0 & 0 & 0 \\ 0 & 0 & 0 \end{pmatrix}$$

We see from these examples that the additive inverse for the n by n matrix $A = (a_{ij})$ can be obtained by simply forming the new matrix $-A = (-a_{ij})$.

When one speaks of *the inverse of a matrix* in practice, he is referring to *the multiplicative inverse.* The multiplicative inverse is somewhat troublesome for two reasons.

1. The given matrix may not possess a multiplicative inverse, and
2. It is much more difficult to determine A^{-1} than $-A$ even if it does exist.

For the moment, we will restrict our study to 2 by 2 matrices.

Example 3.

Let $A = \begin{pmatrix} a & b \\ c & d \end{pmatrix}.$ Find $A^{-1}.$

Solution:

$$\begin{pmatrix} a & b \\ c & d \end{pmatrix} \begin{pmatrix} x & y \\ z & w \end{pmatrix} = \begin{pmatrix} 1 & 0 \\ 0 & 1 \end{pmatrix}$$

(I) $ax + bz = 1$ (III) $ay + bw = 0$

(II) $cx + dz = 0$ (IV) $cy + dw = 1$

To solve for x and z, we solve I and II simultaneously by the method of substitution.

Equation II can be rewritten in the form

$$z = -\frac{c}{d} x$$

If we substitute this into I , we have

$$ax + b\left(-\frac{c}{d} x \right) = 1$$

$$x\left(a - \frac{bc}{d} \right) = 1$$

$$x\left(\frac{ad - bc}{d} \right) = 1$$

$$x(ad - bc) = d$$

$$x = \frac{d}{ad - bc} \qquad (ad - bc \neq 0)$$

Substituting this value of x into

$$z = (-c/d)x$$

gives

$$z = \left(-\frac{c}{d}\right)\frac{d}{ad - bc}$$

$$z = \frac{-c}{ad - bc}$$

In a similar manner one obtains from III and IV the solution

$$y = \frac{-b}{ad - bc} \qquad \text{and} \qquad w = \frac{a}{ad - bc}$$

Therefore,

$$A^{-1} = \begin{pmatrix} \dfrac{d}{ad - bc} & \dfrac{-b}{ad - bc} \\ \dfrac{-c}{ad - bc} & \dfrac{a}{ad - bc} \end{pmatrix}$$

$$= \frac{1}{ad - bc}\begin{pmatrix} d & -b \\ -c & a \end{pmatrix}$$

Example 4.   Find A^{-1} for $A = \begin{pmatrix} 2 & 3 \\ 4 & 7 \end{pmatrix}$.

Solutions:

$$a = 2, b = 3, c = 4, \text{ and } d = 7$$
$$ad - bc = (2)(7) - (4)(3)$$
$$= 2$$

Therefore,

$$A^{-1} = \begin{pmatrix} 7/2 & -3/2 \\ -2 & 1 \end{pmatrix}$$

Checking this, we have

$$AA^{-1} = \begin{pmatrix} 2 & 3 \\ 4 & 7 \end{pmatrix}\begin{pmatrix} 7/2 & -3/2 \\ -2 & 1 \end{pmatrix}$$

$$= \begin{pmatrix} 1 & 0 \\ 0 & 1 \end{pmatrix}$$

$$= 1$$

Example 5.   The matrix $A = \begin{pmatrix} 3 & 6 \\ 2 & 4 \end{pmatrix}$ has no inverse since the expression $ad - bc$ equals zero. This means that the determination of the elements of A^{-1} by the method of Example 1 would involve *division by zero*, which *is undefined*; hence A^{-1} does not exist.

The result obtained in Example 3 essentially completes the study of the multiplicative inverse for the class of 2 by 2 matrices. A similar result for matrices larger than 2 by 2 would be both difficult to obtain and to use. A practical algorithm for finding the inverse of a matrix larger than 2 by 2 will be given in Sec. 3-6. A second method of finding the inverse as well as a test to determine if the inverse exists will be taken up in Sec. 4-5. The next section illustrates an application of the inverse of a matrix once it has been found.

PROBLEMS

1. Compute the additive inverse for the following matrices:

   (a) $\begin{pmatrix} 2 & 1 \\ 5 & 6 \end{pmatrix}$

   (b) $\begin{pmatrix} 3 & 2 & 8 \\ 4 & 5 & 2 \\ 1 & 7 & 6 \end{pmatrix}$

2. Compute the multiplicative inverse, A^{-1}, for the matrix $A = \begin{pmatrix} 5 & 2 \\ 6 & 1 \end{pmatrix}$.

3. Check your result in Prob. 2 by multiplication.

4. Compute A^{-1} if $A = \begin{pmatrix} 3 & 4 \\ 5 & 2 \end{pmatrix}$ and check your result by multiplication.

5. Determine the matrices that do not have a multiplicative inverse.

   (a) $\begin{pmatrix} 2 & 4 \\ 4 & 8 \end{pmatrix}$

   (c) $\begin{pmatrix} 1 & 3 \\ 3 & 9 \end{pmatrix}$

   (b) $\begin{pmatrix} 3 & 6 \\ 6 & 18 \end{pmatrix}$

   (d) $\begin{pmatrix} 1 & 2 \\ 2 & 4 \end{pmatrix}$

6. Do the matrices that do not have an inverse in Prob. 5 have any common characteristic that you can notice?

7. Verify by multiplication that $\begin{pmatrix} 1 & 0 & -2 \\ 0 & \frac{1}{3} & 0 \\ 0 & 0 & 1 \end{pmatrix}$ is the inverse of $\begin{pmatrix} 1 & 0 & 2 \\ 0 & 3 & 0 \\ 0 & 0 & 1 \end{pmatrix}$.

8. Solve equations **III** and **IV** in Example 3 of this section for y and w.

9. Use the definition of A^{-1} to find the inverse of

$$A = \begin{pmatrix} a & 0 & 0 \\ 0 & b & 0 \\ 0 & 0 & c \end{pmatrix} \quad \text{where } a, b, \text{ and } c \neq 0$$

10. Use the result of Prob. 9 to find

$$\begin{pmatrix} 2 & 0 & 0 \\ 0 & 3 & 0 \\ 0 & 0 & -4 \end{pmatrix}^{-1}$$

Remark: Finding A^{-1} is not usually this easy.

3-5 THE APPLICATION OF THE INVERSE OF A MATRIX TO SOLVE SYSTEMS OF EQUATIONS

The reader will recall that in Sec. 2-5 we discussed the possibility of writing a system of linear equations in n unknowns as a single matrix equation. For the case where $m = n$, such matrix equations have the form $A\mathbf{x} = \mathbf{b}$, where A is the n by n matrix of coefficients of the given system, $\mathbf{x}$ is the n by 1 matrix of unknowns, and $\mathbf{b}$ is the n by 1 matrix of right-hand sides. We now have enough algebra for square matrices to do the following examples.

Example 1.   Let A be an n by n matrix which possesses an inverse. Solve the matrix equation $A\mathbf{x} = \mathbf{b}$, where $\mathbf{x}$ and $\mathbf{b}$ are both n by 1 matrices (i.e., column vectors).

Solution:

$$A\mathbf{x} = \mathbf{b}$$
$$A^{-1}A\mathbf{x} = A^{-1}\mathbf{b} \qquad \text{\textit{multiplication by } } A^{-1}, \text{\textit{ which is known to exist}}$$
$$I\mathbf{x} = A^{-1}\mathbf{b} \qquad \text{\textit{definition of } } A^{-1}$$
$$\mathbf{x} = A^{-1}\mathbf{b} \qquad \text{\textit{definition of the multiplicative identity}}$$

Example 2.   Solve the matrix equation

$$\begin{pmatrix} 2 & 3 \\ 4 & 7 \end{pmatrix} \begin{pmatrix} x \\ y \end{pmatrix} = \begin{pmatrix} 1 \\ 2 \end{pmatrix}$$

Solution: We know from Example 4 of the previous section that the inverse of the coefficient matrix $A = \begin{pmatrix} 2 & 3 \\ 4 & 7 \end{pmatrix}$ is $A^{-1} = \begin{pmatrix} \tfrac{7}{2} & -\tfrac{3}{2} \\ -2 & 1 \end{pmatrix}$.

$$\begin{pmatrix} \tfrac{7}{2} & -\tfrac{3}{2} \\ -2 & 1 \end{pmatrix} \begin{pmatrix} 2 & 3 \\ 4 & 7 \end{pmatrix} \begin{pmatrix} x \\ y \end{pmatrix} = \begin{pmatrix} \tfrac{7}{2} & -\tfrac{3}{2} \\ -2 & 1 \end{pmatrix} \begin{pmatrix} 1 \\ 2 \end{pmatrix} \qquad \begin{array}{l} \text{\textit{multiplying both}} \\ \text{\textit{sides by } } A^{-1} \end{array}$$

$$\begin{pmatrix} 1 & 0 \\ 0 & 1 \end{pmatrix} \begin{pmatrix} x \\ y \end{pmatrix} = \begin{pmatrix} \tfrac{1}{2} \\ 0 \end{pmatrix}$$

$$\begin{pmatrix} x \\ y \end{pmatrix} = \begin{pmatrix} \tfrac{1}{2} \\ 0 \end{pmatrix} \qquad x = \tfrac{1}{2} \text{ \textit{and} } y = 0 \text{ \textit{is the solution}}$$

Example 3.   Solve the system of equations

$$2x + 3y = 1$$
$$4x + 7y = 2$$

by the method of elimination.

Solution:

$$\begin{array}{ll} 4x + 6y = 2 & \\ \underline{4x + 7y = 2} & \qquad \text{\textit{subtracting the first equation from the second}} \\ y = 0 & \end{array}$$

$$4x + 7(0) = 2$$
$$x = \tfrac{1}{2} \qquad \textit{as found in Example 2}$$

A study of these examples reveals that the inverse of a matrix can be used to solve systems of equations. In fact, if we look carefully at the solution of Example 1, we see that the n by 1 matrix of unknowns is equal to the n by n inverse of the coefficient matrix times the n by 1 matrix of right-hand sides. Once this multiplication has been performed, the solution of the system can be written down immediately by definition of equality of vectors.

Example 4. Given that the inverse of $\begin{pmatrix} 1 & 2 & 3 \\ 1 & 3 & 5 \\ 2 & 5 & 9 \end{pmatrix}$ is $\begin{pmatrix} 2 & -3 & 1 \\ 1 & 3 & -2 \\ -1 & -1 & 1 \end{pmatrix}$, solve the following system of linear equations.

$$x + 2y + 3z = 1$$
$$x + 3y + 5z = 2$$
$$2x + 5y + 9z = 3$$

Solution: If we write this system as a matrix equation, we have

$$\begin{pmatrix} 1 & 2 & 3 \\ 1 & 3 & 5 \\ 2 & 5 & 9 \end{pmatrix}\begin{pmatrix} x \\ y \\ z \end{pmatrix} = \begin{pmatrix} 1 \\ 2 \\ 3 \end{pmatrix}$$

If we multiply both sides by the inverse we get

$$\begin{pmatrix} 2 & -3 & 1 \\ 1 & 3 & -2 \\ -1 & -1 & 1 \end{pmatrix}\begin{pmatrix} 1 & 2 & 3 \\ 1 & 3 & 5 \\ 2 & 5 & 9 \end{pmatrix}\begin{pmatrix} x \\ y \\ z \end{pmatrix}$$

$$= \begin{pmatrix} 2 & -3 & 1 \\ 1 & 3 & -2 \\ -1 & -1 & 1 \end{pmatrix}\begin{pmatrix} 1 \\ 2 \\ 3 \end{pmatrix}$$

$$\begin{pmatrix} 1 & 0 & 0 \\ 0 & 1 & 0 \\ 0 & 0 & 1 \end{pmatrix}\begin{pmatrix} x \\ y \\ z \end{pmatrix} = \begin{pmatrix} -1 \\ 1 \\ 0 \end{pmatrix} \qquad \textit{by definition of } A^{-1}$$

$$\begin{pmatrix} x \\ y \\ z \end{pmatrix} = \begin{pmatrix} -1 \\ 1 \\ 0 \end{pmatrix} \qquad \textit{by definition of the multiplicative identity}$$

Therefore, the solution is $x = -1, y = 1, z = 0$, by definition of equality of vectors.

If we check this answer by direct substitution, we get

$$-1 + 2 + 0 = 1$$
$$-1 + 3 + 0 = 2$$
$$-2 + 5 + 0 = 3$$

which proves that this is indeed the solution of the system.

Example 5. Solve the new system obtained from the system given in Example 4 by changing the constant column from $\begin{pmatrix} 1 \\ 2 \\ 3 \end{pmatrix}$ to $\begin{pmatrix} 2 \\ 3 \\ 4 \end{pmatrix}$.

Solution: Based on the work done for Example 4, we can go directly to

$$\begin{pmatrix} x \\ y \\ z \end{pmatrix} = \begin{pmatrix} 2 & -3 & 1 \\ 1 & 3 & -2 \\ -1 & -1 & 1 \end{pmatrix} \begin{pmatrix} 2 \\ 3 \\ 4 \end{pmatrix}$$

$$\begin{pmatrix} x \\ y \\ z \end{pmatrix} = \begin{pmatrix} -1 \\ 3 \\ -1 \end{pmatrix}$$

$x = -1, y = 3, z = -1$

We recall from Sec. 2-5 that the normal equations used to fit $\hat{y} = a + bx$ to data can be expressed in matrix form as follows:

$$\begin{pmatrix} n & \sum_{i=1}^{n} x_i \\ \sum_{i=1}^{n} x_i & \sum_{i=1}^{n} x_i^2 \end{pmatrix} \begin{pmatrix} a \\ b \end{pmatrix} = \begin{pmatrix} \sum_{i=1}^{n} y_i \\ \sum_{i=1}^{n} x_i y_i \end{pmatrix}$$

Example 6. Use the above matrix equation to calculate a and b of Example 4 of Sec. 1-8.

Solution:

$$n = 5 \text{ observations}$$

$$\sum_{i=1}^{5} x_i y_i = 133{,}000$$

$$\sum_{i=1}^{5} x_i = 1500$$

$$\sum_{i=1}^{5} y_i = 400$$

$$\sum_{i=1}^{5} x_i^2 = 550{,}000$$

Substitution gives the matrix equation

$$\begin{pmatrix} 5 & 1500 \\ 1500 & 550{,}000 \end{pmatrix} \begin{pmatrix} a \\ b \end{pmatrix} = \begin{pmatrix} 400 \\ 133{,}000 \end{pmatrix}$$

$$\begin{pmatrix} a \\ b \end{pmatrix} = \begin{pmatrix} 5 & 1500 \\ 1500 & 550{,}000 \end{pmatrix}^{-1} \begin{pmatrix} 400 \\ 133{,}000 \end{pmatrix}$$

$$= \frac{1}{5(550{,}000) - (1500)^2} \begin{pmatrix} 550{,}000 & -1500 \\ -1500 & 5 \end{pmatrix} \begin{pmatrix} 400 \\ 133{,}000 \end{pmatrix}$$

$$= \frac{1}{500{,}000} \begin{pmatrix} 20{,}500{,}000 \\ 65{,}000 \end{pmatrix}$$

$$= \begin{pmatrix} 41.00 \\ 0.13 \end{pmatrix}$$

$a = 41$ and $b = 0.13$, as expected.

PROBLEMS

1. Given the system of equations

$$2x + 3y = 4$$
$$x - 2y = -5$$

   (a) Write the above as a matrix equation.

   (b) Verify that $\begin{pmatrix} \frac{2}{7} & \frac{3}{7} \\ \frac{1}{7} & -\frac{2}{7} \end{pmatrix}$ is the inverse of the matrix of coefficients.

   (c) Use the inverse to solve for x and y.

Perform the following operations for the systems of equations given in Probs. 2 through 4.

   (a) Write the system as a matrix equation.

   (b) Find the inverse of the matrix of coefficients.

   (c) Solve the system for x and y.

2. $2x - y = 3$
   $3x - y = 4$

3. $x + y = 4$
   $3x - y = 2$

4. $2x + 3y = -4$
   $4x + 6y = -5$

5. Given the following system:

$$3x_1 + 2x_2 + 2x_3 = 4$$
$$x_2 = 5$$
$$2x_1 + 2x_2 + 2x_3 = 6$$

   (a) Write the system as a matrix equation.

   (b) Verify that $\begin{pmatrix} 1 & 0 & -1 \\ 0 & 1 & 0 \\ -1 & -1 & \frac{3}{2} \end{pmatrix}$ is the inverse of the matrix of coeffi-

   cients.

   (c) Use the inverse to solve for x_1, x_2, and x_3.

6. Use the normal equations written in matrix form to calculate a and b for the data of Prob. 5 in Sec. 1-8.

7. Use the normal equations written in matrix form to fit a straight line to the data in Prob. 6 of Sec. 1-8.

8. Use the normal equations written in matrix form to fit a straight line to the following set of data:

x	1	1	2	2	3	3	4	4
y	8	10	6	7	4	6	4	5

9. In Sec. 1-8 we gave the explicit formula

$$b = \frac{n \sum_{i=1}^{n} x_i y_i - \sum_{i=1}^{n} x_i \sum_{i=1}^{n} y_i}{n \sum_{i=1}^{n} x_i^2 - (\sum_{i=1}^{n} x_i)^2}$$

   (a) Use the normal equations written in matrix form to derive this formula for b.

   (b) Use the normal equations written in matrix form to give an explicit formula for a.

10. Write the following system of linear equations in matrix form:

$$x_1 = a_{11}x_1 + a_{12}x_2 + \cdots + a_{1n}x_n + d_1$$
$$x_2 = a_{21}x_1 + a_{22}x_2 + \cdots + a_{22}x_n + d_2$$

$$\cdot \qquad \cdot \qquad \cdot \qquad \cdot \qquad \cdot \qquad \cdot$$

$$x_n = a_{n1}x_1 + a_{n2}x_2 + \cdots + a_{nn}x_n + d_n$$

11. Express $\mathbf{x} = A\mathbf{x} + \mathbf{d}$ in the form $(I - A)\mathbf{x} = \mathbf{d}$.

12. Express the solution of $(I - A)\mathbf{x} = \mathbf{d}$ in terms of the inverse of $I - A$ and the column vector $\mathbf{d}$.

3-6   AN ALGORITHM FOR FINDING THE INVERSE OF A MATRIX

We saw in the last section that the inverse of a matrix can be used to solve systems of linear equations once the inverse of the coefficient matrix is known. In this section we will describe a method of finding the inverse of a matrix. The process of finding the multiplicative inverse of a matrix is sometimes called inverting the matrix.

Let A be an n by n matrix. Form an n by $2n$ matrix by writing A and the n by n identity matrix side by side with A on the left. This matrix will be called the *composite matrix*. Then perform row operations (to be described below) on this composite matrix until the first n columns are transformed into the identity matrix. If this can be done, then the other n columns (i.e., the right half) of the composite matrix will be the inverse of A.

The permissible row operations are:

1. A row can be multiplied by any nonzero real number.
2. A constant times any row can be added to or subtracted from any other row.
3. Any pair of rows can be interchanged.

The procedure described above is illustrated in the following examples. A justification of this algorithm is given after these illustrative examples.

Example 1.   Use the procedure described above to find the inverse of

$$A = \begin{pmatrix} 2 & 1 \\ 1 & 1 \end{pmatrix}$$

Solution:

a. $\begin{pmatrix} 2 & 1 & \vdots & 1 & 0 \\ 1 & 1 & \vdots & 0 & 1 \end{pmatrix}$

b. $\begin{pmatrix} 1 & 0 & \vdots & 1 & -1 \\ 1 & 1 & \vdots & 0 & 1 \end{pmatrix}$ *by subtracting row 2 from row 1 of (a)*

c. $\begin{pmatrix} 1 & 0 & \vdots & 1 & -1 \\ 0 & 1 & \vdots & -1 & 2 \end{pmatrix}$ *by subtracting row 1 from row 2 of (b)*

Since the matrix $\begin{pmatrix} 2 & 1 \\ 1 & 1 \end{pmatrix}$ in the left half of (a) has been transformed into the

identity $\begin{pmatrix} 1 & 0 \\ 0 & 1 \end{pmatrix}$ in (c), it follows that A^{-1} can be read off from the right half

of (c). This gives $A^{-1} = \begin{pmatrix} 1 & -1 \\ -1 & 2 \end{pmatrix}$.

Example 2.   Find the inverse of $A = \begin{pmatrix} 3 & 2 & 2 \\ 0 & 1 & 0 \\ 2 & 2 & 2 \end{pmatrix}$.

Solution:

a. $\begin{pmatrix} 3 & 2 & 2 & \vdots & 1 & 0 & 0 \\ 0 & 1 & 0 & \vdots & 0 & 1 & 0 \\ 2 & 2 & 2 & \vdots & 0 & 0 & 1 \end{pmatrix}$

b. $\begin{pmatrix} 1 & 0 & 0 & \vdots & 1 & 0 & -1 \\ 0 & 1 & 0 & \vdots & 0 & 1 & 0 \\ 2 & 2 & 2 & \vdots & 0 & 0 & 1 \end{pmatrix}$ *subtracting row 3 from row 1 of (a)*

c. $\begin{pmatrix} 1 & 0 & 0 & \vdots & 1 & 0 & -1 \\ 0 & 1 & 0 & \vdots & 0 & 1 & 0 \\ 0 & 2 & 2 & \vdots & -2 & 0 & 3 \end{pmatrix}$ *subtracting two times row 1 from row 3 of (b)*

d. $\begin{pmatrix} 1 & 0 & 0 & \vdots & 1 & 0 & -1 \\ 0 & 1 & 0 & \vdots & 0 & 1 & 0 \\ 0 & 0 & 2 & \vdots & -2 & -2 & 3 \end{pmatrix}$ *subtracting two times row 2 from row 3 of (c)*

e. $\begin{pmatrix} 1 & 0 & 0 & \vdots & 1 & 0 & -1 \\ 0 & 1 & 0 & \vdots & 0 & 1 & 0 \\ 0 & 0 & 1 & \vdots & -1 & -1 & \frac{3}{2} \end{pmatrix}$ *dividing row 3 of (d) by 2, i.e., multiplying by $\frac{1}{2}$*

Then

$$A^{-1} = \begin{pmatrix} 1 & 0 & -1 \\ 0 & 1 & 0 \\ -1 & -1 & \frac{3}{2} \end{pmatrix}$$

Example 3.   Find the inverse of $A = \begin{pmatrix} 1 & 2 & 3 \\ 1 & 3 & 5 \\ 2 & 5 & 9 \end{pmatrix}$.

Solution:

$\begin{pmatrix} 1 & 2 & 3 & \vdots & 1 & 0 & 0 \\ 1 & 3 & 5 & \vdots & 0 & 1 & 0 \\ 2 & 5 & 9 & \vdots & 0 & 0 & 1 \end{pmatrix}$

We subtract row one from row two, and subtract twice row one from row three. This gives

a. $\begin{pmatrix} 1 & 2 & 3 & \vdots & 1 & 0 & 0 \\ 0 & 1 & 2 & \vdots & -1 & 1 & 0 \\ 0 & 1 & 3 & \vdots & -2 & 0 & 1 \end{pmatrix}$

If we subtract row two from row three of (a), we get

b. $\begin{pmatrix} 1 & 2 & 3 & \vdots & 1 & 0 & 0 \\ 0 & 1 & 2 & \vdots & -1 & 1 & 0 \\ 0 & 0 & 1 & \vdots & -1 & -1 & 1 \end{pmatrix}$

Subtract twice row two from row one of (b) to get $a_{12} = 0$.

c. $\begin{pmatrix} 1 & 0 & -1 & \vdots & 3 & -2 & 0 \\ 0 & 1 & 2 & \vdots & -1 & 1 & 0 \\ 0 & 0 & 1 & \vdots & -1 & -1 & 1 \end{pmatrix}$

Adding row three to row one of (c) to get $a_{13} = 0$ gives

d. $\begin{pmatrix} 1 & 0 & 0 & \vdots & 2 & -3 & 1 \\ 0 & 1 & 2 & \vdots & -1 & 1 & 0 \\ 0 & 0 & 1 & \vdots & -1 & -1 & 1 \end{pmatrix}$

Subtract twice row three from row two of (d) to get $a_{23} = 0$.

e. $\begin{pmatrix} 1 & 0 & 0 & \vdots & 2 & -3 & 1 \\ 0 & 1 & 0 & \vdots & 1 & 3 & -2 \\ 0 & 0 & 1 & \vdots & -1 & -1 & 1 \end{pmatrix}$

Therefore,

$$A^{-1} = \begin{pmatrix} 2 & -3 & 1 \\ 1 & 3 & -2 \\ -1 & -1 & 1 \end{pmatrix}$$

Remarks: If the given matrix A has no inverse, it will be impossible to complete the transformation of A into the identity matrix using only permissible row operations. An alternative test for the existence of the inverse of a matrix is given in Sec. 4-5 of the next chapter.

The following explanation for the algorithm described above was suggested by Dr. Allan E. Andersen.

Let A be a given n by n matrix. Form the matrix equation $A\mathbf{x} = I\mathbf{y}$, where $\mathbf{x}$ and $\mathbf{y}$ are both n by 1 column vectors. This matrix equation is equivalent to the system of linear equations (1).

$$\begin{array}{l} a_{11}x_1 + a_{12}x_2 + \cdots + a_{1n}x_n = y_1 + Oy_2 + \cdots + Oy_n \\ a_{21}x_1 + a_{22}x_2 + \cdots + a_{2n}x_n = Oy_1 + y_2 + \cdots + Oy_n \\ \phantom{a_{}} \vdots \\ a_{n1}x_1 + a_{n2}x_2 + \cdots + a_{nn}x_n = Oy_1 + Oy_2 + \cdots + y_n \end{array}$$

$$(1) \qquad A\mathbf{x} = I\mathbf{y}$$

Assume system (1) has a solution and that it has been solved by the method of elimination to give (2).

$$\begin{array}{l} x_1 + Ox_2 + \cdots + Ox_n = m_{11}y_1 + m_{12}y_2 + \cdots + m_{1n}y_n \\ Ox_1 + x_2 + \cdots + Ox_n = m_{21}y_1 + m_{22}y_2 + \cdots + m_{2n}y_n \\ \vdots \\ Ox_1 + Ox_2 + \cdots + x_n = m_{n1}y_1 + m_{n2}y_2 + \cdots + m_{nn}y_n \end{array}$$

$$(2) \qquad I\mathbf{x} = M\mathbf{y}$$

A procedure for obtaining (2) from (1) would involve a repeated application of the three rules listed below:

1. Any pair of equations can be interchanged.
2. An equation can be multiplied by any nonzero real number.
3. A constant times any equation can be added to or subtracted from any other equation.

The system (1) is equivalent to the composite matrix (3).

$$\begin{pmatrix} a_{11} & a_{12} & \cdots & a_{1n} & 1 & 0 & \cdots & 0 \\ a_{21} & a_{22} & \cdots & a_{2n} & 0 & 1 & \cdots & 0 \\ \cdot & \cdot & \cdot & \cdot & \cdot & \cdot & \cdot & \cdot \\ \cdot & \cdot & \cdot & \cdot & \cdot & \cdot & \cdot & \cdot \\ \cdot & \cdot & \cdot & \cdot & \cdot & \cdot & \cdot & \cdot \\ a_{n1} & a_{n2} & \cdots & a_{nn} & 0 & 0 & \cdots & 1 \end{pmatrix} \qquad (3) \qquad (A|I)$$

Also, system (2) is equivalent to the composite matrix (4).

$$\begin{pmatrix} 1 & 0 & \cdots & 0 & m_{11} & m_{12} & \cdots & m_{1n} \\ 0 & 1 & \cdots & 0 & m_{21} & m_{22} & \cdots & m_{2n} \\ \cdot & \cdot & \cdot & \cdot & \cdot & \cdot & \cdot & \cdot \\ \cdot & \cdot & \cdot & \cdot & \cdot & \cdot & \cdot & \cdot \\ \cdot & \cdot & \cdot & \cdot & \cdot & \cdot & \cdot & \cdot \\ 0 & 0 & \cdots & 1 & m_{n1} & m_{n2} & \cdots & m_{nn} \end{pmatrix} \qquad (4) \qquad (I|M)$$

It is important to note that the permissible *row operations* listed at the beginning of this section can be obtained from the three rules given above by simply replacing the word "equation" with the word "row." It follows that the use of row operations to go from (3) to (4) is equivalent to solving system (1) for x in terms of y. This statement plus the fact that $M = A^{-1}$ should convince the reader that the algorithm is valid.

To see that $M = A^{-1}$, we rewrite the equations $Ax = Iy$ and $Ix = My$ in the forms $Ax = y$ and $x = My$, respectively. Combining these two equations we have

$$y = Ax$$
$$y = A(My)$$
$$y = (AM)y \qquad \text{\textit{by use of the associative law for matrix multiplica-}}$$
$$\text{\textit{tion}}$$

Since the matrix AM times y equals y for any column vector y, it follows that $AM = I$ and, therefore, $M = A^{-1}$.

PROBLEMS

1. Set up the composite matrix for the following matrices:

   (a) $\begin{pmatrix} 2 & 0 \\ 1 & 1 \end{pmatrix}$

   (b) $\begin{pmatrix} 1 & 0 \\ 2 & 2 \end{pmatrix}$

2. Using row operations, find the inverse of the matrices given in Prob. 1.

3. Set up the composite matrix and find the inverse for the following matrices:

   (a) $\begin{pmatrix} 5 & 2 \\ 6 & 1 \end{pmatrix}$ **(b)** $\begin{pmatrix} 3 & 4 \\ 5 & 2 \end{pmatrix}$

4. Set up the composite matrix for the following matrices:

   (a) $\begin{pmatrix} 2 & 3 \\ 1 & -2 \end{pmatrix}$ **(b)** $\begin{pmatrix} 1 & 3 & -2 \\ 0 & 1 & 4 \\ 0 & 0 & 2 \end{pmatrix}$

5. Use row operations to find the inverse of the matrices given in Prob. 4.

6. Use row operations to find the inverse of $\begin{pmatrix} 3 & 0 & 1 \\ 4 & 2 & 1 \\ 3 & 0 & 1 \end{pmatrix}$, if it exists.

7. Use row operations to find the inverse of $\begin{pmatrix} 4 & 2 & 0 \\ 3 & 0 & 0 \\ 6 & 1 & 1 \end{pmatrix}$. Check your result by multiplication.

8. Write

$$y_1 = ax_1 + bx_2$$
$$y_2 = cx_1 + dx_2$$

   where $ad - bc \neq 0$ (1)

   in the form

$$x_1 = a'y_1 + b'y_2$$
$$x_2 = c'y_1 + d'y_2$$

       (2)

9. Show that (2) in Prob. 8 has the form $\begin{pmatrix} x_1 \\ x_2 \end{pmatrix} = \begin{pmatrix} a & b \\ c & d \end{pmatrix}^{-1} \begin{pmatrix} y_1 \\ y_2 \end{pmatrix}$.

10. Find the inverse of $A = \begin{pmatrix} 3 & 2 & 2 \\ 0 & 1 & 0 \\ 2 & 2 & 2 \end{pmatrix}$ as follows:

    (a) Rewrite the system

$$y_1 = 3x_1 + 2x_2 + 2x_3$$
$$y_2 = \qquad x_2$$
$$y_3 = 2x_1 + 2x_2 + 2x_3$$

    in the form

$$x_1 = b_{11}y_1 + b_{12}y_2 + b_{13}y_3$$
$$x_2 = b_{21}y_1 + b_{22}y_2 + b_{23}y_3$$
$$x_3 = b_{31}y_1 + b_{32}y_2 + b_{33}y_3$$

    (b) Observe that $B = (b_{ij}) = A^{-1}$.

    Remark: This matrix is inverted in Example 2.

11. Use the procedure outlined in Prob. 10 to find the inverse of

$$A = \begin{pmatrix} 1 & 2 & 3 \\ 1 & 3 & 5 \\ 2 & 5 & 9 \end{pmatrix} \text{ of Example 3.}$$

3-7   INPUT-OUTPUT ANALYSIS

Input-output analysis is a concept invented by Wassily Leontief about 40 years ago. He has the distinction not only of having single-handedly invented this field, but also of having trained a good number of its practitioners. The value of this concept is now being realized with the development of the high-speed computer. Originally the purpose of the input-output model was to try to relate one industry's activities to broad economic aggregates, such as gross national product or personal consumption expenditures. It is now being used by companies rather than government to forecast market trends. A comprehension of the concepts of identity matrix, matrix inversion, and matrix multiplication is a requirement for an understanding of this section.

In input-output analysis the basic tool is a table which, as we have seen in previous sections, can also be called a matrix. On the left side of the table is a list of industries, one row for each industry. The rows show the sales, called *outputs*, that each industry makes to the others. Across the top of the table, the original industries appear again, one to each column. The columns show the purchases, called *inputs*, that each industry makes from the others. These industries compose what we will call the processing sector. There are two additional columns. The first represents final demand, which includes items such as purchases by households and government, exports, and accumulation to inventory. The last column represents total output.

Example 1.   Interpret the following table which assumes an economy of two industries.

		Purchases (inputs) in millions of $		Final Demand	Total Output
		Industry 1	Industry 2		
Sales (outputs) in millions of $	Industry 1	280	1420	1100	2800
	Industry 2	840	710	2000	3550

Solution: Reading across row 1 we see that Industry 1 had a total output (sales) of $2800 million. This is accounted for by intraindustry sales of $280 million, sales of $1420 million to Industry 2, and sales of $1100 million to households, etc. Reading down column 1, we see that there were $280 million of intraindustry purchases (inputs) and purchases of $840 million from Industry 2.

After an input-output table has been constructed for a given year, a table of input, or *technological coefficients*, can be developed from it. This is done by dividing the total output of a given industry into each of the inputs of the supplying industries. Each result is a fraction expressed as a decimal. A technological coefficient is the amount of input required from each industry to produce one dollar's worth of the output of a given industry. These figures are more important than dollar volume in examining the structure of an industry's market, because they can be applied to any level of sales.

Example 2. Formulate a table of technological coefficients using the data presented in Example 1.

Solution: Dividing all the entries in each industry's column by the total output for that industry results in the following table:

	Industry 1	Industry 2
Industry 1	0.1	0.4
Industry 2	0.3	0.2

This table can be interpreted as follows. Each dollar's worth of production in Industry 1 will require

Intraindustry purchase	$0.10
Purchase from Industry 2	0.30

Each dollar's worth of production in Industry 2 will require

Purchase from Industry 1	$0.40
Intraindustry purchase	0.20

To supply an increase of $1 in final demand in just one industry, we must

1. Increase total output in this industry by more than $1.
2. Increase total output in other industries even though they experience no increase in final demand.

These increases result from the existence of intraindustry requirements.

The determination of the new output levels required in all industries to meet a change in final demand is the main problem of input-output analysis. A method of solution based on matrix concepts follows.

Example 3.   Express the table of technological coefficients as a matrix called A, and total output as a column vector called $\mathbf{x}$. Use the data in Examples 1 and 2.

Solution:

$$A = \begin{pmatrix} a_{11} & a_{12} \\ a_{21} & a_{22} \end{pmatrix} = \begin{pmatrix} 0.1 & 0.4 \\ 0.3 & 0.2 \end{pmatrix}$$

$$\mathbf{x} = \begin{pmatrix} x_1 \\ x_2 \end{pmatrix} = \begin{pmatrix} 2800 \\ 3550 \end{pmatrix}$$

Using the matrix of technological coefficients and the total output vector we can then express interindustry requirements as

Interindustry requirements $= A\mathbf{x}$

As we mentioned before, we must also satisfy final demand. If we let final demand for the industries be represented by the column vector $\mathbf{d}$, we can then express total output as

Total output = Interindustry requirements + Final demand

$$\mathbf{x} = A\mathbf{x} + \mathbf{d}$$

The question is: What must total output be to satisfy the interindustry requirements and final demand? We can answer this question by solving the matrix equation above for $\mathbf{x}$.

$$\mathbf{x} = A\mathbf{x} + \mathbf{d}$$
$$I\mathbf{x} = A\mathbf{x} + \mathbf{d} \qquad \text{i.e., } \mathbf{x} = I\mathbf{x}$$
$$I\mathbf{x} - A\mathbf{x} = \mathbf{d}$$
$$(I - A)\mathbf{x} = \mathbf{d} \qquad \qquad \textit{Right-hand Distributive Law}$$
$$(I - A)^{-1}(I - A)\mathbf{x} = (I - A)^{-1}\mathbf{d}$$
$$I\mathbf{x} = (I - A)^{-1}\mathbf{d}$$
$$\mathbf{x} = (I - A)^{-1}\mathbf{d}$$

Example 4.   Using the result obtained above, solve for $\mathbf{x}$ given $A = \begin{pmatrix} 0.1 & 0.4 \\ 0.3 & 0.2 \end{pmatrix}$ and $\mathbf{d} = \begin{pmatrix} 1100 \\ 2000 \end{pmatrix}$.

Solution:

$$(I - A)^{-1} = \begin{pmatrix} \frac{4}{3} & \frac{2}{3} \\ \frac{1}{2} & \frac{3}{2} \end{pmatrix}$$

$$\mathbf{x} = (I - A)^{-1}\mathbf{d}$$

$$\mathbf{x} = \begin{pmatrix} \frac{4}{3} & \frac{2}{3} \\ \frac{1}{2} & \frac{3}{2} \end{pmatrix} \begin{pmatrix} 1100 \\ 2000 \end{pmatrix} = \begin{pmatrix} 2800 \\ 3550 \end{pmatrix}$$

The reader should refer back to see that this value for final demand is in fact the same as the one in the table in Example 1, since A was developed from this table.

Given any expected level of final demand, one can forecast required output by computing $(I - A)^{-1}$. Note that this inverse must only be calculated once.

Example 5.

If a decrease from 1100 to 1000 occurs in final demand for Industry 1, and the final demand for Industry 2 remains constant, what would be the required total output for both industries?

Solution:

$$\mathbf{x} = (I - A)^{-1}\mathbf{d}$$

$$\mathbf{x} = \begin{pmatrix} 4\frac{1}{3} & 2\frac{2}{3} \\ 1\frac{1}{2} & 3\frac{1}{2} \end{pmatrix} \begin{pmatrix} 1000 \\ 2000 \end{pmatrix} = \begin{pmatrix} 2667 \\ 3500 \end{pmatrix}$$

Examining these results, we see that a $100 million decrease in final demand for Industry 1 results in the following decreases in total output:

Industry 1 $133 million

Industry 2   50 million

This is caused by the decrease in interindustry requirements as well as the decrease in final demand. Hence, if you were in charge of production for Industry 2, you would decrease total output by $50 million if you anticipated that your final demand would remain constant as Industry 1's final demand decreased from $1100 to $1000 million.

We have looked at a simple situation. If there were 286 industries, we would have a little trouble inverting a 286 by 286 matrix. However, it should be clear that input-output analysis is an important tool in forecasting. For large-scale problems we would use a computer.

PROBLEMS

1. Verify that $\begin{pmatrix} 0.9 & -0.4 \\ -0.3 & 0.8 \end{pmatrix}^{-1} = \begin{pmatrix} 4\frac{1}{3} & 2\frac{2}{3} \\ 1\frac{1}{2} & 1\frac{1}{2} \end{pmatrix}$.

2. What would $\mathbf{x}$ have been in Example 5 if $\mathbf{d}$ were equal to $\begin{pmatrix} 1200 \\ 2000 \end{pmatrix}$?

3. Assuming $\mathbf{d} = \begin{pmatrix} 1100 \\ 2000 \end{pmatrix}$ as in Example 4, but that $A = \begin{pmatrix} 0.2 & 0.4 \\ 0.3 & 0.2 \end{pmatrix}$ or $a_{11} = 0.2$ instead of 0.1, find $(I - A)^{-1}$.

4. Solve for $\mathbf{x}$ using the information in Prob. 3.

Given the following in millions:

	Industry 1	Industry 2	Industry 3	Final Demand	Total Output
Industry 1	20	50	40	90	200
Industry 2	10	5	20	65	100
Industry 3	10	15	5	70	100

5. Construct the matrix of technological coefficients A.
6. Interpret a_{21}.
7. Find $(I - A)$.
8. If
$$(I - A)^{-1} = \begin{pmatrix} 1.18788 & 0.728387 & 0.653506 \\ 0.07828 & 1.13683 & 0.272294 \\ 0.07488 & 0.217835 & 1.13002 \end{pmatrix} \quad \text{and} \quad d = \begin{pmatrix} 90 \\ 65 \\ 70 \end{pmatrix}$$
find x.
9. Using the inverse in Prob. 8, find x if
$$d = \begin{pmatrix} 100 \\ 65 \\ 70 \end{pmatrix}$$
10. Given $A = \begin{pmatrix} 0.2 & 0.4 \\ 0.3 & 0.1 \end{pmatrix}$.
    (a) Find $I - A$.
    (b) Find $(I - A)^{-1}$.
11. Using the result of Prob. 10, find x if $d = \begin{pmatrix} 300 \\ 600 \end{pmatrix}$.
12. Using the result of Prob. 10, find x if $d = \begin{pmatrix} 330 \\ 600 \end{pmatrix}$.
13. Interpret the results of Probs. 11 and 12.
14. It follows from $x = Ax + d$ that
$$b_{11}\,\Delta x_1 + b_{12}\,\Delta x_2 = \Delta d_1$$
$$b_{21}\,\Delta x_1 + b_{22}\,\Delta x_2 = \Delta d_2, \qquad \text{where } B = I - A$$
Let $\Delta d_1 = 1$ and $\Delta d_2 = 0$.
    (a) Solve for Δx_1, Δx_2 in terms of the elements of B.
    (b) Use the results of (a) to solve for Δx_1 and Δx_2 given the technological coefficient matrix $A = \begin{pmatrix} 0.1 & 0.4 \\ 0.3 & 0.2 \end{pmatrix}$.

FOUR

Determinants and solutions of systems of linear equations

In this chapter we will introduce the concept of the determinant of a square matrix. Determinants can be used to determine if a given square matrix has a multiplicative inverse, or if certain systems of linear equations have solutions. Determinants can also be used to solve systems of n linear equations in n unknowns.

In Sec. 3-4 of Chap. 3 we derived a formula for finding the inverse of a 2 by 2 matrix. It was found that if

$$A = \begin{pmatrix} a & b \\ c & d \end{pmatrix}$$

then

$$A^{-1} = \begin{pmatrix} \dfrac{d}{ad-bc} & \dfrac{-b}{ad-bc} \\[2ex] \dfrac{-c}{ad-bc} & \dfrac{a}{ad-bc} \end{pmatrix}$$

Now the expression $ad - bc$, which appears as the denominator of each of the elements of A^{-1}, is called the determinant of A. We will study this expression further before giving a definition of the determinant of an n by n matrix.

Writing the expression $ad - bc$ in the form $ad + (-bc)$, we see that it is a sum of signed products. Furthermore, each product contains exactly one element from each row and one element from each column. In the first product, *ad*, "*a*" is from the first row and the first column while "*d*" is from the second row and the second column. In the second product, $-bc$, "*b*" is from the first row and the second column. We shall soon see that the determinant of an *n* by *n* matrix is defined in terms of these ideas.

Next we introduce the term *transposition* as used in the definition of determinant given below. Imagine a set of positive integers listed in some definite order, let us say 5, 2, 1, 3, 4. We use the term transposition to describe an *interchange* in the order of any single *adjacent pair* of integers in such a list. One example of a transposition of the given list of integers is 5, 2, 3, 1, 4, and another example is 2, 5, 1, 3, 4.

Example 1. Use transpositions to rearrange the integers 5, 2, 1, 3, 4 into the *natural order* 1, 2, 3, 4, 5 in two different ways.

Solution:

5, 2, 1, 3, 4	5, 2, 1, 3, 4
5, 1, 2, 3, 4	5, 2, 1, 4, 3
1, 5, 2, 3, 4	2, 5, 1, 4, 3
1, 2, 5, 3, 4	2, 5, 1, 3, 4
1, 2, 3, 5, 4	2, 1, 5, 3, 4
1, 2, 3, 4, 5	1, 2, 5, 3, 4
	1, 2, 3, 5, 4
	1, 2, 3, 4, 5

In the first case *five* transpositions are used and in the second case *seven* transpositions are used. In both cases we needed an *odd number* of steps to restore the set of integers 5, 2, 1, 3, 4 to the natural order. This situation did not happen by chance. Mathematicians have proved that given a list of integers the number of steps needed to restore the natural order $1, 2, 3, \ldots, n$, using only transpositions, is always either *even* or *odd*, regardless of the number of steps actually taken to do this.

DEFINITION 4.1. *Part A. Let A be an n by n matrix. The determinant of A denoted by |A| is defined to be the sum of all possible signed products that can be formed by choosing exactly one element from each row and exactly one element from each column of A.*

Part B. Let each product be arranged so that the first subscripts of the factors are in the natural order, $1, 2, 3, \ldots, n$. The number of transpositions required to restore the second subscripts of a particular product to the natural order, $1, 2, 3, \ldots, n$, determines the sign of that product. If the number of transpositions required is odd, the product receives a minus sign, and if the number of transpositions is even or zero, the product receives a plus sign.

Example 2.

Let $A = \begin{pmatrix} a_{11} & a_{12} \\ a_{21} & a_{22} \end{pmatrix}$. Find the determinant of A.

Solution: There are two possible products, $a_{11}a_{22}$ and $a_{12}a_{21}$.

$a_{11}a_{22}$ receives a plus sign since the second subscripts are in the natural order. $a_{12}a_{21}$ receives a *minus sign* since it requires *one* transposition to *restore* the *second subscripts* to the natural order.

Therefore, the determinant of the matrix $\begin{pmatrix} a_{11} & a_{12} \\ a_{21} & a_{22} \end{pmatrix}$ is $a_{11}a_{22} + (-a_{12}a_{21}) = a_{11}a_{22} - a_{12}a_{21}$.

Example 3.

Given the 3 by 3 matrix $A = \begin{pmatrix} a_{11} & a_{12} & a_{13} \\ a_{21} & a_{22} & a_{23} \\ a_{31} & a_{32} & a_{33} \end{pmatrix}$, find the determinant of A by Definition 4.1.

Solution: The possible products are $a_{11}a_{22}a_{33}$, $a_{12}a_{23}a_{31}$, $a_{13}a_{21}a_{32}$, $a_{13}a_{22}a_{31}$, $a_{11}a_{23}a_{32}$, and $a_{12}a_{21}a_{33}$.

Analyzing the product $a_{13}a_{21}a_{32}$, we have the order 312 for the *second subscripts*. $312 \rightarrow 132 \rightarrow 123$. *Two* transpositions are required to *restore* the natural order. Therefore, the product $a_{12}a_{21}a_{32}$ receives a *plus sign*. Similarly, for the product $a_{13}a_{22}a_{31}$, we have $321 \rightarrow 312 \rightarrow 132 \rightarrow 123$ or *three* necessary transpositions. Therefore, this product receives a *minus sign*.

Further analysis on the part of the reader will reveal that the first three products receive plus signs and the second three products receive minus signs. Hence, the determinant of A is

$$|A| = a_{11}a_{22}a_{33} + a_{12}a_{23}a_{31} + a_{13}a_{21}a_{32}$$
$$- a_{13}a_{22}a_{31} - a_{11}a_{23}a_{32} - a_{12}a_{21}a_{33}$$

Example 4.

Compute $\begin{vmatrix} 2 & 3 & 4 \\ 1 & 7 & 6 \\ 4 & 2 & 3 \end{vmatrix}$.

Solution: Using the result of Example 3, we have

$$\begin{vmatrix} 2 & 3 & 4 \\ 1 & 7 & 6 \\ 4 & 2 & 3 \end{vmatrix} = (2)(7)(3) + (3)(6)(4) + (4)(1)(2) - (4)(7)(4)$$
$$- (2)(6)(2) - (3)(1)(3)$$
$$= 42 + 72 + 8 - 112 - 24 - 9$$
$$= 122 - 145$$
$$= -23$$

Beginning students sometimes confuse the terms matrix and determinant. A *matrix* is simply a rectangular array of numbers. A *determinant*, which is only defined for square matrices, is a real number associated with a given square matrix that can be calculated by Definition 4.1.

For example, $A = \begin{pmatrix} 2 & 3 & 4 \\ 1 & 7 & 6 \\ 4 & 2 & 3 \end{pmatrix}$ is a 3 by 3 matrix. On the other hand,

$|A| = \begin{vmatrix} 2 & 3 & 4 \\ 1 & 7 & 6 \\ 4 & 2 & 3 \end{vmatrix} = -23$ is the determinant of this matrix.

PROBLEMS

1. Find all the possible products that can be formed by choosing exactly one element from each row and exactly one element from each column of the following matrices:

   (a) $\begin{pmatrix} 4 & 2 \\ 1 & 3 \end{pmatrix}$ (c) $\begin{pmatrix} 2 & 3 & 4 \\ 5 & 6 & 2 \\ 1 & 7 & 4 \end{pmatrix}$

   (b) $\begin{pmatrix} c_{11} & c_{12} \\ c_{21} & c_{22} \end{pmatrix}$ (d) $\begin{pmatrix} x & y \\ 2 & 8 \end{pmatrix}$

2. Find all the possible products that can be formed by choosing exactly one element from each row and exactly one element from each column of the following matrices:

   (a) $\begin{pmatrix} x_{11} & x_{12} \\ x_{21} & x_{22} \end{pmatrix}$ (b) $\begin{pmatrix} x & 3 & 9 \\ 8 & 4 & 2 \\ 6 & 8 & 1 \end{pmatrix}$

3. How many transpositions are required to rearrange the following lists of integers into the natural order?
   (a) 2, 3, 1   (c) 4, 5, 2, 3, 1
   (b) 3, 2, 1, 4   (d) 5, 7, 8, 10, 9

4. Using only transpositions, rearrange the integers 4, 3, 2, 1 into the natural order 3 different ways.

5. Using only transpositions, rearrange the integers 1, 3, 5, 2, 4 into the natural order 2 different ways.

6. Was the number of transpositions in Prob. 5 even or odd?

7. Given the following products:
   (a) $a_{33} \cdot a_{22} \cdot a_{11}$ (b) $a_{31} \cdot a_{23} \cdot a_{12}$
   Arrange each product so that the first subscripts of the factors are in the natural order.

8. Given the following products whose first subscripts are in the natural order, how many transpositions are required to get the second subscripts in the natural order? (Show all steps.)
   (a) $b_{12} \cdot b_{21} \cdot b_{33}$ (b) $b_{13} \cdot b_{22} \cdot b_{31}$

9. What sign should be attached to the products in Prob. 8?

10. $a_{13}a_{21} x\, a_{42}$ is one of twenty-four possible signed products of a 4 by 4 determinant.
    (a) Solve for x.
    (b) Choose the correct sign for this particular product.

11. Given the following products:
     (a) $a_{32} \cdot a_{21} \cdot a_{13}$ (c) $a_{32} \cdot a_{23} \cdot a_{11}$
     (b) $a_{31} \cdot a_{22} \cdot a_{13}$ (d) $a_{33} \cdot a_{21} \cdot a_{12}$
     After arranging the products so that the first subscripts of the factors are in the natural order, restore the second subscript to the natural order by transpositions and attach the correct sign to the product.

12. Given the 3 by 3 matrix
$$B = \begin{pmatrix} b_{11} & b_{12} & b_{13} \\ b_{21} & b_{22} & b_{23} \\ b_{31} & b_{32} & b_{33} \end{pmatrix}$$
     find the determinant of B by Definition 4.1.

13. Given that the matrix $A = \begin{pmatrix} a_{11} & a_{12} \\ a_{21} & a_{22} \end{pmatrix}$ has as its determinant $|A| = a_{11}a_{22} - a_{12}a_{21}$. compute
     (a) $\begin{vmatrix} 6 & 3 \\ 2 & 1 \end{vmatrix}$ (b) $\begin{vmatrix} 7 & 8 \\ 16 & 4 \end{vmatrix}$

14. Given that $|A| = a_{11}a_{22}a_{33} + a_{12}a_{23}a_{31} + a_{13}a_{21}a_{32}$
$$- a_{13}a_{22}a_{31} - a_{11}a_{23}a_{32} - a_{12}a_{21}a_{33}.$$
     Compute
     (a) $\begin{vmatrix} 2 & 4 & 8 \\ 1 & 6 & 2 \\ 3 & 0 & 4 \end{vmatrix}$ (b) $\begin{vmatrix} 6 & 0 & 0 \\ 2 & 1 & 3 \\ 4 & 2 & 1 \end{vmatrix}$

4-2   EVALUATION OF DETERMINANTS OF 2 × 2 AND 3 × 3 MATRICES

The following scheme can be used to evaluate determinants of 2 by 2 and 3 by 3 matrices.

Case 1.   2 by 2 matrices

$$\begin{vmatrix} a_{11} & a_{12} \\ a_{21} & a_{22} \end{vmatrix} = a_{11}a_{22} - a_{12}a_{21} \qquad \textit{by Definition 4.1}$$

Now draw 2 arrows in the matrix $\begin{pmatrix} a_{11} & a_{12} \\ a_{21} & a_{22} \end{pmatrix}$ as follows:

Interpret the arrow pointing *down and to the right* as an instruction to *multiply and use a plus sign.* Interpret the arrow pointing *upward and to the right* as an instruction to *multiply and use a minus sign.* This scheme gives

$$\begin{vmatrix} a_{11} & a_{12} \\ a_{21} & a_{22} \end{vmatrix} = a_{11}a_{22} - a_{12}a_{21}$$

Example 1.   Evaluate $\begin{vmatrix} 2 & 3 \\ 1 & 5 \end{vmatrix}$ by the above scheme.

Solution:

$$\begin{vmatrix} 2 & 3 \\ 1 & 5 \end{vmatrix} = +(2)(5) - (1)(3)$$

$$= 10 - 3$$
$$= 7$$

Example 2.   Evaluate the determinant of $\begin{pmatrix} 3 & -2 \\ -3 & 5 \end{pmatrix}$ using this scheme.

Solution: Determinant of $\begin{pmatrix} 3 & -2 \\ -3 & 5 \end{pmatrix}$

$$= \begin{vmatrix} 3 & -2 \\ -3 & 5 \end{vmatrix}$$

$$= +(3)(5) - (-3)(-2)$$
$$= 15 - 6$$
$$= 9$$

Case 2.   3 by 3 matrices

It was shown in the previous section using Definition 4.1 that

$$\begin{vmatrix} a_{11} & a_{12} & a_{13} \\ a_{21} & a_{22} & a_{23} \\ a_{31} & a_{32} & a_{33} \end{vmatrix} = a_{11}a_{22}a_{33} + a_{12}a_{23}a_{31} + a_{13}a_{32}a_{21} \\ - a_{31}a_{22}a_{13} - a_{32}a_{23}a_{11} - a_{33}a_{12}a_{21}$$

The correct products with the appropriate sign are indicated by the following scheme where the arrows that *start down and to the right* indicate a *plus sign* and the arrows *starting up and to the right indicate a minus sign.*

$$\begin{vmatrix} a_{11} & a_{12} & a_{13} \\ a_{21} & a_{22} & a_{23} \\ a_{31} & a_{32} & a_{33} \end{vmatrix}$$

$$= a_{11}a_{22}a_{33} + a_{12}a_{23}a_{31} + a_{13}a_{32}a_{21} - a_{31}a_{22}a_{13} - a_{32}a_{23}a_{11} - a_{33}a_{12}a_{21}$$

Example 3.   Use the above scheme to evaluate the determinant in Example 4 of Sec. 4-1.

Solution:

$$\begin{vmatrix} 2 & 3 & 4 \\ 1 & 7 & 6 \\ 4 & 2 & 3 \end{vmatrix}$$

$$= (2)(7)(3) + (3)(6)(4) + (4)(2)(1) - (4)(7)(4) - (2)(6)(2) - (3)(3)(1)$$
$$= 42 + 72 + 8 - 112 - 24 - 9$$
$$= 122 - 145 = -23, \text{ as found previously}$$

107

Example 4. Evaluate the determinant of $\begin{pmatrix} 2 & 3 & 4 \\ 1 & -2 & 1 \\ 4 & 6 & 8 \end{pmatrix}$.

Solution:

$$\begin{vmatrix} 2 & 3 & 4 \\ 1 & -2 & 1 \\ 4 & 6 & 8 \end{vmatrix}$$

$$= -32 + 12 + 24 + 32 - 12 - 24$$
$$= 0$$

The scheme given above *does not work* for determinants of matrices with size greater than 3 by 3!

An alternative method of evaluation of determinants of any size is given in the next section.

PROBLEMS

Use the scheme of drawing arrows to evaluate the following determinants:

1. $\begin{vmatrix} 3 & 2 \\ 6 & 1 \end{vmatrix}$

2. $\begin{vmatrix} 4 & 9 \\ 8 & 0 \end{vmatrix}$

3. $\begin{vmatrix} 4 & 2 & 6 \\ 1 & 8 & 4 \\ 3 & 2 & 1 \end{vmatrix}$

4. $\begin{vmatrix} 5 & 7 & 2 \\ 1 & 8 & 7 \\ 3 & 4 & 4 \end{vmatrix}$

5. $\begin{vmatrix} b_{11} & b_{12} & b_{13} \\ b_{21} & b_{22} & b_{23} \\ b_{31} & b_{32} & b_{33} \end{vmatrix}$

6. Compare the result of Prob. 5 with the result of Prob. 12, Sec. 4-1.

7. Solve for x in the equation
$$\begin{vmatrix} x & 3 \\ 2 & 2 \end{vmatrix} = 0$$

8. Show that $\begin{vmatrix} x & y & z \\ 2 & 1 & 3 \\ 3x & 3y & 3z \end{vmatrix} = 0$ for any choice of x, y, and z.

4-3 THE METHOD OF COFACTORS

In Sec. 4-1 it was found that the determinant of the matrix

$$A = \begin{pmatrix} a_{11} & a_{12} & a_{13} \\ a_{21} & a_{22} & a_{23} \\ a_{31} & a_{32} & a_{33} \end{pmatrix}$$

is given by the expression

$$|A| = a_{11}a_{22}a_{33} + a_{12}a_{23}a_{31} + a_{13}a_{21}a_{32} \\ - a_{13}a_{22}a_{31} - a_{11}a_{23}a_{32} - a_{12}a_{21}a_{33} \quad (1)$$

One of several possible rearrangements of this expression is as follows:

$$|A| = a_{11}(a_{22}a_{33} - a_{23}a_{32}) - a_{12}(a_{21}a_{33} - a_{23}a_{31}) \\ + a_{13}(a_{21}a_{32} - a_{22}a_{31}) \quad (2)$$

A careful look at the three "differences" inside the parentheses above reveals that they are simply the values of certain 2 by 2 determinants. Therefore, we can write $|A|$ in terms of other determinants as

$$|A| = a_{11} \begin{vmatrix} a_{22} & a_{23} \\ a_{32} & a_{33} \end{vmatrix} - a_{12} \begin{vmatrix} a_{21} & a_{23} \\ a_{31} & a_{33} \end{vmatrix} + a_{13} \begin{vmatrix} a_{21} & a_{22} \\ a_{31} & a_{32} \end{vmatrix} \quad (3)$$

This is a specific case of the very important theorem for determinants that asserts that an *n* by *n* determinant can be expressed in terms of the elements of any row or column times certain $n - 1$ by $n - 1$ determinants. Before stating this theorem, we need to define two more terms.

DEFINITION 4.2. *Let a_{ij} be the element in the ith row and jth column of the n by n matrix A. Then the minor of a_{ij} is the $n - 1$ by $n - 1$ determinant formed by deleting the ith row and jth column of A.*

DEFINITION 4.3. *Let a_{ij} be an element of the matrix A. The cofactor of a_{ij} = the minor of a_{ij} if $i + j$ is even. If $i + j$ is odd, then the cofactor of a_{ij} = the negative of the minor of a_{ij}. The cofactor of a_{ij} is denoted by A_{ij}.*

Example 1. Let $A = \begin{pmatrix} 2 & 3 & 1 \\ 4 & 7 & 2 \\ 3 & 1 & 2 \end{pmatrix}$. Find the minors of a_{12} and a_{33}.

Solution:

$$\begin{matrix} 2 & 3 & 1 \\ 4 & 7 & 2 \\ 3 & 1 & 2 \end{matrix} \qquad \text{minor of } a_{12} \text{ is } \begin{vmatrix} 4 & 2 \\ 3 & 2 \end{vmatrix} = 8 - 6 = 2$$

$$\begin{matrix} 2 & 3 & 1 \\ 4 & 7 & 2 \\ 3 & 1 & 2 \end{matrix} \qquad \text{minor of } a_{33} \text{ is } \begin{vmatrix} 2 & 3 \\ 4 & 7 \end{vmatrix} = 14 - 12 = 2$$

Example 2. Using the determinant and the results of Example 1, find the cofactors a_{12} and a_{33}.

Solution:

$$\text{Cofactor of } a_{12} = -\begin{vmatrix} 4 & 2 \\ 3 & 2 \end{vmatrix}$$
$$= -2$$

The minus sign is used since $1 + 2 = 3$ is odd.

$$\text{Cofactor of } a_{33} = \begin{vmatrix} 2 & 3 \\ 4 & 7 \end{vmatrix}$$
$$= 2 \qquad \text{\textit{since } } 3 + 3 = 6 \text{ \textit{is even}}$$

THEOREM 4.1.   *Let A be an n by n matrix. Then the determinant of A can be found by computing the sum of the elements in any row or column times their corresponding cofactors.*

The proof of this theorem for the general case is beyond the scope of this text. However, our result (3), which was obtained from Definition 4.1, is in agreement with Theorem 4.1.

$$A_{11} = \text{Cofactor of } a_{11} = \begin{vmatrix} a_{22} & a_{23} \\ a_{32} & a_{33} \end{vmatrix}$$

$$A_{12} = \text{Cofactor of } a_{12} = -\begin{vmatrix} a_{21} & a_{23} \\ a_{31} & a_{33} \end{vmatrix}$$

$$A_{13} = \text{Cofactor of } a_{13} = \begin{vmatrix} a_{21} & a_{22} \\ a_{31} & a_{32} \end{vmatrix}$$

Hence, by Theorem 4.1,

$$\begin{vmatrix} a_{11} & a_{12} & a_{13} \\ a_{21} & a_{22} & a_{23} \\ a_{31} & a_{32} & a_{33} \end{vmatrix} = a_{11} \text{ cofactor of } a_{11} + a_{12} \text{ cofactor of } a_{12} + a_{13}$$
$$\text{cofactor of } a_{13}$$

$$= a_{11} \begin{vmatrix} a_{22} & a_{23} \\ a_{32} & a_{33} \end{vmatrix} - a_{12} \begin{vmatrix} a_{21} & a_{23} \\ a_{31} & a_{33} \end{vmatrix} + a_{13} \begin{vmatrix} a_{21} & a_{22} \\ a_{31} & a_{32} \end{vmatrix} \qquad (3)$$

Example 3. | Evaluate the determinant $\begin{vmatrix} 2 & 1 & 3 \\ 1 & 2 & 4 \\ 2 & 1 & 5 \end{vmatrix}$ by the method of cofactors in two different ways.

Solution: By using row two, we have

$$\begin{vmatrix} 2 & 1 & 3 \\ 1 & 2 & 4 \\ 2 & 1 & 5 \end{vmatrix} = -1 \begin{vmatrix} 1 & 3 \\ 1 & 5 \end{vmatrix} + 2 \begin{vmatrix} 2 & 3 \\ 2 & 5 \end{vmatrix} - 4 \begin{vmatrix} 2 & 1 \\ 2 & 1 \end{vmatrix}$$
$$= -1(5 - 3) + 2(10 - 6) - 4(2 - 2)$$
$$= -1(2) + 2(4) - 4(0)$$
$$= -2 + 8 - 0$$
$$= 6$$

By using column one, we have

$$\begin{vmatrix} 2 & 1 & 3 \\ 1 & 2 & 4 \\ 2 & 1 & 5 \end{vmatrix} = 2\begin{vmatrix} 2 & 4 \\ 1 & 5 \end{vmatrix} - 1\begin{vmatrix} 1 & 3 \\ 1 & 5 \end{vmatrix} + 2\begin{vmatrix} 1 & 3 \\ 2 & 4 \end{vmatrix}$$

$$= 2(10 - 4) - 1(5 - 3) + 2(4 - 6)$$
$$= 2(6) - 1(2) + 2(-2)$$
$$= 12 - 2 - 4$$
$$= 6$$

Next we illustrate a fact about determinants which will be needed in Sec. 4-5.

THEOREM 4.2. *If the cofactors of the elements of any row or column of an n by n determinant are multiplied by the corresponding elements in some other row or column and then added together, the result is zero.*

Example 4. (Partial proof of Theorem 4.2 for 3 by 3 case.) Compute the quantity $a_{11}A_{21} + a_{12}A_{22} + a_{13}A_{23}$ for the matrix $A = \begin{pmatrix} a_{11} & a_{12} & a_{13} \\ a_{21} & a_{22} & a_{23} \\ a_{31} & a_{32} & a_{33} \end{pmatrix}$.

Solution:

$$A_{21} = \text{Cofactor of } a_{21} = -\begin{vmatrix} a_{12} & a_{13} \\ a_{32} & a_{33} \end{vmatrix}$$

$$A_{22} = \text{Cofactor of } a_{22} = \begin{vmatrix} a_{11} & a_{13} \\ a_{31} & a_{33} \end{vmatrix}$$

$$A_{23} = \text{Cofactor of } a_{23} = -\begin{vmatrix} a_{11} & a_{12} \\ a_{31} & a_{32} \end{vmatrix}$$

The desired quantity is given by

$$-a_{11}(a_{12}a_{33} - a_{32}a_{13}) + a_{12}(a_{11}a_{33} - a_{31}a_{13}) - a_{13}(a_{11}a_{32} - a_{31}a_{12})$$
$$= -a_{11}a_{12}a_{33} + a_{11}a_{32}a_{13} + a_{12}a_{11}a_{33} - a_{12}a_{31}a_{13} - a_{11}a_{13}a_{32} + a_{13}a_{31}a_{12}$$
$$= (a_{12}a_{11}a_{33} - a_{11}a_{12}a_{33}) + (a_{11}a_{32}a_{13} - a_{11}a_{13}a_{32}) + (a_{13}a_{31}a_{12} - a_{12}a_{31}a_{13})$$
$$= 0 + 0 + 0$$
$$= 0$$

PROBLEMS

1. Find the minor of the elements b_{31} and b_{23} given that
$$B = \begin{pmatrix} b_{11} & b_{12} & b_{13} \\ b_{21} & b_{22} & b_{23} \\ b_{31} & b_{32} & b_{33} \end{pmatrix}$$

2. Find the minor of a_{31}, a_{32}, a_{33} if
$$A = \begin{pmatrix} 2 & 6 & 1 \\ 3 & 4 & 2 \\ 8 & 1 & 6 \end{pmatrix}$$

3. Find the cofactor of a_{31}, a_{32}, a_{33} in Prob. 2.

4. Use the results of Example 3 to evaluate the determinant of A in Prob. 2.

5. Given the matrix $\begin{pmatrix} 4 & 1 & 0 \\ 3 & 6 & 2 \\ 2 & 0 & 1 \end{pmatrix}$, evaluate the determinant by computing the sum of the elements in column three times their corresponding cofactors.

6. Evaluate the determinant of the matrix in Example 5 by computing the sum of the elements in column two times their corresponding cofactors.

7. Evaluate the following determinants by the method of cofactors:

   (a) $\begin{vmatrix} 2 & 1 & 4 \\ 3 & 6 & 1 \\ 2 & 1 & 2 \end{vmatrix}$ (b) $\begin{vmatrix} 4 & 1 & 3 \\ 3 & 0 & 0 \\ 2 & 1 & 6 \end{vmatrix}$

8. Evaluate the following determinants by the method of cofactors:

   (a) $\begin{vmatrix} 3 & 1 & 2 \\ 5 & 1 & 3 \\ 2 & 4 & 6 \end{vmatrix}$ (b) $\begin{vmatrix} 4 & 1 & 3 \\ 3 & 0 & 1 \\ 4 & 0 & 2 \end{vmatrix}$

9. Illustrate Theorem 4.2 by summing the cofactors of column three times the corresponding elements of column two for the following:

$$\begin{vmatrix} 6 & 2 & 1 \\ 4 & 0 & 2 \\ 3 & 1 & 4 \end{vmatrix}$$

10. Illustrate Theorem 4.2 for the following:

   (a) $\begin{vmatrix} 3 & 2 & 1 \\ 6 & 8 & 4 \\ 2 & 1 & 3 \end{vmatrix}$ (b) $\begin{vmatrix} 6 & 2 & 1 \\ 3 & 1 & 1 \\ 2 & 4 & 5 \end{vmatrix}$

11. Evaluate the determinant of the following matrix:

$$\begin{pmatrix} 6 & 8 & 4 & 2 \\ 1 & 3 & 2 & 0 \\ 0 & 1 & 4 & 2 \\ 0 & 1 & 2 & 3 \end{pmatrix}$$

   i.e., continue the following partial solution:

$$6\begin{vmatrix} 3 & 2 & 0 \\ 1 & 4 & 2 \\ 1 & 2 & 3 \end{vmatrix} + 8(-)\begin{vmatrix} 1 & 2 & 0 \\ 0 & 4 & 2 \\ 0 & 2 & 3 \end{vmatrix} + 4\begin{vmatrix} 1 & 3 & 0 \\ 0 & 1 & 2 \\ 0 & 1 & 3 \end{vmatrix} + 2(-)\begin{vmatrix} 1 & 3 & 2 \\ 0 & 1 & 4 \\ 0 & 1 & 2 \end{vmatrix}$$

$$6\begin{vmatrix} 3 & 2 & 0 \\ 1 & 4 & 2 \\ 1 & 2 & 3 \end{vmatrix} - 8\begin{vmatrix} 1 & 2 & 0 \\ 0 & 4 & 2 \\ 0 & 2 & 3 \end{vmatrix} + 4\begin{vmatrix} 1 & 3 & 0 \\ 0 & 1 & 2 \\ 0 & 1 & 3 \end{vmatrix} - 2\begin{vmatrix} 1 & 3 & 2 \\ 0 & 1 & 4 \\ 0 & 1 & 2 \end{vmatrix}$$

12. Evaluate the following determinants:

   (a) $\begin{vmatrix} 2 & 1 & 0 & 3 \\ 4 & 2 & 1 & 6 \\ 2 & 3 & 2 & 1 \\ 4 & 5 & 0 & 2 \end{vmatrix}$ (b) $\begin{vmatrix} 3 & 2 & 1 & 1 \\ 0 & 2 & 1 & 0 \\ 4 & 6 & 3 & 1 \\ 2 & 5 & 2 & 2 \end{vmatrix}$

4-4 CRAMER'S RULE

In Sec. 4-1 it was pointed out that the expression $ad - bc$ occurs in a natural way when we attempt to find the inverse of the square matrix

$A = \begin{pmatrix} a & b \\ c & d \end{pmatrix}$. The reader will recall that $ad - bc = \begin{vmatrix} a & b \\ c & d \end{vmatrix}$.

Next we show that this same quantity also occurs when the system of equations

$$ax + by = k_1$$
$$cx + dy = k_2$$

is solved by the method of elimination.

Multiply the first equation by d and the second equation by b to get

$$adx + bdy = k_1 d$$
$$bcx + bdy = k_2 b$$

Subtract the second equation from the first to get

$$adx - bcx = k_1 d - k_2 b$$
$$(ad - bc)x = k_1 d - k_2 b$$

For $ad - bc \neq 0$, we have $x = \dfrac{k_1 d - k_2 b}{ad - bc}$. Similarly, multiplying the first equation by c and the second equation by a and subtracting gives $y = \dfrac{k_2 a - k_1 c}{ad - bc}$.

Note that both denominators are given by $ad - bc$, i.e., $\begin{vmatrix} a & b \\ c & d \end{vmatrix}$. In fact, the numerators can also be expressed as the determinants $\begin{vmatrix} k_1 & b \\ k_2 & d \end{vmatrix}$ and $\begin{vmatrix} a & k_1 \\ c & k_2 \end{vmatrix}$. Note: the k column has been substituted into the two determinants.

In summary, the system

$$\begin{aligned} ax + by &= k_1 \\ cx + dy &= k_2 \end{aligned} \qquad ad - bc \neq 0$$

has the solution

$$x = \frac{\begin{vmatrix} k_1 & b \\ k_2 & d \end{vmatrix}}{\begin{vmatrix} a & b \\ c & d \end{vmatrix}}, \quad y = \frac{\begin{vmatrix} a & k_1 \\ c & k_2 \end{vmatrix}}{\begin{vmatrix} a & b \\ c & d \end{vmatrix}}$$

This result is a special case of a theorem called *Cramer's rule*.

THEOREM 4.3.   *The system of n equations in n unknowns*

$$\begin{aligned} a_{11}x_1 + a_{12}x_2 + \cdots + a_{1n}x_n &= c_1 \\ a_{21}x_1 + a_{22}x_2 + \cdots + a_{2n}x_n &= c_2 \\ &\ \ \vdots \\ a_{n1}x_1 + a_{n2}x_2 + \cdots + a_{nn}x_n &= c_n \end{aligned}$$

where

$$D_n = \begin{vmatrix} a_{11} & a_{12} & \cdots & a_{1n} \\ a_{21} & a_{22} & \cdots & a_{2n} \\ \cdot & \cdot & \cdot & \cdot \\ \cdot & \cdot & \cdot & \cdot \\ \cdot & \cdot & \cdot & \cdot \\ a_{n1} & a_{n2} & \cdots & a_{nn} \end{vmatrix} \neq 0$$

has as its solution

$$x_1 = \frac{\begin{vmatrix} c_1 & a_{12} & a_{13} & \cdots & a_{1n} \\ c_2 & a_{22} & a_{23} & \cdots & a_{2n} \\ \cdot & \cdot & \cdot & \cdot & \cdot \\ \cdot & \cdot & \cdot & \cdot & \cdot \\ c_n & a_{n2} & a_{n3} & \cdots & a_{nn} \end{vmatrix}}{D_n},$$

$$x_2 = \frac{\begin{vmatrix} a_{11} & c_1 & a_{13} & \cdots & a_{1n} \\ a_{21} & c_2 & a_{23} & \cdots & a_{2n} \\ \cdot & \cdot & \cdot & \cdot & \cdot \\ \cdot & \cdot & \cdot & \cdot & \cdot \\ a_{n1} & c_n & a_{n3} & \cdots & a_{nn} \end{vmatrix}}{D_n} \quad \cdots, \quad x_n = \frac{\begin{vmatrix} a_{11} & a_{12} & \cdots & c_1 \\ a_{21} & a_{22} & \cdots & c_2 \\ \cdot & \cdot & \cdot & \cdot \\ \cdot & \cdot & \cdot & \cdot \\ a_{n1} & a_{n2} & \cdots & c_n \end{vmatrix}}{D_n}$$

Example 1. | Use Cramer's rule to solve the linear system

$$x + 2y + 3z = 1$$
$$x + 3y + 5z = 2$$
$$2x + 5y + 9z = 3$$

Solution:

$$D_3 = \begin{vmatrix} 1 & 2 & 3 \\ 1 & 3 & 5 \\ 2 & 5 & 9 \end{vmatrix} = 1(27 - 25) - 1(18 - 15) + 2(10 - 9) = 1$$

By using the method of cofactors and column one, we have

$$x = \frac{\begin{vmatrix} 1 & 2 & 3 \\ 2 & 3 & 5 \\ 3 & 5 & 9 \end{vmatrix}}{D_3} = \frac{1(27 - 25) - 2(18 - 15) + 3(10 - 9)}{1} = -1$$

$$y = \frac{\begin{vmatrix} 1 & 1 & 3 \\ 1 & 2 & 5 \\ 2 & 3 & 9 \end{vmatrix}}{D_3} = \frac{1}{1}$$

$$z = \frac{\begin{vmatrix} 1 & 2 & 1 \\ 1 & 3 & 2 \\ 2 & 5 & 3 \end{vmatrix}}{D_3} = \frac{0}{1} = 0$$

Hence, the solution is $x = -1$, $y = 1$, $z = 0$.

Example 2.   Evaluate the determinant of the coefficient matrix for the system

$$\begin{pmatrix} 1 & 0 & 1 \\ 2 & 1 & 0 \\ 3 & 0 & 1 \end{pmatrix} \begin{pmatrix} x \\ y \\ z \end{pmatrix} = \begin{pmatrix} 1 \\ 3 \\ 5 \end{pmatrix}$$

Solution: The coefficient matrix is

$$A = \begin{pmatrix} 1 & 0 & 1 \\ 2 & 1 & 0 \\ 3 & 0 & 1 \end{pmatrix} \quad \text{and} \quad |A| = 1 + 0 + 0 - 3 - 0 - 0 = -2$$

using the scheme of Sec. 4-2

PROBLEMS

1.   **(a)**   By Cramer's rule, solve $x + y = 1$
                                     $x - y = 4$
    (b)   Verify your answer by the method of elimination.

2.   Given the following matrix equation:

$$\begin{pmatrix} 1 & 2 & 3 \\ 0 & 1 & 2 \\ 2 & 1 & 4 \end{pmatrix} \begin{pmatrix} x \\ y \\ z \end{pmatrix} = \begin{pmatrix} 4 \\ -2 \\ 6 \end{pmatrix}$$

    (a)   What is the determinant of the matrix of coefficients?
    (b)   Solve for y using Cramer's rule.

3.   Given the system

$$2x + 3y + 4z = 4$$
$$x + 2y + 5z = 0$$
$$4x + y + z = 5$$

    Solve for x by Cramer's rule.

4.   Given the system

$$2x + 2z = 2$$
$$5x + 4y + z = 3$$
$$2x + 6z = 4$$

    (a)   What is the determinant of the matrix of coefficients?
    (b)   Solve for x, y, and z using Cramer's rule.

5.   Given the system

$$a + b + c = -2$$
$$8a + 4b + 2c = 6$$
$$-a + b - c = 0$$

    Solve for a, b, and c using Cramer's rule.

Problems 6 through 9 are based on Leontief's input-output analysis concepts.

6.   Use Cramer's rule to solve Prob. 14 of Sec. 3-7.

7.   Recall the system

$$b_{11}\Delta x_1 + b_{12}\Delta x_2 = \Delta d_1$$

$$b_{21}\Delta x_1 + b_{22}\Delta x_2 = \Delta d_2$$

    from Prob. 14 of Sec. 3-7. Use Cramer's rule to solve for Δx_1 and Δx_2 in terms of Δd_1, Δd_2, and the elements of B, where $B = I - A$.

8. Using the results of Prob. 7, determine Δx_1 and Δx_2 if $\Delta d_1 = 2$, $\Delta d_2 = 3$, and $B = \begin{pmatrix} 0.9 & -0.4 \\ -0.3 & 0.8 \end{pmatrix}$.

9. Use the results of Prob. 7 to obtain the required output for both industries in Examples 4 and 5 of Sec. 3-7.

4-5 THE USE OF DETERMINANTS FOR FINDING THE INVERSE OF A MATRIX

In Sec. 3-4 we solved a system of 4 equations in 4 unknowns and found that if

$$A = \begin{pmatrix} a & b \\ c & d \end{pmatrix}$$

then

$$A^{-1} = \begin{pmatrix} \dfrac{d}{ad - bc} & \dfrac{-b}{ad - bc} \\[2mm] \dfrac{-c}{ad - bc} & \dfrac{a}{ad - bc} \end{pmatrix}$$

Noting that $ad - bc = |A|$ and using the definition of multiplication of a matrix by a scalar, we have

$$A^{-1} = \frac{1}{|A|} \begin{pmatrix} d & -b \\ -c & a \end{pmatrix}$$

If A is written in subscript notation

$$A = \begin{pmatrix} a_{11} & a_{12} \\ a_{21} & a_{22} \end{pmatrix}$$

then

$$A^{-1} = \frac{1}{|A|} \begin{pmatrix} a_{22} & -a_{12} \\ -a_{21} & a_{11} \end{pmatrix} \tag{1}$$

Example 1. Use the above formula to find the inverse of $A = \begin{pmatrix} 2 & 3 \\ 2 & 4 \end{pmatrix}$.

Solution:

$$a_{11} = 2,\ a_{12} = 3,\ a_{21} = 2,\ a_{22} = 4$$

$$\begin{vmatrix} 2 & 3 \\ 2 & 4 \end{vmatrix} = 8 - 6 = 2$$

$$A^{-1} = \frac{1}{2} \begin{pmatrix} a_{22} & -a_{12} \\ -a_{21} & a_{11} \end{pmatrix}$$

$$= \frac{1}{2} \begin{pmatrix} 4 & -3 \\ -2 & 2 \end{pmatrix}$$

$$A^{-1} = \begin{pmatrix} 2 & -\frac{3}{2} \\ -1 & 1 \end{pmatrix}$$

Before we continue with a discussion of the inverse of a square matrix, we need the following matrix concept.

DEFINITION 4.4.   *Let A be an m by n matrix. Then the n by m matrix A^t, which is obtained by interchanging the rows and columns of A, is called the transpose of A.*

The next two examples illustrate the definition of the transpose of a matrix.

1. If $A = \begin{pmatrix} 1 & 3 & 5 \\ 4 & 5 & 3 \end{pmatrix}$, then $A^t = \begin{pmatrix} 1 & 4 \\ 3 & 5 \\ 5 & 3 \end{pmatrix}$.

2. If $B = \begin{pmatrix} 3 & 8 \\ 6 & 2 \end{pmatrix}$, then $B^t = \begin{pmatrix} 3 & 6 \\ 8 & 2 \end{pmatrix}$.

Example 2.   Given the matrix $A = \begin{pmatrix} a_{11} & a_{12} \\ a_{21} & a_{22} \end{pmatrix}$, form a new matrix B by replacing each element of A by its cofactor.

Solution:

$$A_{11} = a_{22}$$
$$A_{21} = -a_{12}$$
$$A_{12} = -a_{21}$$
$$A_{22} = a_{11}$$

Therefore, the desired matrix is

$$B = \begin{pmatrix} a_{22} & -a_{21} \\ -a_{12} & a_{11} \end{pmatrix}$$

Example 3.   Find the transpose of the matrix B of Example 2.

Solution:

$$B = \begin{pmatrix} a_{22} & -a_{21} \\ -a_{12} & a_{11} \end{pmatrix}$$

$$B^t = \begin{pmatrix} a_{22} & -a_{12} \\ -a_{21} & a_{11} \end{pmatrix}$$

If we multiply the matrix B^t of Example 3 by the scalar quantity $1/|A|$ and compare the resulting matrix with (1), we see that this is A^{-1}, the multiplicative inverse of A. $|A|$ must not be zero, of course. This would be written symbolically as

$$A^{-1} = \frac{1}{|A|} B^t$$

if

$$|A| \neq 0$$

Next we give an extension of this method. This extension can be used to find the inverse of an n by n matrix.

PROCEDURE

Step 1:   Calculate the determinant of the given matrix. If this determinant is not zero, go on to step 2.

Step 2:   Form a new matrix B by replacing each element in the given matrix by its cofactor. B will be called the *matrix of cofactors.*

Step 3:   Take the transpose of the matrix of cofactors.

Step 4:   The inverse of the given matrix is found by multiplying the matrix in step 3 by the scalar $1/|A|$.

Before commenting on the validity and the usefulness of the above procedure, we will illustrate the procedure by a numerical example.

Example 4.

Use the above procedure to find the inverse of the matrix

$$A = \begin{pmatrix} 1 & 2 & 3 \\ 1 & 3 & 5 \\ 2 & 5 & 9 \end{pmatrix}$$

Solution:

Step 1.

$$\begin{vmatrix} 1 & 2 & 3 \\ 1 & 3 & 5 \\ 2 & 5 & 9 \end{vmatrix} = 1 \qquad \text{from Example 1 in the previous section}$$

Step 2.   The cofactor of 9 is

$$\begin{vmatrix} 1 & 2 \\ 1 & 3 \end{vmatrix} = 3 - 2 = 1 \qquad \text{(sample calculation)}$$

The matrix of cofactors is

$$B = \begin{pmatrix} 2 & 1 & -1 \\ -3 & 3 & -1 \\ 1 & -2 & 1 \end{pmatrix}$$

Step 3.

$$B^t = \begin{pmatrix} 2 & -3 & 1 \\ 1 & 3 & -2 \\ -1 & -1 & 1 \end{pmatrix} \qquad \text{interchanging rows and columns}$$

Step 4.

$$A^{-1} = \frac{1}{|A|} B^t$$

$$\begin{pmatrix} 1 & 2 & 3 \\ 1 & 3 & 5 \\ 2 & 5 & 9 \end{pmatrix}^{-1} = \frac{1}{1} \begin{pmatrix} 2 & -3 & 1 \\ 1 & 3 & -2 \\ -1 & -1 & 1 \end{pmatrix}$$

$$A^{-1} = \begin{pmatrix} 2 & -3 & 1 \\ 1 & 3 & -2 \\ -1 & -1 & 1 \end{pmatrix}$$

Note: This matrix was also inverted by row operations in Sec. 3-6.

Remarks:

1. If the determinant of the given matrix turns out to be zero, then the matrix does not have a multiplicative inverse. This test for the existence of the inverse of a matrix can also be used in conjunction with the algorithm of Sec. 3-6.

2. We must point out that even though the four-step procedure given above can be used to find the inverse of a matrix of size greater than 3 by 3, the procedure is very long and tedious for matrices of size 4 by 4 and greater. Our use of this method in later sections will be limited to 3 by 3 matrices.

Finally, we prove the validity of the procedure for the special case of a 3 by 3 matrix. Let

$$A = \begin{pmatrix} a_{11} & a_{12} & a_{13} \\ a_{21} & a_{22} & a_{23} \\ a_{31} & a_{32} & a_{33} \end{pmatrix}$$

If we denote the cofactor of a_{ij} by A_{ij}, we have

$$B = \begin{pmatrix} A_{11} & A_{12} & A_{13} \\ A_{21} & A_{22} & A_{23} \\ A_{31} & A_{32} & A_{33} \end{pmatrix} \qquad \textit{the matrix of cofactors}$$

$$B^t = \begin{pmatrix} A_{11} & A_{21} & A_{31} \\ A_{12} & A_{22} & A_{32} \\ A_{13} & A_{23} & A_{33} \end{pmatrix}$$

$$\frac{1}{|A|} \begin{pmatrix} A_{11} & A_{21} & A_{31} \\ A_{12} & A_{22} & A_{32} \\ A_{13} & A_{23} & A_{33} \end{pmatrix} \qquad \textit{is the alleged inverse by step 4}$$

To check this we must show that $A\left(\dfrac{1}{|A|}B^t\right) = \begin{pmatrix} 1 & 0 & 0 \\ 0 & 1 & 0 \\ 0 & 0 & 1 \end{pmatrix}$.

Now,

$$\begin{pmatrix} a_{11} & a_{12} & a_{13} \\ a_{21} & a_{22} & a_{23} \\ a_{31} & a_{32} & a_{33} \end{pmatrix} \frac{1}{|A|} \begin{pmatrix} A_{11} & A_{21} & A_{31} \\ A_{12} & A_{22} & A_{32} \\ A_{13} & A_{23} & A_{33} \end{pmatrix}$$

$$= \frac{1}{|A|} \begin{pmatrix} a_{11}A_{11} + a_{12}A_{12} + a_{13}A_{13} & a_{11}A_{21} + a_{12}A_{22} + a_{13}A_{31} \\ a_{21}A_{11} + a_{22}A_{12} + a_{23}A_{13} & a_{21}A_{21} + a_{22}A_{22} + a_{23}A_{23} \\ a_{31}A_{31} + a_{32}A_{12} + a_{33}A_{13} & a_{31}A_{21} + a_{32}A_{22} + a_{33}A_{23} \end{pmatrix}$$

$$\begin{matrix} a_{11}A_{31} + a_{12}A_{32} + a_{13}A_{33} \\ a_{21}A_{31} + a_{22}A_{32} + a_{23}A_{33} \\ a_{31}A_{31} + a_{32}A_{32} + a_{33}A_{33} \end{matrix}$$

119

$$= \frac{1}{|A|} \begin{pmatrix} |A| & 0 & 0 \\ 0 & |A| & 0 \\ 0 & 0 & |A| \end{pmatrix} \qquad \text{by Theorems 4.1 and 4.2}$$

$$= \begin{pmatrix} 1 & 0 & 0 \\ 0 & 1 & 0 \\ 0 & 0 & 1 \end{pmatrix} \qquad \text{as shown}$$

PROBLEMS

1. Use the formula $A^{-1} = \dfrac{1}{|A|} \begin{pmatrix} a_{22} & -a_{12} \\ -a_{21} & a_{11} \end{pmatrix}$ to find the inverse of the following matrices:

   (a) $\begin{pmatrix} 6 & 4 \\ 3 & 1 \end{pmatrix}$ (b) $\begin{pmatrix} 9 & 2 \\ 4 & 3 \end{pmatrix}$

2. Find the transpose of the following matrices:

   (a) $(3, 2, 6)$ (c) $\begin{pmatrix} 2 & 1 \\ 5 & 6 \end{pmatrix}$

   (b) $\begin{pmatrix} 4 & 2 & 1 \\ 8 & 3 & 4 \end{pmatrix}$ (d) $\begin{pmatrix} a_{11} & a_{12} \\ a_{21} & a_{22} \end{pmatrix}$

3. Find the transpose of the following matrices:

   (a) $\begin{pmatrix} 6 & 5 & 4 \\ 2 & 3 & 1 \\ 6 & 8 & 9 \end{pmatrix}$ (c) $\begin{pmatrix} 2 \\ 6 \\ 1 \end{pmatrix}$

   (b) $\begin{pmatrix} c_{11} & c_{12} \\ c_{21} & c_{22} \\ c_{31} & c_{32} \end{pmatrix}$ (d) $\begin{pmatrix} 2 & 3 \\ 4 & 5 \\ 6 & 7 \end{pmatrix}$

4. Given the matrix $\begin{pmatrix} 4 & 3 \\ 6 & 9 \end{pmatrix}$.

   (a) Find the matrix of cofactors.
   (b) Find the transpose of the matrix of cofactors.

5. Given that $B = \begin{pmatrix} 4 & 2 \\ 8 & 6 \end{pmatrix}$.

   (a) Find the determinant of B.
   (b) Find the matrix of cofactors.
   (c) Find the transpose of the matrix of cofactors.
   (d) Find B^{-1}.

6. Show that the result in Example 5, part (d) is indeed the inverse of B (i.e., $B \cdot B^{-1} = I$).

7. Calculate the inverse of each of the following matrices using the 4-step procedure outlined in this section.

   (a) $\begin{pmatrix} 3 & 0 & 1 \\ 4 & 2 & 1 \\ 3 & 0 & 1 \end{pmatrix}$ (b) $\begin{pmatrix} 4 & 2 & 0 \\ 3 & 0 & 0 \\ 6 & 1 & 1 \end{pmatrix}$

8. Does the following system of equations have a unique solution?

$$x + 2y = 3$$
$$2x + 4y = 6$$

[*Hint:* Is the determinant of the matrix of coefficients equal to zero?]

9. Calculate the inverse of C and show that this is indeed the inverse, i.e.,

$$C\left[\frac{1}{|C|} B^t\right] = I, \qquad C = \begin{pmatrix} c_{11} & c_{12} & c_{13} \\ c_{21} & c_{22} & c_{23} \\ c_{31} & c_{32} & c_{33} \end{pmatrix}$$

10. (a) Show that $(A^t)^t = A$.
(b) Show that $(A + B)^t = A^t + B^t$.

11. Recalling the definition of the *trace* of a matrix as the sum of elements on its principal diagonal, write out the trace of AB^t, where A and B are n by n matrices.

12. The following result is given by Campbell[1]:
The total revenue of a transportation industry maintaining regular service between n stations is given by the trace of AB^t, where a_{ij} = number of passengers transported from station i to station j, and b_{ij} = cost of a ticket from station i to station j. See Prob. 11 for the definition of the trace of a matrix.
Draw a schematic diagram and establish the result for the special case $n = 3$.

13. Use the result in Prob. 12 to compute the average daily revenue for the Fast Service Transit Company given the following data for cities x, y, and z.

AVERAGE PASSENGER USE

		To		
		x	y	z
	x	0	200	105
From	y	160	0	125
	z	80	110	0

TICKET PRICES IN DOLLARS

		To		
		x	y	z
	x	0	15	50
From	y	15	0	30
	z	50	30	0

14. Does $B^t = B$ in Prob. 13? Could we use AB instead of AB^t in this case to compute the total revenue?

---

1. Hugh G. Campbell, *Matrices with Applications.* New York: Appleton-Century-Crofts, 1968, p. 55.

4-6 SUMMARY OF METHODS FOR SOLVING SYSTEMS OF EQUATIONS

In this section we will solve a system of linear equations by three different methods. In the first example, the system is solved by the method of elimination. In the second example, the system is solved by Cramer's rule. Finally, in the last example, the system is solved by first finding the inverse of the coefficient matrix by the algorithm of Sec. 3-6, and then multiplying both sides of the matrix equation by this inverse.

Example 1. Solve the following linear system by the method of elimination.

e_1: $2x + 6y + 4z = -12$
e_2: $6x + 6y + 4z = 8$
e_3: $3x + 2y + 4z = 13$

Solution: By subtracting e_2 from e_1, we have

$$
\begin{array}{r}
2x + 6y + 4z = -12 \\
6x + 6y + 4z = 8 \\
\hline
-4x + 0 + 0 = -20
\end{array}
$$

Therefore, e_4: $x = 5$.

Subtract e_3 from e_2.

$$
\begin{array}{r}
6x + 6y + 4z = 8 \\
3x + 2y + 4z = 13 \\
\hline
\end{array}
$$

e_5: $3x + 4y = -5$

By substituting e_4 into e_5, we get

$3(5) + 4(y) = -5$
$ 4y = -20$
$ y = -5$

If we substitute $x = 5$ and $y = -5$ into e_1, we have

$2(5) + 6(-5) + 4z = -12$
$ 4z = -12 - 10 + 30$
$ 4z = 8$
$ z = 2$

The solution of the given system is $x = 5$, $y = -5$, and $z = 2$.

Example 2. Use Cramer's rule to solve the system in Example 1.

Solution:

$$
D_3 = \begin{vmatrix} 2 & 6 & 4 \\ 6 & 6 & 4 \\ 3 & 2 & 4 \end{vmatrix}
$$

$$
= 2(24 - 8) - 6(24 - 12) + 4(12 - 18)
$$
$$
= 2(16) - 6(12) + 4(-6)
$$

$$= 32 - 72 - 24$$
$$= -64 \qquad \text{by the method of cofactors and the first row}$$

$$x = \frac{\begin{vmatrix} -12 & 6 & 4 \\ 8 & 6 & 4 \\ 13 & 2 & 4 \end{vmatrix}}{D_3}, \qquad y = \frac{\begin{vmatrix} 2 & -12 & 4 \\ 6 & 8 & 4 \\ 3 & 13 & 4 \end{vmatrix}}{D_3}, \quad \text{and}$$

$$z = \frac{\begin{vmatrix} 2 & 6 & -12 \\ 6 & 6 & 8 \\ 3 & 2 & 13 \end{vmatrix}}{D_3}, \qquad \text{where } D_3 = -64$$

By the method of cofactors and column three we have

$$x = \frac{4(16 - 78) - 4(-24 - 78) + 4(-72 - 48)}{-64}$$

$$x = \frac{4(-62 + 102 - 120)}{-64} = \frac{4(-80)}{-64} = 5$$

Use the scheme of Sec. 4-2, which works for 2 by 2 and 3 by 3 determinants only, and

$$y = \frac{64 - 144 + 312 - 96 - 104 + 288}{-64}$$

$$y = \frac{320}{-64} = -5$$

Finally, a similar calculation gives $z = -128/-64 = 2$, and the solution is $x = 5$, $y = -5$, and $z = 2$, the same answers found in Example 1.

Example 3.

Solve the system given in Example 1 by finding the inverse of the coefficient matrix and multiplying by this inverse.

Solution: The coefficient matrix of the system is $A = \begin{pmatrix} 2 & 6 & 4 \\ 6 & 6 & 4 \\ 3 & 2 & 4 \end{pmatrix}$. The given system can be written as the matrix equation

$$\begin{pmatrix} 2 & 6 & 4 \\ 6 & 6 & 4 \\ 3 & 2 & 4 \end{pmatrix} \begin{pmatrix} x \\ y \\ z \end{pmatrix} = \begin{pmatrix} -12 \\ 8 \\ 13 \end{pmatrix}$$

Use the algorithm from Sec. 3-6.

$$(A|I) = \begin{pmatrix} 2 & 6 & 4 & | & 1 & 0 & 0 \\ 6 & 6 & 4 & | & 0 & 1 & 0 \\ 3 & 2 & 4 & | & 0 & 0 & 1 \end{pmatrix} \qquad \text{(a)}$$

Subtract row 2 from row 1 of (a) to get $b_{12} = 0$, $b_{13} = 0$; this gives

$$(B|X_1) = \begin{pmatrix} -4 & 0 & 0 & | & 1 & -1 & 0 \\ 6 & 6 & 4 & | & 0 & 1 & 0 \\ 3 & 2 & 4 & | & 0 & 0 & 1 \end{pmatrix} \qquad \text{(b)}$$

123

Subtract row 3 from row 2 of (b) to get $c_{23} = 0$; this gives

$$(C|X_2) = \begin{pmatrix} -4 & 0 & 0 & | & 1 & -1 & 0 \\ 3 & 4 & 0 & | & 0 & 1 & -1 \\ 3 & 2 & 4 & | & 0 & 0 & 1 \end{pmatrix} \tag{c}$$

Subtract row 2 from row 3 of (c) to get $d_{31} = 0$.

$$(D|X_3) = \begin{pmatrix} -4 & 0 & 0 & | & 1 & -1 & 0 \\ 3 & 4 & 0 & | & 0 & 1 & -1 \\ 0 & -2 & 4 & | & 0 & -1 & 2 \end{pmatrix} \tag{d}$$

Multiply row 1 by $\frac{3}{4}$ and then subtract from row 2 of (d) to get $e_{12} = 0$.

$$(E|X_4) = \begin{pmatrix} -4 & 0 & 0 & | & 1 & -1 & 0 \\ 0 & 4 & 0 & | & \frac{3}{4} & \frac{1}{4} & -1 \\ 0 & -2 & 4 & | & 0 & -1 & 2 \end{pmatrix} \tag{e}$$

Multiply row 2 by $-\frac{1}{2}$ and then subtract row 2 from row 3 of (e) to get $f_{32} = 0$. This gives

$$(F|X_5) = \begin{pmatrix} -4 & 0 & 0 & | & 1 & -1 & 0 \\ 0 & -2 & 0 & | & -\frac{3}{8} & -\frac{1}{8} & \frac{1}{2} \\ 0 & 0 & 4 & | & \frac{3}{8} & -\frac{7}{8} & \frac{3}{2} \end{pmatrix} \tag{f}$$

Multiply row 1 by $\frac{1}{4}$, row 2 by $-\frac{1}{2}$, row 3 by $\frac{1}{4}$. We now have

$$(I|A^{-1}) = \begin{pmatrix} 1 & 0 & 0 & | & -\frac{1}{4} & \frac{1}{4} & 0 \\ 0 & 1 & 0 & | & \frac{3}{16} & \frac{1}{16} & -\frac{1}{4} \\ 0 & 0 & 1 & | & \frac{3}{32} & -\frac{7}{32} & \frac{3}{8} \end{pmatrix} \tag{g}$$

Therefore,

$$A^{-1} = \begin{pmatrix} -\frac{1}{4} & \frac{1}{4} & 0 \\ \frac{3}{16} & \frac{1}{16} & -\frac{1}{4} \\ \frac{3}{32} & -\frac{7}{32} & \frac{3}{8} \end{pmatrix}$$

The solution of the given system can now be obtained by multiplying both sides of the matrix equation

$$\begin{pmatrix} 2 & 6 & 4 \\ 6 & 6 & 4 \\ 3 & 2 & 4 \end{pmatrix} \begin{pmatrix} x \\ y \\ z \end{pmatrix} = \begin{pmatrix} -12 \\ 8 \\ 13 \end{pmatrix}$$

by A^{-1}.

This gives

$$\begin{pmatrix} 1 & 0 & 0 \\ 0 & 1 & 0 \\ 0 & 0 & 1 \end{pmatrix} \begin{pmatrix} x \\ y \\ z \end{pmatrix} = \begin{pmatrix} -\frac{1}{4} & \frac{1}{4} & 0 \\ \frac{3}{16} & \frac{1}{16} & -\frac{1}{4} \\ \frac{3}{32} & -\frac{7}{32} & \frac{3}{8} \end{pmatrix} \begin{pmatrix} -12 \\ 8 \\ 13 \end{pmatrix}$$

$$\begin{pmatrix} x \\ y \\ z \end{pmatrix} = \begin{pmatrix} 3 + 2 + 0 \\ -\frac{36}{16} + \frac{8}{16} - \frac{13}{4} \\ -\frac{36}{32} - \frac{56}{32} + \frac{39}{8} \end{pmatrix} = \begin{pmatrix} 5 \\ -5 \\ 2 \end{pmatrix}$$

Therefore, $x = 5$, $y = -5$, and $z = 2$, as found in Examples 1 and 2.

PROBLEMS

Solve the following by the method of elimination, by the use of the inverse of the matrix of coefficients, and by Cramer's rule.

1. $x + y = 2$
    $x - y = 5$

2. $3x - 2y = 4$
    $-x - 2y = 6$

3. $x + y + z = 1$
    $x - y \quad\;\; = 4$
    $x + y - 2z = 4$

4. $2x \quad\quad + 2z = 2$
    $5x + 4y + z = 3$
    $2x \quad\quad + 6z = 4$

5. $2x + 3y + 4z = 4$
    $x + 2y + 5z = 0$
    $4x + y + z = 5$

6. $\begin{pmatrix} 1 & 2 & 3 \\ 0 & 1 & 2 \\ 2 & 1 & 4 \end{pmatrix} \begin{pmatrix} x \\ y \\ z \end{pmatrix} = \begin{pmatrix} 4 \\ -2 \\ 6 \end{pmatrix}$

7. $x_1 + x_2 + x_3 = -2$
    $8x_1 + 4x_2 + 2x_3 = 6$
    $-x_1 + x_2 - x_3 = 0$

8. You are currently manufacturing a product that can be sold for $100.00 per unit. You have available the figures in Table 4-1 on output and costs.

TABLE 4-1

Year	Quarter	x_1 (output)	x_2 (total cost)
1	1	9,000	$ 875,000
	2	11,000	960,000
	3	12,000	1024,000
	4	10,000	920,000
2	1	10,500	920,000
	2	11,800	1045,000
	3	14,000	1280,000
	4	12,500	1120,000
3	1	13,000	1200,000
	2	15,000	1325,000
	3	16,500	1420,000
	4	14,500	1285,000

(a) Prepare a scatter diagram of total cost versus output.

(b) Fit a linear cost function of the form $x_2 = a + bx_1$ to these data using the method of least squares.

(c) Plot the estimated cost function and the revenue function on a chart.

(d) Use the cost function of (c) to estimate the break-even point. (Set revenue = cost.)

(e) Write the cost and revenue equations as a matrix equation.

(f) What is the determinant of the matrix of coefficients?

(g)   What is the inverse of the matrix of coefficients?

(h)   Solve the system using determinants and/or matrix algebra.

(i)   Use the cost equation calculated in (b) to estimate profit if output is expected to be 20,000 units.

REFERENCES

Books

Andree, Richard V. *Selections from Modern Abstract Algebra.* New York: Henry Holt and Co., 1958.

Campbell, Hugh G. *Matrices with Applications.* New York: Appleton-Century-Crofts, 1968.

Corcoran, A. Wayne. *Mathematical Applications in Accounting.* New York: Harcourt Brace Jovanovich, 1968.

Curtis, Charles W. *Linear Algebra, An Introductory Approach.* Boston: Allyn and Bacon, Inc., 1963.

Draper, N. R., and Smith, H. *Applied Regression Analysis.* New York: John Wiley & Sons, Inc., 1966.

Kemeny, John G., Schleifer, A., Snell, J. R., and Thompson, G. L. *Finite Mathematics with Business Applications.* Englewood Cliffs, N.J.: Prentice-Hall, Inc., 1964.

Leontief, Wassily. *Input-Output Economics.* New York: Oxford University Press, Inc., 1966.

Levin, Richard I., and Kirkpatrick, C. A. *Quantitative Approaches to Management.* New York: McGraw-Hill Book Co., Inc., 1965.

Miernyk, William H. *The Elements of Input-Output Analysis.* New York: Random House, Inc., 1965.

Parker, William Vann, and Eaves, James Clifton. *Matrices.* New York: The Ronald Press Co., 1960.

Springer, Clifford H., Herlihy, R. E., and Beggs, R. I. *Basic Mathematics.* Homewood, Ill.: Richard D. Irwin, Inc., 1965.

Articles

"Criteria for Entering an Industry." *Sales Management:* Oct. 15, 1969.

"Marketers Meet 'Input-Output'." *Business Week:* Oct. 29, 1966.

"Planners Put Big Picture on a Grid." *Business Week:* Sept. 23, 1967.

"They Call It 'Instant Research'." *Business Week:* Jan. 25, 1969.

FIVE

Linear programming

5-1 INTRODUCTION

Linear programming is a mathematical technique used to maximize or minimize the value of a linear function. This linear function is called the *objective function*. The maximum or minimum is determined in the presence of known or assumed restrictions. The restrictions are called *constraints*.

Linear programming can be used to solve a variety of business problems that involve the allocation of limited resources in an optimal manner. The following example is an allocation problem that involves profit maximization. The treatment of linear programming in this text is limited to maximization problems.

Example 1. A certain manufacturer produces two products called ZIPS and ZAPS. The production of ZIPS and ZAPS requires the use of two machines. The production of a ZIP requires 3 minutes on machine I and 1 minute on machine II. The production of one ZAP requires 3 minutes on machine I and 5 minutes on machine II. The total time available on machine I is 2400 minutes, and the total time available on machine II is 1600 minutes. The company realizes a profit of $4.00 for each ZIP that is produced and a $4.50 profit for each ZAP that is produced. Determine the number of ZIPS and ZAPS that should be produced to give the largest possible profit.

Solution: (*set-up only*) To translate this word problem into a mathematical model, we let x denote the number of ZIPS and y denote the number of ZAPS. Clearly, the variables x and y must take on nonnegative values only.

127

This involves two restrictions or constraints on the variables x and y. Using the symbols for inequalities, we have

$x \geq 0$
$y \geq 0$

Since only 2400 minutes are available on machine I, we have $3x + 3y \leq 2400$. For machine II, we obtain the inequality $x + 5y \leq 1600$.

From the profit contribution of $4.00 for each ZIP and $4.50 for each ZAP, we can express the total profit as a linear function of the variables x and y as follows: $P = 4x + 4.5y$, where P denotes total profit in dollars.

Finally, the mathematical model is:

Maximize the *objective function* $P = 4x + 4.5y$ subject to the *constraints:*
$x \geq 0$ (*x and y denote amounts of products*)
$y \geq 0$
$3x + 3y \leq 2400$ (*machine I*)
$\quad x + 5y \leq 1600$ (*machine II*)

Example 2.   In addition to the data given in Example 1, assume that each ZIP and each ZAP requires 4 minutes on a third machine that has 1600 minutes of available time. Set up the mathematical model for this new situation.

Solution: (*set-up only*) The new mathematical model is:

Maximize the *objective function* $P = 4x + 4.5y$ subject to the *constraints:*
$x \geq 0$
$y \geq 0$
$3x + 3y \leq 2400$
$\quad x + 5y \leq 1600$
$4x + 4y \leq 1600$ (*machine III*)

PROBLEMS

Set up the mathematical model corresponding to the realistic situations described below. Assume that the goal is to maximize profit.

1. A manufacturer can produce two products A and B. To produce each product requires processing in two departments, Department I and Department II. Department I has 36 hours available. Department II has 40 hours available. To manufacture a unit of Product A requires 4 hours in Department I and 2 hours in Department II. Product B requires 1 hour in Department I and 4 hours in Department II. The contribution to profit is $6 per unit of Product A and $5 per unit of Product B.

2. Assume that the products in Prob. 1 also require processing in a third department. This department has 20 hours available. Product A requires 2 hours and Product B requires 1 hour in Department III. Redo Prob. 1 with these new conditions.

3. A manufacturer produces two products, Product A and Product B. To produce each product requires processing in two departments, Department I and Department II. Department I has 200 hours available. Department II has 150 hours available. To manufacture a unit of Product A requires 5 hours in Department I and 5 hours in Department II. Product

B requires 4 hours in Department I and 2 hours in Department II. The contribution to profit per unit is $2 for Product *A* and $1 for Product *B*.

4. The products in Prob. 3 require additional processing in a third department. This department has 350 hours available. Product *A* requires 10 hours and Product *B* requires 7 hours in Department III. Redo Prob. 3 with these new conditions.

5-2 THE GRAPHICAL METHOD

We will now present the graphical method for solving linear programming problems that involve only two independent variables. Although the graphical method is not practical for the solution of linear programming problems that involve more than two independent variables, it does provide some insight into the more involved problems.

The graphical method involves three basic steps. These steps are explained in this section in connection with the mathematical model that was obtained in Example 1 of the last section (i.e., maximize $P = 4x + 4.5y$ subject to $x \geq 0$, $y \geq 0$, $3x + 3y \leq 2400$, and $x + 5y \leq 1600$).

Step 1:   Determine the solution space for the system of inequalities involved in the given problem. Applying the techniques of Sec. 1-8 to the above system of inequalities leads to the solution space shown in **Fig. 5-1**.

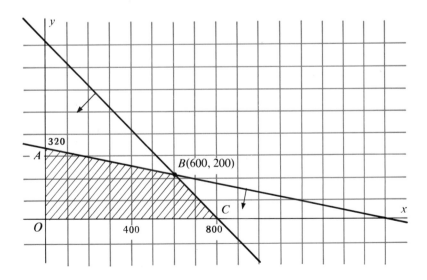

F I G U R E 5-1

Step 2: Determine the value of the objective function at the *upper left-hand corner* of the solution space in Step 1. For the present problem, this is the point $(0, 320)$ and the value of the objective function is given by

$$P = 4(0) + 4.5(320)$$
$$= 0 + 1440$$
$$P = 1440$$

Next, graph the equation of the straight line that results when this value is substituted into the objective function. For this problem we have the equation $4x + 4.5y = 1440$. The graph of this equation is shown below.

$L_1: 4x + 4.5y = 1440$

x	360	0
y	0	320

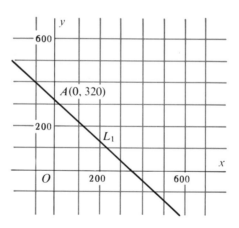

F I G U R E 5-2

Step 3: Determine the point or points of the solution space through which a line L_2 parallel to L_1 of Step 2 can be drawn with the restriction that L_2 be *as far from the origin* as possible. (*Note:* L_2 may coincide with L_1.) The location of such a point or points and the corresponding value of the objective function constitutes the solution of the given linear programming problem. The line L_2 for the present problem is shown below.

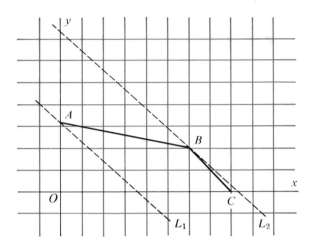

F I G U R E 5-3

It is clear from the figure above that point B (600, 200) is the desired point.

$$P_{max} = 4(600) + 4.5(200)$$
$$= 2400 + 900$$
$$= 3300$$

The three step procedure outlined above is based on the fact that the maximum value of the objective function occurs at a corner of the *solution space* of the system of inequalities given by the constraints. It should be clear that the maximum value *never* occurs at an *interior point* of the solution space since the value of the objective function could then be increased either by moving horizontally to the right-hand boundary or vertically to the upper boundary. This means that the solution of the given problem is to be sought somewhere on the boundary of the solution space. It can be shown further that the maximum value of the objective function occurs at a corner of this boundary. It can happen that more than one corner gives the same maximum value of the objective function. In this case, the maximum value occurs at any point on the line segment joining the two points just described.

This point is illustrated by the table below. This table is based on the problem solved in this section.

TABLE 5-1

Coordinates	Type of Point	Value of the Objective Function
(0, 320)	Corner	$1440
(590, 200)	Interior point	$3260
(600, 200)	Corner	$3300 (Maximum Value)
(600, 190)	Interior point	$3255
(800, 0)	Corner	$3200
(0, 0)	Corner	$0

Example 1. Use the graphical method to solve the linear programming problem of Example 2 of the previous section. Maximize $P = 4x + 4.5y$ subject to $x \geq 0$, $y \geq 0$, $3x + 3y \leq 2400$, $x + 5y \leq 1600$, and $4x + 4y \leq 1600$.

Solution: Lines L_1 and L_2 and the solution space are shown in the figure below.

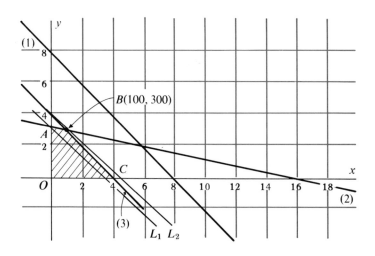

F I G U R E 5-4

The point can be found algebraically by solving the system:

$$x + 5y = 1600$$
$$4x + 4y = 1600$$

$$4x + 20y = 6400 \qquad y = 300$$
$$4x + 4y = 1600 \qquad x = 1600 - 1500 = 100$$

$$\overline{16y = 4800}$$

P_{max}, which occurs at (100, 300), is given by

$$P_{max} = 4(100) + 4.5(300)$$
$$= 400 + 1350$$
$$P_{max} = \$1750$$

Example 2. Check the profit at the corners O, A, and C and compare them with the profit at B.

Solution: At the origin, $P = 4(0) + 4.5(0) = 0$.
At A, $P = 4(0) + 4.5(320) = \$1440$.
At C, $P = 4(400) + 4.5(0) = \$1600$.

Corner	Profit
O	0
A	\$1440
B	\$1750 (P_{max})
C	\$1600

PROBLEMS

Problems 1 through 4 are the mathematical models for the first four problems of Sec. 5-1. Use the graphical method to find P_{max} for each of these problems.

1. Maximize $P = 6x + 5y$ subject to $x \geq 0$, $y \geq 0$, $4x + y \leq 36$, and $2x + 4y \leq 40$.

2. Maximize $P = 6x + 5y$ subject to $x \geq 0$, $y \geq 0$, $4x + y \leq 36$, $2x + 4y \leq 40$, and $2x + y \leq 20$.

3. Maximize $P = 2x + y$ subject to $x \geq 0$, $y \geq 0$, $5x + 4y \leq 200$, $5x + 2y \leq 150$.

4. Maximize $P = 2x + y$ subject to $x \geq 0$, $y \geq 0$, $5x + 4y \leq 200$, $5x + 2y \leq 150$, and $10x + 7y \leq 350$.

5. Solve Prob. 1 by finding the coordinates of each corner of the solution space and comparing the value of P at these points. Your result should be the same as in Prob. 1.

6. Solve Prob. 4 by checking the value of P at each corner of the solution space.

7. Maximize $P = 3x + y$ subject to $x \geq 0$, $y \geq 1$, and $x + y \leq 8$.

8. Maximize $P = x + 2y$ subject to $x \geq 0$, $y \geq 1$, and $x + y \leq 8$.

5-3   TABLE 1 OF THE SIMPLEX METHOD

The simplex method is a numerical algorithm for solving linear programming problems. This method involves a sequence of tables the last of which indicates the solution of the given problem. Our introduction to the simplex method is built around the problem that was solved graphically in the previous section, namely, maximize $P = 4x + 4.5y$ subject to $x \geq 0$, $y \geq 0$, $3x + 3y \leq 2400$, and $x + 5y \leq 1600$.

First we introduce two new variables w and z, called *slack variables*. These variables enable us to rewrite the inequalities $3x + 3y \leq 2400$ and $x + 5y \leq 1600$ as a pair of linear equations in x, y, w, and z.

$$3x + 3y + 1w + 0z = 2400$$
$$x + 5y + 0w + 1z = 1600 \tag{1}$$

Next we interpret variables w and z. The reader will recall that x and y represent amounts of *real* products, in this case ZIPS and ZAPS. In contrast, the slack variables w and z can be thought of as representing amounts of two *imaginary* products. The coefficients of w and z in Eq. 1 above indicate that the imaginary product corresponding to w requires one minute on machine I and no time on machine II. Similarly, the other imaginary product requires no time on machine I and one minute on machine II. The fact that the company cannot realize a profit by producing an imaginary product is expressed mathematically by introducing the new objective function

$$P = 0w + 0z + 4x + 4.5y \tag{2}$$

To provide a smoother lead-in to Table 1 of the simplex method, we write Eq. 1 in matrix form as follows:

$$\begin{pmatrix} 1 & 0 & 3 & 3 \\ 0 & 1 & 1 & 5 \end{pmatrix} \begin{pmatrix} w \\ z \\ x \\ y \end{pmatrix} = \begin{pmatrix} 2400 \\ 1600 \end{pmatrix} \tag{3}$$

Using a standard simplex method format, we rewrite the above information in tabular form as follows:

TABLE 1 (Partial)

	Solution Variables		Variables not in the Solution		
	w	z	x	y	Constants
w	1	0	3	3	2400
z	0	1	1	5	1600
CTPPU	0	0	4	4.5	

The reader should note the similarity of the w and z rows of this table to the matrix equation, Eq. 3, and the similarity of the CTPPU row to the objective function, Eq. 2. In fact, the letters CTPPU stand for the words "contribution to profit per unit."

Variables, which are used as row headings, are called *solution variables*. In Table 1 (partial), the solution variables are w and z. The remaining variables, in this case x and y, are said to be *not in the solution*.

If no ZIPS and ZAPS are to be produced, then $x = 0$ and $y = 0$. If we substitute these values into Eq. 3, we have

$$\begin{pmatrix} 1 & 0 & 3 & 3 \\ 0 & 1 & 1 & 5 \end{pmatrix} \begin{pmatrix} w \\ z \\ 0 \\ 0 \end{pmatrix} = \begin{pmatrix} 2400 \\ 1600 \end{pmatrix}$$

$$\begin{pmatrix} w \\ z \end{pmatrix} = \begin{pmatrix} 2400 \\ 1600 \end{pmatrix}$$

This gives $w = 2400$ and $z = 1600$. Note that these values can also be read directly from the constant column of Table 1 (partial). From the new objective function, Eq. 2, we have

$$P = 0(2400) + 0(1600) + 4(0) + 4.5(0)$$
$$P = 0$$

This value can also be obtained by multiplying the row vector $(0, 0)$, which comes from the CTPPU row (*using the solution variable entries only*), times the constant column $\begin{pmatrix} 2400 \\ 1600 \end{pmatrix}$ as follows:

$$(0, 0)\begin{pmatrix} 2400 \\ 1600 \end{pmatrix} = 0(2400) + 0(1600) = 0$$

Next, we define five column vectors **w**, **z**, **x**, **y**, and **c** as follows:

$$\mathbf{w} = \begin{pmatrix} 1 \\ 0 \end{pmatrix}, \mathbf{z} = \begin{pmatrix} 0 \\ 1 \end{pmatrix}, \mathbf{x} = \begin{pmatrix} 3 \\ 1 \end{pmatrix}, \mathbf{y} = \begin{pmatrix} 3 \\ 5 \end{pmatrix}, \text{ and } \mathbf{c} = \begin{pmatrix} 2400 \\ 1600 \end{pmatrix}$$

For Table 1, the components of these vectors can be interpreted either as machine times or as coefficients in vector equations.

Machine time interpretation of the components of **w** *and* **x**

$\mathbf{w} = \begin{pmatrix} 1 \\ 0 \end{pmatrix}$ *means that the production of one unit of the imaginary product corresponding to* **w** *takes one minute on machine I and no time on machine II*

$\mathbf{x} = \begin{pmatrix} 3 \\ 1 \end{pmatrix}$ *means that it takes 3 minutes on machine I and 1 minute on machine II to produce a ZIP*

Coefficient interpretation of the components of **w** *and* **x**

$\mathbf{w} = 1\mathbf{w} + 0\mathbf{z}$ $\mathbf{x} = 3\mathbf{w} + 1\mathbf{z}$

$\mathbf{w} = 1\begin{pmatrix} 1 \\ 0 \end{pmatrix} + 0\begin{pmatrix} 0 \\ 1 \end{pmatrix}$ $\mathbf{x} = 3\begin{pmatrix} 1 \\ 0 \end{pmatrix} + 1\begin{pmatrix} 0 \\ 1 \end{pmatrix}$

$\mathbf{w} = \begin{pmatrix} 1 \\ 0 \end{pmatrix} + \begin{pmatrix} 0 \\ 0 \end{pmatrix}$ $\mathbf{x} = \begin{pmatrix} 3 \\ 0 \end{pmatrix} + \begin{pmatrix} 0 \\ 1 \end{pmatrix}$

$\mathbf{w} = \begin{pmatrix} 1 \\ 0 \end{pmatrix}$ $\mathbf{x} = \begin{pmatrix} 3 \\ 1 \end{pmatrix}$

It is very important to see that the *components* of the vectors **w**, **z**, **x**, and **y** are coefficients of the *vectors that correspond to solution variables* (i.e., row headings). The coefficient interpretation of the components will be used throughout the remainder of this chapter.

A complete Table 1 for the simplex method consists of Table 1 (partial), which is described above, plus two additional rows with headings DIOFPU and NET, respectively. DIOFPU stands for the words "decrease in the objective function per unit" and NET denotes the net increase in the objective function per unit. The only entries made in these two rows are for the variables not in the solution.

The introduction of one unit of x requires three units of w and one unit of z (i.e., $\mathbf{x} = \begin{pmatrix} 3 \\ 1 \end{pmatrix}$ or $\mathbf{x} = 3\mathbf{w} + 1\mathbf{z}$).

The resulting decrease in the objective function is given by the following calculation.

DIOFPU = 3(contribution to profit per unit of w)
$$+ \; 1(\text{contribution to profit per unit of } z)$$
DIOFPU = 3(0) + 1(0)
DIOFPU = 0

This result is expected since only imaginary products with a price of zero are being produced.

We then enter 0 in the row labelled decrease in the objective function per unit (DIOFPU) and under the column x. Note that this entry can be obtained by multiplying the CTPPU row (using the solution variable entries only) times the column vector $\begin{pmatrix} 3 \\ 1 \end{pmatrix}$ from the x column.

$$(0, 0)\begin{pmatrix} 3 \\ 1 \end{pmatrix} = 0$$

TABLE 1 (Complete)

	w	z	x	y	Constant
w	1	0	3	3	2400
z	0	1	1	5	1600
CTPPU	0	0	$4.00	$4.50	
DIOFPU			0	0	
NET			$4.00	$4.50	

The decrease in the objective function, which results when a unit of y is brought into the solution, is zero, as in the case for x. This follows from $(0, 0)\begin{pmatrix} 3 \\ 5 \end{pmatrix} = 0$.

The net increase in the objective function is then calculated by subtracting the DIOFPU row from the CTPPU row. Doing this we get $4.00 and $4.50 for x and y, respectively. This completes the first table, and we move on to the second table in the next section. We will continue forming new tables as long as there is at least one positive entry in the NET row.

PROBLEMS

In Probs. 1 through 4 list the systems of inequalities for problems 1 through 4 of Sec. 5-1. In each of these problems, introduce slack variables and write the resulting system of equations as a single matrix equation.

1. $4x + y \leq 36$ and $2x + 4y \leq 40$.
2. $4x + y \leq 36$, $2x + 4y \leq 40$, and $2x + y \leq 20$.
3. $5x + 4y \leq 200$ and $5x + 2y \leq 150$.
4. $5x + 4y \leq 200$, $5x + 2y \leq 150$, and $10x + 7y \leq 350$.
5. Set up Table 1 of the simplex method for Prob. 1 above. $P = 6x + 5y$.
6. Set up Table 1 of the simplex method for Prob. 2 above. $P = 6x + 5y$.
7. Set up Table 1 of the simplex method for Prob. 3 above. $P = 2x + y$.
8. Set up Table 1 of the simplex method for Prob. 4 above. $P = 2x + y$.

5-4   SIMPLEX METHOD CONTINUED

It is clear from Table 1 that for each unit of x brought into the solution the objective function is increased by $4.00, and for each unit of y brought into the solution the objective function is increased by $4.50. This means that the next step in our search for production levels that give the maximum profit will be to increase y as much as possible. There are now two questions to be answered:

1. *How much can y be increased with the machine time which is available?*
2. *Which of the solution variables w or z should be replaced by y?*

The production levels indicated by Table 1 are $x = 0$, $y = 0$, $w = 2400$, and $z = 1600$. For each unit of y brought into the solution, 3 units of w must be taken out of the solution. The maximum number of units of y that could be brought into the solution if this were the only constraint present is obtained by dividing 2400 by 3, which gives 800. Similarly, 5 units of z must be taken out of the solution for each unit of y that is included. This leads to a maximum value of y of 320, which is obtained by dividing 1600 by 5. Choosing the minimum of these two numbers so that both constraints will be satisfied, we see that the largest number of units of y which can be brought into the solution is 320. This means that y replaces z and the solution variables are now w and y.

The new production levels are $x = 0$, $y = 320$, $z = 0$, and $w = 1440$, where w is obtained as follows.

$w = 2400 - 3(320)$
$ = 2400 - 960$
$w = 1440$

The information obtained so far is displayed below.

TABLE 2 (Partial)

	w	y	x	z	Constant
w					1440
y					320
CTPPU	0	4.50	4.00	0	

We are ready to express the variables x and z, which are not in the solution, in terms of the solution variables w and y. This can be done using vector methods as follows.

In Sec. 5-3 we defined the vectors $\mathbf{w} = \begin{pmatrix} 1 \\ 0 \end{pmatrix}$, $\mathbf{z} = \begin{pmatrix} 0 \\ 1 \end{pmatrix}$, $\mathbf{x} = \begin{pmatrix} 3 \\ 1 \end{pmatrix}$, and $\mathbf{y} = \begin{pmatrix} 3 \\ 5 \end{pmatrix}$.

Starting with the vector equation $\mathbf{x} = k_1\mathbf{w} + k_2\mathbf{y}$, where k_1 and k_2 are scalars to be determined, we have

$$\begin{pmatrix} 3 \\ 1 \end{pmatrix} = k_1 \begin{pmatrix} 1 \\ 0 \end{pmatrix} + k_2 \begin{pmatrix} 3 \\ 5 \end{pmatrix}$$

$$\begin{pmatrix} 3 \\ 1 \end{pmatrix} = \begin{pmatrix} 1k_1 \\ 0k_1 \end{pmatrix} + \begin{pmatrix} 3k_2 \\ 5k_2 \end{pmatrix}$$

$$1k_1 + 3k_2 = 3$$

$$0k_1 + 5k_2 = 1$$

$$\begin{pmatrix} 1 & 3 \\ 0 & 5 \end{pmatrix}\begin{pmatrix} k_1 \\ k_2 \end{pmatrix} = \begin{pmatrix} 3 \\ 1 \end{pmatrix} \qquad \textit{writing the above system in matrix form}$$

$$\begin{pmatrix} k_1 \\ k_2 \end{pmatrix} = \begin{pmatrix} 1 & 3 \\ 0 & 5 \end{pmatrix}^{-1} \begin{pmatrix} 3 \\ 1 \end{pmatrix} \qquad \textit{multiplying by the inverse}$$

$$\begin{pmatrix} k_1 \\ k_2 \end{pmatrix} = \begin{pmatrix} 1 & -0.6 \\ 0 & 0.2 \end{pmatrix}\begin{pmatrix} 3 \\ 1 \end{pmatrix}$$

$$\begin{pmatrix} k_1 \\ k_2 \end{pmatrix} = \begin{pmatrix} 2.4 \\ 0.2 \end{pmatrix}$$

or $k_1 = 2.4$ and $k_2 = 0.2$.

Similarly, the solution of $\mathbf{z} = k_3\mathbf{w} + k_4\mathbf{y}$ leads to the matrix equation

$$\begin{pmatrix} 1 & 3 \\ 0 & 5 \end{pmatrix}\begin{pmatrix} k_3 \\ k_4 \end{pmatrix} = \begin{pmatrix} 0 \\ 1 \end{pmatrix}$$

$$\begin{pmatrix} k_3 \\ k_4 \end{pmatrix} = \begin{pmatrix} 1 & 3 \\ 0 & 5 \end{pmatrix}^{-1}\begin{pmatrix} 0 \\ 1 \end{pmatrix}$$

$$\begin{pmatrix} k_3 \\ k_4 \end{pmatrix} = \begin{pmatrix} 1 & -0.6 \\ 0 & 0.2 \end{pmatrix}\begin{pmatrix} 0 \\ 1 \end{pmatrix} \qquad \text{\textit{recalling the inverse from the calculation for x}}$$

$$k_3 = -0.6$$
$$k_4 = 0.2$$

Using the obvious fact that $\mathbf{w} = 1\mathbf{w} + 0\mathbf{y}$ and $\mathbf{y} = 0\mathbf{w} + 1\mathbf{y}$ and the values for k_1, k_2, k_3, and k_4 found above, we have the necessary information to complete the following table.

TABLE 2 (Partial)

	w	y	x	z	Constant
w	1	0	$k_1 = 2.4$	$k_3 = -0.6$	1440
y	0	1	$k_2 = 0.2$	$k_4 = 0.2$	320
CTPPU	0	4.50	4.00	0	

We point out that the new constant column $\begin{pmatrix} 1440 \\ 320 \end{pmatrix}$ could have been found by multiplying $\mathbf{c} = \begin{pmatrix} 2400 \\ 1600 \end{pmatrix}$ by the inverse of $\begin{matrix} w & y \\ \begin{pmatrix} 1 & 3 \\ 0 & 5 \end{pmatrix} \end{matrix}$.

Returning momentarily to a machine time interpretation, we have from the vector equation $\mathbf{z} = -0.6\mathbf{w} + 0.2\mathbf{y}$ that the production of one unit of z requires 0.2 units of y and at the same time *frees* enough time to produce 0.6 units of w. The following calculation shows that this is the correct interpretation of the *minus sign* in Table 2 (partial).

$$0.2\mathbf{y} = 0.2\begin{pmatrix} 3 \\ 5 \end{pmatrix}$$

$$0.2\mathbf{y} = \begin{pmatrix} 0.6 \\ 1.0 \end{pmatrix}$$

or 0.6 minutes on machine I and 1 minute on machine II.

Now, $0.2\mathbf{y} = \begin{pmatrix} 0.6 \\ 1 \end{pmatrix}$ exceeds $\mathbf{z} = \begin{pmatrix} 0 \\ 1 \end{pmatrix}$ by $\begin{pmatrix} 0.6 \\ 1 \end{pmatrix} - \begin{pmatrix} 0 \\ 1 \end{pmatrix} = \begin{pmatrix} 0.6 \\ 0 \end{pmatrix}$, so that taking 0.2 units of y out of the solution *frees* 0.6 minutes on machine I.

To complete Table 2 we need the entries in the DIOFPU and NET rows. The entries in the DIOFPU row can be computed by vector multiplication as follows:

$$(0, 4.5)\begin{pmatrix} 2.4 \\ 0.2 \end{pmatrix} = 0.9$$

gives the entry in the x column.

$$(0, 4.5)\begin{pmatrix} -0.6 \\ 0.2 \end{pmatrix} = 0.9$$

gives the entry in the z column.

The net figure entries are obtained by subtracting the entries in the decrease row from the entries in the CTPPU row.

TABLE 2 (Complete)

	w	y	x	z	Constant
w	1	0	2.4	-0.6	1440
y	0	1	0.2	0.2	320
CTPPU	0	4.5	4.0	0	
DIOFPU			0.9	0.9	
NET			3.10	-0.9	

The positive entry, 3.10, in the net row in the above table indicates that the objective function can be further increased. This can be accomplished by bringing x into the solution. The variable to be replaced by x is w since the ratio 1440/2.4 is less than the ratio 320/0.2.

The solution variables for Table 5-2 are x and y. The entries for Table 5-2 can be obtained by multiplying the vectors **w**, **z**, and **c** by the

inverse of the matrix $\begin{matrix} x & y \\ \begin{pmatrix} 3 & 3 \\ 1 & 5 \end{pmatrix} \end{matrix}$, which is $\begin{pmatrix} 5/12 & -3/12 \\ -1/12 & 3/12 \end{pmatrix}$.

It is *important* to note that the vectors **w**, **z**, and **c** used to form Table 5-2 are column vectors from Table 1 and *not* vectors from the preceding table.

TABLE 5-2

	x	y	w	z	Constant
x	1	0	$5/12$	$-3/12$	600
y	0	1	$-1/12$	$+3/12$	200
CTPPU	4.00	4.50	0	0	
DIOFPU			1.2917	0.125	
NET			-1.2917	-0.125	

We see that 600 units of x were brought in, leaving enough capacity for 200 units of y to be produced using up $600 \begin{pmatrix} 3 \\ 1 \end{pmatrix} + 200 \begin{pmatrix} 3 \\ 5 \end{pmatrix}$, or the total time available on each machine. The resulting profit is given by $600(\$4.00) + 200(\$4.50) = \$3300$.

It is impossible to increase the objective function any further, since both entries in the net row are negative. This means that the optimum solution has been obtained and is $x = 600$ and $y = 200$, with $P_{\max} = \$3300$, as found graphically in Sec. 5-2. In other words, the company can make the maximum profit by producing 600 ZIPS and 200 ZAPS.

Before going on to another example, it is interesting and quite important to look at the DIOFPU row of the last table. Note that to bring one w into the solution results in a decrease in the objective function of $1.2917. Checking the original column vectors, we see that to make a unit of w requires one minute on machine I and no time on machine II. By making a unit of w, we are reducing the time available on machine I by one minute. Since this results in a decrease in the objective function of $1.2917, one minute on machine I must be worth $1.2917. Similarly, to produce one unit of z requires one minute on machine II and no minutes on machine I. Since the objective function is reduced by $0.125, if one unit of z is produced, one minute of time on machine II must be worth $0.125.

Therefore, the total worth of machine time is

$$2400(\$1.2917) + 1600(\$0.125) = \$3300$$

The fact that this is equal to the maximum value of the objective function is no mere coincidence. This aspect is discussed in more extensive treatments of linear programming.

PROBLEMS

1. Use the simplex method to solve Prob. 1 of Sec. 5-1, i.e., maximize $P = 6x + 5y$ subject to $x \geq 0, y \geq 0, 4x + y \leq 36$, and $2x + 4y \leq 40$. Compare your result with the graphical solution of Prob. 1, Sec. 5-2.

2. Use the simplex method to solve Prob. 3 of Sec. 5-1 (i.e., maximize $P = 2x + y$ subject to $x \geq 0, y \geq 0, 5x + 4y \leq 200$, and $5x + 2y \leq 150$). Compare your result with the graphical solution of Prob. 3, Sec. 5-2.

3. Find the inverse of the 2 by 2 matrix $\begin{pmatrix} 3 & 3 \\ 1 & 5 \end{pmatrix}$ by some previous method. Compare your result with the inverse given in the text.

4. Multiply the column vectors $\mathbf{w} = \begin{pmatrix} 1 \\ 0 \end{pmatrix}$, $\mathbf{z} = \begin{pmatrix} 0 \\ 1 \end{pmatrix}$, and $\mathbf{c} = \begin{pmatrix} 2400 \\ 1600 \end{pmatrix}$ by the inverse found in Prob. 3 above to verify the entries in Table 5-2 of this section.

5. How were the entries in the DIOFPU and NET rows of Table 5-2 of this section obtained?

141

5-5 THE SIMPLEX METHOD—A MAXIMIZATION PROBLEM AND A SUMMARY

In this section we will further illustrate the simplex method by solving the linear programming problem given in Example 2 of Sec. 5-1. The reader will recall that one additional constraint is present in that problem. This constraint resulted from a third machine. This additional constraint causes the optimum solution to involve a slack variable. Some of the data from that example are repeated below.

In order to produce a ZIP, four minutes on machine III are now required in addition to the three minutes on machine I and one minute on machine II. In order to produce a ZAP, four minutes are also required on machine III in addition to three minutes on machine I and five minutes on machine II. The three constraints are:

$$3x + 3y \leq 2400 \text{ min.} \qquad (\textit{Machine I})$$

$$1x + 5y \leq 1600 \qquad (\textit{Machine II})$$

$$4x + 4y \leq 1600 \qquad (\textit{Machine III})$$

Remember: The coefficients of x read as follows: to produce one unit of x requires 3 minutes on machine I, one minute on machine II, and four minutes on machine III; it does not mean that 3 x's and 3 y's can be made in one minute using machine I.

To change the inequalities to equalities it is necessary to introduce three slack variables, each of which requires one minute on one machine only. This results in the following three equations:

$$3x + 3y + 1w + 0z + 0t = 2400 \qquad (\textit{Machine I})$$

$$1x + 5y + 0w + 1z + 0t = 1600 \qquad (\textit{Machine II})$$

$$4x + 4y + 0w + 0z + 1t = 1600 \qquad (\textit{Machine III})$$

We now have the same problem as before, which is to allocate machine time in order to maximize the objective function,

$$P = 4.00x + 4.50y + 0w + 0z + 0t$$

TABLE 5-3

	w	z	t	x	y	Constant
w	1	0	0	3	3	2400
z	0	1	0	1	5	1600
t	0	0	1	4	4	1600
CTPPU				4.00	4.50	
DIOFPU				0	0	
NET				4.00	4.50	

As usual, the initial solution involves only slack variables and the initial solution matrix is the 3 by 3 identity matrix. The entries in the last row of Table 5-3 above correspond to the fact that if one unit of x is introduced into the solution the objective function will be increased by $4.00, whereas if one unit of y is brought into the solution the objective function will be increased by $4.50. Since 4.5 > 4.0, we bring y into the solution.

Next we must determine how many units of y can be introduced. The largest amount of y that can be brought into the solution is given by the positive minimum of the ratios: 2400/3, 1600/5, and 1600/4, or 320 units of y. Since the minimum ratio 320 = 1600/5 corresponds to z, we know that z must be taken out of the solution. The following vector calculation illustrates these points further.

$$\begin{pmatrix} 2400 \\ 1600 \\ 1600 \end{pmatrix} - 320 \begin{pmatrix} 3 \\ 5 \\ 4 \end{pmatrix} = \begin{pmatrix} 1440 \\ 0 \\ 320 \end{pmatrix} \quad \begin{matrix} w \\ z \\ t \end{matrix}$$

where

$$\begin{pmatrix} 2400 \\ 1600 \\ 1600 \end{pmatrix} = \mathbf{c}$$

and

$$\begin{pmatrix} 3 \\ 5 \\ 4 \end{pmatrix} = \mathbf{y}$$

To obtain the entries in Table 5-4, we multiply by the inverse of a certain 3 by 3 matrix. The matrix to be inverted is

$$A = \begin{pmatrix} 1 & 3 & 0 \\ 0 & 5 & 0 \\ 0 & 4 & 1 \end{pmatrix}$$

which is obtained by replacing the second column of the identity matrix by the y column of Table 5-3.

Using the procedure given in Sec. 4-5 for finding the inverse of a matrix, we have

$|A| = 1$ cofactor of $a_{11} + 0$ cofactor of $a_{21} + 0$ cofactor of a_{31}

$|A| = (1)(5) \qquad\qquad + \quad 0 \qquad\qquad + \quad 0$

$|A| = \qquad 5$

The matrix of cofactors is

$$B = \begin{pmatrix} 5 & 0 & 0 \\ -3 & 1 & -4 \\ 0 & 0 & 5 \end{pmatrix}$$

Therefore,

$$A^{-1} = \begin{pmatrix} 1 & -0.6 & 0 \\ 0 & 0.2 & 0 \\ 0 & -0.8 & 1 \end{pmatrix}$$

Multiply the matrix A^{-1} times the *original* column vectors from Table 5-3 to get the entries in Table 5-4 for rows w, y, and t. The entries in the DIOFPU row are given by:

$$x = (0, 4.5, 0) \begin{pmatrix} 2.4 \\ 0.2 \\ 3.2 \end{pmatrix} = 0.90$$

$$y = (0, 4.5, 0) \begin{pmatrix} -0.6 \\ 0.2 \\ -0.8 \end{pmatrix} = 0.90$$

Subtract the entries in the DIOFPU row from the corresponding entries in the CTPPU row. We see that the objective function will be increased by \$3.10 for each unit of x brought into the solution.

TABLE 5-4

	w	y	t	x	z	Constant
w	1	0	0	2.4	−0.6	1440
y	0	1	0	0.2	0.2	320
t	0	0	1	3.2	−0.8	320
CTPPU	0	4.50	0	4.00	0	
DIOFPU				0.90	0.90	
NET				3.10	−0.90	

The maximum number of x's that can be brought into the solution is the positive minimum of 1440/2.4, 320/0.2, 320/3.2, or 100 units of x.

If we bring 100 units of x into the solution, it results in

$$\begin{pmatrix} 1440 \\ 320 \\ 320 \end{pmatrix} - 100 \begin{pmatrix} 2.4 \\ 0.2 \\ 3.2 \end{pmatrix} = \begin{pmatrix} 1200 \\ 300 \\ 0 \end{pmatrix} \begin{matrix} w \\ y \\ t \end{matrix}$$

Hence t is to be taken out of the solution.

TABLE 5-5

	w	y	x	t	z	Constant
w	1	0	0	−0.75	0	1200
y	0	1	0	$-\frac{1}{16}$	0.25	300
x	0	0	1	$\frac{5}{16}$	−0.25	100
CTPPU	0	4.50	4.00	0	0	
DIOFPU				0.96875	0.125	
NET				−0.96875	−0.125	

The new entries in the first 3 rows of Table 5-5 were obtained by

multiplying the inverse of $A = \begin{pmatrix} 1 & 3 & 3 \\ 0 & 5 & 1 \\ 0 & 4 & 4 \end{pmatrix}$ times the column vectors of

Table 5-3, where

$$A^{-1} = \begin{pmatrix} 1 & 0 & -\tfrac{3}{4} \\ 0 & \tfrac{1}{4} & -\tfrac{1}{16} \\ 0 & -\tfrac{1}{4} & \tfrac{5}{16} \end{pmatrix}$$

A look at the NET row reveals that it is impossible to further increase the objective function. The optimum solution then is to produce 100 units of x and 300 units of y, giving \$1750 as the maximum obtainable profit (i.e., $P_{max} = 100(4.00) + 300(4.50) = \$1750$). This result was also obtained graphically in Example 1 of Sec. 5.2.

The total time used is 1200 minutes on machine I, 1600 minutes on machine II, and 1600 minutes on machine III, as shown by

$$300\begin{pmatrix} 3 \\ 5 \\ 4 \end{pmatrix} + 100\begin{pmatrix} 3 \\ 1 \\ 4 \end{pmatrix} = \begin{pmatrix} 1200 \\ 1600 \\ 1600 \end{pmatrix}$$

The fact that 1200 minutes went unused on machine I is indicated by the presence of the slack variable w in the final solution. This happens because to produce one unit of w requires one minute on machine I only. It should be noted that the presence of a slack variable in the solution is always an indication of unused capacity.

If we were to decide on expanding capacity, clearly it would not be to our advantage to increase the capacity of machine I.

Note that the entries in the DIOFPU row times the capacity of the machine needed to produce 1600 units of z and 1600 units of t results in

$$\$0.125(1600) + \$0.96875(1600) = \$200 + \$1550 = \$1750$$

which is the maximum value of the objective function. Hence, in this case, the value of one minute on machine II is \$0.125 and the value of one minute of time on machine III is \$0.96875.

SUMMARY OF THE SIMPLEX METHOD

1. Set up Table 1 (see Sec. 5-3). If there is a positive entry in the NET row, then the objective function can be increased and Table 2 should be formed. If not, the solution can be read from Table 1.

2. To form the next table, choose a variable that has the maximum entry in the NET row. This variable now becomes a solution variable. Divide the entries in this column into the corresponding entries in the constant column. A variable with the minimum positive ratio is the one to be replaced.

3. To get additional entries for this table, compute the inverse of the matrix that is formed by the *original* column vectors of the variables that are now in the solution. Then multiply each *original* column vector by this inverse. Finally, complete the CTPPU, DIOFPU, and NET rows.

4. If there is still a positive entry in the NET row, then the objective function can be increased further. If this is the case, return to Step 2 and form the next table. Continue to form new tables until a table with all negative entries in the NET row is obtained. The solution can then be read from this final table.

PROBLEMS

Problems 1 through 6 refer to material in the body of the text in Sec. 5-5.

1. Write the three equations that precede Table 1 in this section as a matrix equation.

2. Multiply the column vectors $\mathbf{w} = \begin{pmatrix} 1 \\ 0 \\ 0 \end{pmatrix}$, $\mathbf{z} = \begin{pmatrix} 0 \\ 1 \\ 0 \end{pmatrix}$, $\mathbf{t} = \begin{pmatrix} 0 \\ 0 \\ 1 \end{pmatrix}$, $\mathbf{x} = \begin{pmatrix} 3 \\ 1 \\ 4 \end{pmatrix}$, $\mathbf{y} = \begin{pmatrix} 3 \\ 5 \\ 4 \end{pmatrix}$, and $\mathbf{c} = \begin{pmatrix} 2400 \\ 1600 \\ 1600 \end{pmatrix}$ by $\begin{pmatrix} 1 & -0.6 & 0 \\ 0 & 0.2 & 0 \\ 0 & -0.8 & 1 \end{pmatrix}$ in order to verify the entries in Table 5-4.

3. Why was it decided to introduce x as a solution variable in Table 5-5?

4. Find the inverse of the 3 by 3 matrix $\begin{pmatrix} 1 & 3 & 3 \\ 0 & 5 & 1 \\ 0 & 4 & 4 \end{pmatrix}$ by some previous method. Compare your result with the inverse given in the text.

5. Multiply the column vectors $\mathbf{w} = \begin{pmatrix} 1 \\ 0 \\ 0 \end{pmatrix}$, $\mathbf{z} = \begin{pmatrix} 0 \\ 1 \\ 0 \end{pmatrix}$, $\mathbf{t} = \begin{pmatrix} 0 \\ 0 \\ 1 \end{pmatrix}$, $\mathbf{x} = \begin{pmatrix} 3 \\ 1 \\ 4 \end{pmatrix}$, $\mathbf{y} = \begin{pmatrix} 3 \\ 5 \\ 4 \end{pmatrix}$, and $\mathbf{c} = \begin{pmatrix} 2400 \\ 1600 \\ 1600 \end{pmatrix}$ by $\begin{pmatrix} 1 & 0 & -\frac{3}{4} \\ 0 & \frac{1}{4} & -\frac{1}{16} \\ 0 & -\frac{1}{4} & \frac{5}{16} \end{pmatrix}$ in order to verify the entries in Table 5-5.

6. How were the entries in the DIOFPU and the NET rows calculated for Table 5-5?

7. Use the simplex method to solve Prob. 2 of Sec. 5-1, i.e., maximize $P = 6x + 5y$ subject to $x \geq 0$, $y \geq 0$, $4x + y \leq 36$, $2x + 4y \leq 40$, and $2x + y \leq 20$. Compare your result with the graphical solution of Prob. 2, Sec. 5-2.

8. Use the simplex method to solve Prob. 4 of Sec. 5-1, i.e., maximize $P = 2x + y$ subject to $x \geq 0$, $y \geq 0$, $5x + 4y \leq 260$, $5x + 2y \leq 150$, and $10x + 7y \leq 350$. Compare your result with the graphical solution of Prob. 4, Sec. 5-2.

9. A certain firm makes two products, type A and type B. Each product requires 10 man-hours per unit in Department I. Each unit of product A requires 4 man-hours in Department II and each unit of product B requires 8 man-hours in Department II. There are 160 man-hours avail-

able in Department I and 80 man-hours available in Department II per week. The firm earns a profit of $3.00 per unit of product *A* and a profit of $4.00 per unit of product *B*. Assume that it is possible to sell all units produced each week. Find the levels of production which will give the maximum profit.

10. Use the same data given in Prob. 9 except that the firm earns a profit of $6.00 per unit of product *A* and $4.00 per unit of product *B*.

11. Maximize $P = 2x + 3y$ subject to $x \geq 0$, $y \geq 0$, $x + y \leq 10$, and $x + 2y \leq 12$.

12. Use the same data given in Prob. 11 except $P = 9x + 3y$.

REFERENCES

Books

Boulding, Kenneth E. *Linear Programming and the Theory of the Firm*. New York: The MacMillan Company, 1960.

Charnes, A., Cooper, W. W., and Henderson, A. *An Introduction to Linear Programming*. New York: John Wiley and Sons Inc., 1953.

Dantzig, George B. *Linear Programming and Extensions*. Princeton, N.J.: Princeton University Press, 1963.

Dorfman, Robert, Samuelson, Paul A., and Solow, Robert M. *Linear Programming and Economic Analysis*. New York: McGraw-Hill Book Co., Inc., 1958.

Ferguson, Robert O., and Sargent, Lauren F. *Linear Programming: Fundamentals and Applications*. New York: McGraw-Hill Book Co., Inc., 1958.

Gass, Saul I. *Linear Programming; Methods and Applications*. New York: McGraw-Hill Book Co., Inc., 1964.

Levin, Richard I., and Lamone, Rudolph P. *Linear Programming for Management Decisions*. Homewood, Illinois: Richard D. Irwin, Inc., 1969.

Springer, Clifford H., Herlily, R. E., and Beggs, R. I. *Advanced Methods and Models*. Homewood, Illinois: Richard D. Irwin, Inc., 1965.

Stockton, R. Stansbury. *Introduction to Linear Programming*. Boston: Allyn and Bacon, Inc., 1963.

Vajda, Steven. *Readings in Linear Programming*. New York: John Wiley and Sons, Inc., 1958.

Articles

Henderson, Alexander, and Schlaifer, R. "Mathematical Programming Better Information for Better Decision Making." *Harvard Business Review* 32: 73–100.

Mulligan, James E. "Basic Optimization Techniques—A Brief Survey." *The Journal of Industrial Engineering* XVI, 3: 192–197.

Raun, Donald L. "Product-Mix Analysis by Linear Programming." *Management Accounting* XLVII: 3–13.

SIX

Exponents, logarithms, and some important nonlinear functions

Chapter 6 treats the laws of exponents in Sec. 6-1 and the laws of log-arithms in Sec. 6-2. The use of logarithms for computational purposes is covered in Secs. 6-3 and 6-4. Sections 6-5 and 6-6 provide an exposure to logarithmic, exponential, and power functions. The experience gained in graphing these functions will be very useful as background knowledge for the study of calculus in later chapters. In Sec. 6-7 the reader is introduced to the technique of graphing functions on semilog and log-log paper. We point out that each of the three types of functions introduced in Secs. 6-5 and 6-6 graphs as a straight line either on semilog paper or on log-log paper. A procedure for transforming x and/or y values and utilizing the linear regression model which was introduced in Sec. 1-8 is also discussed.

6-1 LAWS OF EXPONENTS

The following laws of exponents are essential in the study of elementary algebra. These laws are valid for real numbers m, n, a, and b. Laws E-2, E-3, and E-4 are used in the study of logarithms and will be discussed later in this chapter. Laws E-5, E-7, and E-8 are used frequently in the study of calculus. Our treatment of calculus will begin in the next chapter.

E-1	$a^0 = 1$, if $a \neq 0$	E-5	$a^{-n} = 1/a^n$, if $a \neq 0$
E-2	$a^m a^n = a^{m+n}$	E-6	$(ab)^n = a^n b^n$
E-3	$a^m/a^n = a^{m-n}$	E-7	$a^{1/n} = \sqrt[n]{a}, a > 0$
E-4	$(a^m)^n = a^{mn}$	E-8	$a^{m/n} = \sqrt[n]{a^m}, a > 0$

Example 1. Use the laws of exponents to calculate $a^5 a^3$ and $(a^5)^3$.

Solution:

$$a^5 a^3 = a^{5+3} \qquad by\ E\text{-}2$$
$$ = a^8$$
$$(a^5)^3 = a^{5(3)} \qquad by\ E\text{-}4$$
$$ = a^{15}$$

Example 2. Calculate a^4/a^0 two different ways, $a \neq 0$.

Solution:

$$a^4/a^0 = a^{4-0} = a^4 \qquad by\ E\text{-}3$$

or

$$a^4/a^0 = a^4/1 \qquad by\ E\text{-}1$$
$$ = a^4$$

Example 3. Express $1/x$ and $\sqrt{x}$ in exponential notation.

Solution:

$$1/x = x^{-1} \qquad by\ E\text{-}5$$
$$\sqrt{x} = \sqrt[2]{x} \qquad (understood)$$
$$\phantom{\sqrt{x}} = x^{1/2} \qquad by\ E\text{-}7$$

Example 4. Use laws of exponents to write $a^4 b^2$ in a different form.

Solution:

$$a^4 b^2 = (a^2)^2 b^2 \qquad by\ E\text{-}4$$
$$ = (a^2 b)^2 \qquad by\ E\text{-}6$$

Example 5. Simplify $4^{1.5}$.

Solution:

$$4^{1.5} = 4^{3/2}$$
$$\phantom{4^{1.5}} = \sqrt[2]{4^3} \qquad by\ E\text{-}8$$
$$\phantom{4^{1.5}} = \sqrt{64}$$
$$\phantom{4^{1.5}} = 8$$
$$4^{3/2} = 8$$

PROBLEMS

1. Rewrite the following expressions in exponential form:

   (a) $\sqrt{x}$ (d) $\sqrt{(xy)^4}$

   (b) $\sqrt[3]{x}$ (e) $x\sqrt{x}$

   (c) $\sqrt{x^3}$ (f) $\sqrt[3]{x+y}$

2. Rewrite the following expressions using radicals:

   (a) $x^{1/2}$ (d) $x^{5/3}$

   (b) $x^{3/2}$ (e) $(x+y)^{1/2}$

   (c) $x^{3/4}$ (f) $x^{-1/4}$

3. Use laws of exponents to simplify the following:

   (a) $3^5/3^2$ (c) 2^{-3}

   (b) x^5/x^2 (d) 3^{-2}

4. Use laws of exponents to show that

   (a) $\sqrt{x}\,\sqrt{y} = \sqrt{xy}$ (b) $\sqrt{x}/\sqrt{y} = \sqrt{x/y}$

5. Use the results of Prob. 4 to find the following square roots:

   (a) $\sqrt{a^2(b+c)^4}$ (c) $\sqrt{25/49}$

   (b) $\sqrt{9/16}$ (d) $\sqrt{13/9}$

6. Solve for x.

   (a) $2^x = 8$ (d) $\sqrt[x]{8} = 2$

   (b) $3^x = 81$ (e) $\sqrt[3]{x} = 4$

   (c) $4^x = 1/4$ (f) $\sqrt{3x} = 4$

7. Solve for x.

   (a) $10^x = 100$ (d) $10^x = 0.1$

   (b) $10^x = 1$ (e) $10^x = 0.01$

   (c) $10^x = 1000$ (f) $10^x = 10,000$

8. Show that $(x^2 + 4)^0 = 1$ for any real number x.

9. Show that $P(1 + i)^n + P(1 + i)^n i = P(1 + i)^{n+1}$.

6-2   DEFINITION AND LAWS OF LOGARITHMS

DEFINITION 6.1.   *Given the positive number b, where $b \neq 1$ and N is any positive real number, then the logarithm to the base b of N denoted by $\log_b N$ is the number that, when used as an exponent of b, gives N. In symbols, $\log_b N = x$ if $b^x = N$.*

Example 1.   Use Definition 6.1 to find $\log_2 8$, $\log_{16} 4$, and $\log_{1/2} (\tfrac{1}{16})$.

Solution:

$$\log_2 8 = 3 \quad \text{since} \quad 2^3 = 8$$

$$\log_{16} 4 = \tfrac{1}{2} \quad \text{since} \quad 16^{1/2} = \sqrt{16} = 4$$

$$\log_{1/2} (\tfrac{1}{16}) = 4 \quad \text{since} \quad (\tfrac{1}{2})^4 = \tfrac{1}{16}$$

In the previous example, we used bases 2, 16, and 1/2 to illustrate Definition 6.1. Although, theoretically, any positive number not equal to one could be used as a base, actually there are only two bases in current use. In the next section we will discuss the *base 10* system. This system is called the *common log system*. The other system, called the *natural log system*, will be taken up later.

Example 2.   Find $\log_{10} 1$, $\log_{10} 10$, $\log_{10} 100$, and $\log_{10} 1000$.

Solution:

$$10^x = 1 \qquad\qquad\qquad\qquad 10^x = 100$$
$$x = 0 \qquad by\ E\text{-}1 \qquad\qquad x = 2$$
$$\log_{10} 1 = 0 \qquad\qquad\qquad \log_{10} 100 = 2$$

$$10^x = 10 \qquad\qquad\qquad\qquad 10^x = 1000$$
$$x = 1 \qquad\qquad\qquad\qquad x = 3$$
$$\log_{10} 10 = 1 \qquad\qquad\qquad \log_{10} 1000 = 3$$

The following laws of logarithms are valid. Let M, N, and b be positive numbers with $b \neq 1$. Then

L-1 $\log_b MN = \log_b M + \log_b N$
L-2 $\log_b M/N = \log_b M - \log_b N$
L-3 $\log_b N^P = P \log_b N$

Proof of L-1.   Let $\log_b M = x$ and $\log_b N = y$. Then, by Definition 6.1, $b^x = M$ and

$$b^y = N$$
$$MN = b^x b^y$$
$$= b^{x+y} \qquad by\ E\text{-}2$$

Therefore,

$$\log_b MN = x + y \qquad\qquad by\ Definition\ 6.1$$
$$\log_b MN = \log_b M + \log_b N$$

(We will omit the proofs of L-2 and L-3.)

Example 3.   Illustrate numerically that $\log_2 16 = \log_2 2 + \log_2 8$.

Solution:

$$\log_2 16 = 4 \qquad \text{since} \qquad 2^4 = 16$$
$$\log_2 2 = 1 \qquad \text{since} \qquad 2^1 = 2$$
$$\log_2 8 = 3 \qquad \text{since} \qquad 2^3 = 8$$

Therefore,

$$\log_2 16 = 4 = 1 + 3 = \log_2 2 + \log_2 8$$

Example 4. | Show that $\log_b \sqrt[n]{M} = 1/n \log_b M$.

Solution:

$$\sqrt[n]{M} = M^{1/n} \qquad\qquad \textit{by E-7}$$
$$\log_b \sqrt[n]{M} = \log_b M^{1/n}$$
$$= 1/n \log_b M \qquad \textit{by L-3}$$

Therefore,

$$\log_b \sqrt[n]{M} = 1/n \log_b M$$

Example 5. | Verify L-2 for the case $\log_2 {}^{16}\!/\!_4 = \log_2 16 - \log_2 4$.

Solution:

$$\log_2 {}^{16}\!/\!_4 = \log_2 4$$
$$= 2 \qquad \text{since} \qquad 2^2 = 4$$
$$\log_2 16 = 4 \qquad \text{and} \qquad \log_2 4 = 2$$

Therefore,

$$\log_2 {}^{16}\!/\!_4 = 2 = \log_2 16 - \log_2 4$$

PROBLEMS

1. Find $\log_3 N$ for the following values of N:

    $N = 9, 81, 27, 1, \frac{1}{3}, \frac{1}{27}, \frac{1}{9}$

2. Find $\log_{1/2} N$ for the following values of N:

    $N = \frac{1}{4}, 1, 2, \frac{1}{2}, \frac{1}{8}, 16$

3. Find $\log_{10} N$ for the following values of N:

    $10^2, 10^{-3}, 10^5, 10^{1/3}, \sqrt{10}, \sqrt[3]{10}, 10^{1/3}, \sqrt[3]{100}$

4. Illustrate numerically that $\log_4 64 = \log_4 4 + \log_4 16$.

5. Illustrate numerically that $\log_2 4^3 = 3 \log_2 4$.

6. Illustrate numerically that $\log_5 {}^{625}\!/\!_{25} = \log_5 625 - \log_5 25$.

7. Prove L-2 and L-3.

8. Find $\log_b x$ given that $\log_b xy = 8$ and that $\log_b (x/y) = 4$.

9. Calculate or rewrite each of the following:

    (a) $\log_b (b^3)$ (c) $\log_b (1/b)$

    (b) $\log_b 1$ (d) $\log_b (ab^3 + b^2)$

10. Show that $\dfrac{\log_b 40 - \log_b 5}{3} = \log_b 2$.

11. Show that $\log_a N = \dfrac{\log_b N}{\log_b a}$ (change of base formula).

12. Illustrate the result in Prob. 11 with $N = 16$, $a = 4$, and $b = 2$.

13. Which of the following expressions can be written as a difference of two logarithms?

(a) $\log_{10} \dfrac{5}{3}$ (b) $\dfrac{\log_{10} 5}{\log_{10} 3}$

14. Express each of the following ratios as a single logarithm.

[*Hint:* Use the result of Prob. 11.]

(a) $\dfrac{\log_{10} 5}{\log_{10} 3}$ (b) $\dfrac{\log_3 81}{\log_3 9}$

15. Rewrite $V_n = P(1 + i)^n$ by taking logarithms of both sides.

6-3 THE USE OF TABLES OF LOGARITHMS

In this section we will use the base 10 system for computations. Since the base 10 is used throughout this section, we will adopt the usual convention and write $\log_{10} N$ as $\log N$.

In all of the numerical examples of the previous section, the logarithms could be obtained by intuition. Clearly, this is not the case for $\log_{10} 110 = \log 110$, for example. In other words, the answer to the question, "Ten to what power equals 110?" is not at all obvious. Fortunately, there are tables of logarithms that provide an easy answer to this type of question. One of the main purposes of this section is to acquaint the reader with the use of such tables. The reader will find a five-place table of common logarithms in Table 1 of Appendix A.

To answer the above question, we know intuitively that $\log 110$ is between 2 and 3. The decimal part of this number is found from Table 1 to be 0.04139. Hence, $\log 110 = 2.04139$. In this example, the decimal 0.04139 is called the *mantissa* of $\log 110$ and the integer 2 is called the *characteristic* of $\log 110$. The terms characteristic and mantissa are illustrated further in the following examples.

Example 1. Find the characteristic and mantissa of $\log 101$ and $\log 1001$.

Solution: It is clear that $\log 101$ is slightly larger than 2; i.e., $\log 100 = 2$; therefore, $\log 101 = 2 \ldots$. The decimal needed to fill in the blank is the mantissa of $\log 101$. From Table 1, we find that $\log 101 = 2.00432$.
The characteristic of $\log 101$ is 2 and the mantissa of $\log 101$ is 0.00432.
Similarly, $\log 1001 = 3.00043$. $\log 1000 = 3$; therefore, the characteristic of $\log 1001$ is 3 and the mantissa is 0.00043.

Example 2. Find the characteristic and mantissa of $\log 11$, $\log 110$, and $\log 1100$.

Solution:

$\log 11 = 1.04139$
$\log 110 = 2.04139$
$\log 1100 = 3.04139$

The characteristics of $\log 11$, $\log 110$, and $\log 1100$ are one, two, and three, respectively. The mantissa, 0.04139, is the same for all of them.

The previous example illustrates the fact that the mantissa of log N is determined by the sequence of digits that make up N with no regard to the decimal point. That is, the logarithms of two different numbers with the same sequence of digits have the same mantissa. For example, log 1.23, log 12.3, and log 123 all have mantissa 0.08991.

The characteristic of log N is determined by the location of the decimal point within the sequence of digits that make up N.

Any real number can be written with the decimal point after the first significant digit times ten to some integral power. The decimal point is then said to be in the *standard position.*

Example 3.   Write the numbers 0.0462 and 398 with the decimal point in standard position and find the logarithms of these numbers.

Solution:

$$0.0462 = 4.62 \times 10^{-2}$$
$$398 = 3.98 \times 10^2$$

$$\begin{aligned}
\log 398 &= \log 3.98 \times 10^2 \\
&= \log 3.98 + \log 10^2 \qquad \textit{by L-1} \\
&= \log 3.98 + 2 \qquad\quad \text{since } \log 10^2 = 2 \\
&\qquad\qquad\qquad\qquad\quad \textit{by Definition 6.1} \\
\\
&= 0.59988 + 2
\end{aligned}$$

Since 3.98 is between one and ten, therefore, its logarithm has characteristic zero.

$$\log 398 = 2.59988$$

By similar reasoning,

$$\begin{aligned}
\log 0.0462 &= \log (4.62 \times 10^{-2}) \\
&= \log 4.62 + \log 10^{-2} \\
&= 0.66464 - 2 \qquad \text{since } \log 10^{-2} = -2 \\
&\qquad\qquad\qquad\qquad \textit{by definition}
\end{aligned}$$

The previous example illustrates the basis of a short-cut method of determining the characteristic of log N. This method consists of counting the number of places the decimal must be moved to put it in standard position. If the decimal must be *moved to the left*, the characteristic is *positive*. It is *negative* if the decimal point must be *moved to the right*.

Example 4.   Use the short-cut method to find log 3.4, log 94, log 9400, and log 0.69.

Solution:

$$\log 3.4 = 0.53148$$
$$\log 94 = 1.97313$$
$$\log 9400 = 3.97313$$

Finally, log 0.69 has mantissa 0.83885 and characteristic -1. Negative characteristics should be written to the right of the mantissa. This gives log 0.69 =

0.83885 − 1. It is also common to express such numbers as follows: log 0.69 = 0.83885 − 1 = 9.83885 − 10.

The mantissa for numbers with no more than four significant digits can be found directly from Table A-1 of the Appendix. A method called *linear interpolation* can be used to approximate the mantissa for a number with five significant digits. This method treats the *nonlinear* function $y = \log x$ as if it were a *straight line* between the tabulated points. The method of linear interpolation is illustrated numerically in the next two examples.

It is to be noted that the first two digits of the mantissa in this table are indicated for groups of mantissas in order to save space. Where an asterisk (*) appears, the first two digits of the next group of mantissas, which are located in the row below, are to be used for the mantissa.

Example 5.   Use linear interpolation and Table A-1 of the Appendix to find log 1.8432.

Solution: Since log 1.8440 = 0.26576, and log 1.8430 = 0.26553, their difference is 0.00023. Adding 2/10 of the difference, log 1.8440 − log 1.8430, to log 1.843, we have

$$\log 1.8432 = 0.26553 + 0.2(0.00023)$$
$$= 0.26553 + 0.000046$$
$$\log 1.8432 = 0.265576$$

This value may be rounded off to 0.26558.

Example 6.   Use Table A-1 of the Appendix and linear interpolation to find log 934.57.

Solution: The mantissa for 934.6 is 0.97063 and the mantissa for 934.5 is 0.97058. Adding 7/10 of the difference, 0.97063 − 0.97058, to 0.97058, the mantissa of the smaller tabulated number, we have

$$\text{mantissa for } 934.57 = 0.97058 + 0.7(0.00005)$$
$$= 0.97058 + 0.000035$$
$$= 0.97062$$

Therefore,

$$\log 934.57 = 2.97062$$

Note that in Example 6, the choice of 0.7 was based on the fact that the fifth digit in 934.57 is seven.

PROBLEMS

1. The logarithm of each of the following numbers is between what two integers?

(a)	84	**(e)**	1562
(b)	97	**(f)**	2437
(c)	154	**(g)**	0.23
(d)	837	**(h)**	0.0087

2. Find the common mantissa for the following numbers:

(a)	0.1234	**(e)**	0.001234
(b)	1.234	**(f)**	12340
(c)	1234	**(g)**	1,234,000
(d)	12.34	**(h)**	1.234×10^8

3. Write each of the following numbers with the decimal point in the standard position.

(a)	482	**(e)**	352×10^4
(b)	5372	**(f)**	4800
(c)	0.043	**(g)**	573,000
(d)	0.87	**(h)**	0.43×10^{-3}

4. Find the mantissa for each of the following numbers:

(a)	4832	**(e)**	0.02391
(b)	3718	**(f)**	0.8
(c)	43.92	**(g)**	712,300
(d)	257.6	**(h)**	0.001

5. Find the characteristic for each of the numbers in Prob. 4.

6. Find the logarithm of each of the numbers in Prob. 4. [*Hint:* Use the results of Probs. 4 and 5.]

7. Use Table A-1 of the Appendix and interpolation to find the logarithm of each of the following numbers:

(a)	48217	**(d)**	8364.9
(b)	0.083175	**(e)**	0.12348
(c)	23.711	**(f)**	7.3463×10^5

8. Simplify $b = \dfrac{\log 10.10 - \log 2}{\log 3 - \log 1}$.

6-4 COMPUTATIONS WITH LOGARITHMS

Before giving some examples to illustrate the use of logarithms, we will define the concept of an *antilogarithm*.

DEFINITION 6.2. *The antilogarithm of a number x, denoted by antilog x, is defined by the relationship antilog $x = N$ if and only if $x = \log N$.*

For the base 10 system, the antilog of x is the number whose logarithm to the base 10 is x. This definition is further illustrated below.

1. antilog $2 = 100$

2. antilog $3 = 1000$

3. antilog $(-1) = 0.1$

   By Definition 6.2, antilog $x = N$ if $x = \log N$.
   By Definition 6.1, $x = \log N$ if $N = 10^x$. Combining these two statements gives antilog $x = 10^x$.

The following examples illustrate the use of logarithms in certain calculations.

Example 1. | Use logarithms to calculate $\sqrt{4}$.

Solution: Let $N = \sqrt{4}$.

$$N = 4^{1/2} \qquad\qquad by\ E\text{-}7$$
$$\log N = 1/2 \log 4 \qquad\qquad by\ L\text{-}3$$
$$= 1/2(0.60206)$$
$$\log N = 0.30103$$

Looking up 0.30103 in Table A-1 of the Appendix, we find that $N = 2$. The answer $N = 2$ in Example 1 is called the antilog of 0.30103.

Example 2. | Calculate $(47)^{0.3}$ using logarithms.

Solution: Let $N = (47)^{0.3}$.

$$\log N = 0.3(1.67210) \qquad\qquad by\ L\text{-}3$$
$$\log N = 0.50163$$
$$N = 3.174$$

Example 3. | Use logarithms to calculate $\dfrac{(283)(8.1)}{2500}$.

Solution: Let $N = \dfrac{(283)(8.1)}{2500}$.

$$\log N = \log 283 + \log 8.1 - \log 2500 \qquad\qquad by\ L\text{-}1\ and\ L\text{-}2$$
$$= 2.45179 + 0.90849 - 3.39794$$
$$= 3.36028 - 3.39794$$
$$\log N = -0.03766$$

The antilog of a negative number cannot be found directly from Table A-1 of the Appendix. By adding and subtracting one to -0.03766, we obtain

$$\log N = 1 - 0.03766 - 1$$
$$\log N = 0.96234 - 1$$
$$N = 0.9169 \qquad\qquad without\ using\ interpolation$$

The technique of adding and subtracting a number large enough to introduce a positive decimal is the standard way of looking up antilogs of negative numbers.

The method of linear interpolation can also be used for finding antilogs. This is illustrated in the next example.

Example 4. | Use Table A-1 of the Appendix and interpolation to find antilog (0.94118).

Solution:

antilog 0.94121 = 8.7340
antilog 0.94118 = 8.733x
antilog 0.94116 = 8.7330

157

$$\frac{x}{10} = \frac{0.94118 - 0.94116}{0.94121 - 0.94116}$$

$$\frac{x}{10} = \frac{0.00002}{0.00005} = \frac{2}{5}$$

$$x = 4$$

antilog $(0.94118) = 8.7334$

Example 5. Find $\sqrt[3]{0.432}$ using logs.

Solution:

$N = (0.432)^{1/3}$
$\log N = \frac{1}{3} \log 0.432$
$\log N = \frac{1}{3}(0.63548 - 1)$
$\log N = \frac{1}{3}(2.63548 - 3)$ *adding and subtracting 2 to obtain*
                                                   a number divisible by 3

$\log N = 0.87849 - 1$
$N = \text{antilog } (0.87849 - 1)$
$\sqrt[3]{0.432} = 0.75595$ *using interpolation and Table A-1*
                                                   of the Appendix in reverse

PROBLEMS

1. Find the following antilogarithms:

    (a) antilog 4   (d) antilog (2.67025)
    (b) antilog (−2)   (e) antilog (0.71037 − 3)
    (c) antilog (0)   (f) antilog (0.66011)

2. Use logarithms to find the following square roots:

    (a) $\sqrt{9}$ (d) $\sqrt{0.63}$
    (b) $\sqrt{432}$ (e) $\sqrt{0.063}$
    (c) $\sqrt{8126}$ (f) $\sqrt{0.0063}$

3. Use logarithms to find the following cube roots:

    (a) $\sqrt[3]{64}$ (c) $\sqrt[3]{360}$
    (b) $\sqrt[3]{432}$ (d) $\sqrt[3]{0.063}$

4. Perform the following multiplications using logarithms:

    (a) (483)(7543)   (d) (9.37)(856)(1432)
    (b) (0.317)(3754)   (e) (16427)(845.21)
    (c) (48212)(672)   (f) (23)(84)(570)(6842)

5. Use logarithms to do the following division problems:

    (a) 8723/415   (c) 0.428/642
    (b) 415/8723   (d) 0.03475/0.004182

6. Use logarithms to perform the indicated operations.

    (a) (234)(8752)/4827   (d) $\sqrt[3]{(856)}/439$
    (b) $\sqrt{(572)(0.459)}$ (e) $437/\sqrt{(848)(5342)}$
    (c) $(8432)\sqrt{954}$ (f) $(0.01245)/\sqrt[5]{(6542)}$

7. Calculate the following quantities using logarithms. Expressions of this form arise in connection with compound interest calculations.
   (a) $2000(1.06)^{10}$
   (b) $(1 + 0.08)^5$
   (c) $1000(1.04)^{20}$

8. Solve $\left(1 + \dfrac{i}{4}\right)^4 = 1.08$ for i.

9. Find antilog $\left(\dfrac{\log 40 - \log 5}{3}\right)$.

10. Determine or simplify the following:
    (a) antilog (log 2)
    (b) antilog (3 log 5)
    (c) antilog (log b)
    (d) antilog (a log b)

6-5 LOG FUNCTIONS

Functions of the form $y = m \log_a x + b$, where a, m, and b are constants, will be discussed in this section.

Example 1. Draw the graph of $y = \log_3 x$.

Solution: $y = \log_3 x$ if and only if $3^y = x$.

x	1	3	9	27	$\frac{1}{3}$	$\frac{1}{9}$
y	0	1	2	3	-1	-2

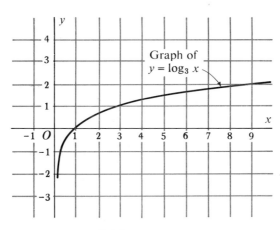

FIGURE 6-1

Analysis: (a) $m = 1$ and $b = 0$.

(b) The function does not cross the y axis and crosses the x axis at $x = 1$.

(c) The function increases at a decreasing rate.

Example 2.

Draw the graph of $y = \log x$.

Solution: $y = \log x$ if and only if $10^y = x$.

x	1	2	3	4	5	10	100	$\frac{1}{10}$
y	0	?	?	?	?	1	2	-1

x	2	3	4	5
y	0.30103	0.47712	0.60206	0.69897

To complete the table the student must use Table A-1 of the Appendix.

x	1	2	3	4	5	10	100	$\frac{1}{10}$
y	0	0.30103	0.47712	0.60206	0.69897	1	2	-1

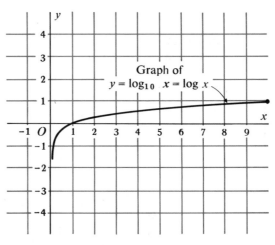

FIGURE 6-2

Analysis: (a) $m = 1$ and $b = 0$.

(b)   The function does not cross the y axis and crosses the x axis at $x = 1$.

(c)   The function increases at a decreasing rate.

Earlier in the text, we briefly mentioned the natural log system. This system of logs has various applications, and is especially important in advanced mathematics. The base for the natural log system is the irrational number e, where $e = 2.7183$ rounded to four decimal places. The reason for the use of this particular irrational number as a base for a log system is to be found in a study of differential calculus. In particular, it is explained in Sec. 8-8 of this text. For the natural log system, we write $\log_e N$ or simply $\ln N$. In other words, $\log N$ refers to the base 10 and $\ln N$ refers to the base e. In the Appendix the reader will find a table of natural logarithms.

Example 3. | Discuss and graph the function $y = \ln x$.

Solution: $y = \ln x$ if and only if $e^y = x$.

x	1	2	2.7183
y	0		1

The entry for y when x is equal to 2 can be found in two ways:
Method I: Starting with $2.7183^y = 2$ and taking the log of both sides, we have

$$y \log 2.7183 = \log 2 \quad \text{or} \quad y = \frac{\log 2.0000}{\log 2.7183}$$

Referring to the table of logs,

$$y = \frac{0.30103}{0.43425} \quad \text{or} \quad y = 0.693$$

The entry when $x = 2$ is $y = 0.693$.
Method II: The second method consists of looking up the number 2 in the table of natural logs. Doing this, we get the number 0.693. From Table A-2 in the Appendix, we have

x	1	2	2.7183	3	4
y	0.000	0.693	1.000	1.099	1.386

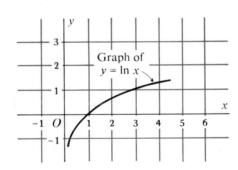

FIGURE 6-3

Analysis: (a) $m = 1$, $b = 0$, and $a = e$ (referring to the form $y = m \log_a x + b$).
(b)   The function does not cross the y axis but crosses the x axis at $x = 1$.

PROBLEMS

1. Draw the graph of the following functions:
   (a) $y = \log_2 x$ (c) $y = 2 \ln x$
   (b) $y = \log_4 x$ (d) $y = \log_{10} x^2$

2. Draw the graphs of the following functions:
   (a) $y = 2 \log x + 3$ (c) $y = \log (2x)$
   (b) $y = 3 \log x + 2$ (d) $y = \log (2x) + 3$

3. Draw the graph of $y = \ln x^2 + 3$.

4. Find the equation of the form $y = m \log x + b$ that passes through the points (1, 2) and (10, 4). Use the method of elimination.

5. Find the equation of the form $y = m \ln x + b$ that passes through the points (1, 3) and (e^2, 4).

6. Find the equation of the form $y = m \log x + b$ that passes through the points (1, 5) and (10, 6). Use the method of elimination.

7. Use the change of base formula of Prob. 11 of Sec. 6-2, $\log_b N / \log_b a = \log_a N$, to show that $\log N = (\log e) \ln N$.

8. Illustrate the result of Prob. 7 for the following values of N:
   (a) $N = 6.5$
   (b) $N = 9.8$
   Note: $\log e = 0.43429448$ accurate to eight decimal places.

6-6 EXPONENTIAL AND POWER FUNCTIONS

The expression $y = ab^x$, where a and b are constants, is called an *exponential function*. Examples of such equations are $y = 3^x$, $y = e^x$, $y = 4(2^x)$, and $y = a(1 + r)^x$.

Example 1.   Draw the graph of $y = 2^x$.

x	-1	0	1	2	3
y	0.5	1	2	4	8

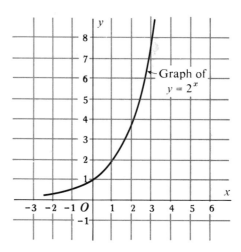

FIGURE 6-4

Analysis: (a) *a* is equal to one and *b* is equal to 2.
(b) The function crosses the *y* axis at $y = 1$ and does not cross the *x* axis.
(c) The function increases at an increasing rate.

Example 2. Draw the graph of $y = e^x$.

Solution: The entries for $x = 2$, 3, etc. can be found in Table A-3 of the Appendix.

x	0	1	2	3
y	1.0	2.72	7.39	20.1

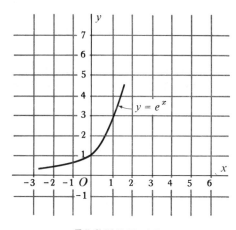

FIGURE 6-5

Analysis: (a) *a* is equal to one and *b* is equal to *e*.
(b) The function increases at an increasing rate.

Example 3. Draw the graph of $y = 5(2^x)$.

Solution:

x	−1	0	1	2	3
y	2.5	5	10	20	40

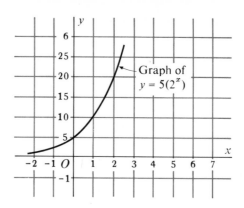

FIGURE 6-6

Analysis: (a) $a = 5$ and $b = 2$.
          (b) The function crosses the y axis at $y = 5$ and does not cross the x axis.
          (c) The function increases at an increasing rate.

The expression $y = ax^b$, where a and b are constants, is called a *power function*. Examples of power functions are $y = x^3$, $y = 4x^2$, $y = x^{1.4}$, and $y = x^e$.

Example 4.   Draw the graph of $y = x^2$.

Solution:

x	0	± 1	± 2	± 3
y	0	1	4	9

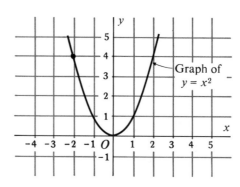

FIGURE 6-7

Analysis: (a) a is equal to one and b is equal to 2.
          (b) The function is increasing at an increasing rate for $x > 0$.

Example 5. | Draw the graph of $y = 2(x^{1.5})$.

Solution:

x	0	1	2	3
y	0	2	5.65	10.39

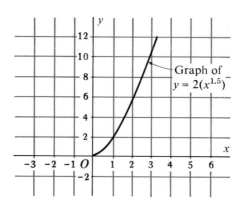

F I G U R E   6-8

To find the values of y when $x = 2$, 3, etc. one must make use of logs. We have then $\log y = \log 2 + 1.5 \log x$.
When x is 2,

$$\log y = \log 2 + 1.5 \log 2$$
$$= 0.301 + 1.5(0.301)$$
$$= 0.301 + 0.4515$$
$$\log y = 0.7525$$
$$y = 5.65$$

Analysis: (a) a is equal to two and b is equal to 1.5.
　　　　　　(b)   The function increases at an increasing rate for $x > 0$.

If $y = kx$, where a is a constant, y is said to be directly proportional to x. More generally, if $y = k f(x)$, where k is a constant, y is said to be *directly proportional to* $f(x)$. The statement "*y varies directly as* $f(x)$" is equivalent to the statement "y is directly proportional to $f(x)$."

Example 6. | Given that w varies directly as the square of z, express w as a function of z.

Solution: w varies directly as the square of z means that w is directly proportional to z^2. Therefore, $w = kz^2$ is the desired function. Note that $f(z) = z^2$ in this example.

PROBLEMS

1. Graph the following functions:

   (a) $y = 3^x$ (c) $y = 3(4)^x$
   (b) $y = 2e^x$ (d) $y = 2(\frac{1}{2})^x$

2. Determine the function of the form $y = 3b^x$ that passes through the point (2, 12) and graph the function.

3. Determine the function of the form $y = ab^x$ that passes through the points (0, 3) and (1, 6). Use the method of elimination. Graph the resulting function.

4. Determine the function of the form $y = ab^x$ that passes through the points (0, 2) and (4, 3). Use the method of elimination. Graph the resulting function.

5. Graph the following functions:

   (a) $y = x^3$ (c) $y = 0.5x^{2.5}$
   (b) $y = 3x^{1/2}$ (d) $y = 2x^{1/3}$

6. Determine the function of the form $y = 2x^b$ that passes through (2, 16). Graph the resulting function.

7. Determine the function of the form $y = ax^b$ that passes through the points (1, 1) and (10, 10). Use the method of elimination.

8. Sales for a certain industry have been growing at an annual rate of 12% for the past four years. Assume that this rate of growth remains constant over the next eight years and that current sales are $20,000,000. Estimate the expected level of sales:
   (a) five years hence
   (b) eight years hence

9. Sales are currently $1,000,000 per year. Annual growth over the next five years is expected to be 10% per year.
   (a) Complete the following table:

x (year)	1	2	3	4	5
y (annual sales at year end in millions)	1.100				

   (b) Determine the function of the form $y \doteq ab^x$ that passes through the two points corresponding to Year 1 and Year 5.

10. Express the following statements functionally and identify the resulting functions by name:
    (a) y is directly proportional to x^3.
    (b) y varies directly as the square root of x.
    (c) w is directly proportional to log z.
    (d) v varies directly as t.
    (e) s is directly proportional to t^2.
    (f) y varies directly as 2^x.
    (g) y is directly proportional to $(1 + r)^x$.

11. Grosch's law (for computers) states that computing power $= k(\text{cost})^2$, where k is a constant.

(a) Express this law verbally.

(b) What type of function is this?

12. Show that $y = ab^x$ can be put in the form $y = ae^{kx}$, where $k = \ln b$.

6-7 SEMILOG AND LOG-LOG PAPER

Consider the equation $y = m \log x + b$, where m and b are constants. The reader will recognize this as a nonlinear function. However, if we think of y as a function of $\log x$ rather than x, we would obtain a linear function with slope m and y intercept b. Semilog paper is constructed in such a way that one of the axes is a *logarithmic* or *ratio scale*. (See Fig. 6-9.) It follows that any function of the form $y = m \log x + b$ will graph as a straight line with slope m and y intercept b on semilog paper.

Example 1. Draw the graph of $y = \log x$ on semilog paper with the x axis in logarithmic scale.

Solution: A table of values and the graph appear below.

x	1	2	3	4	5	10
$y = \log x$	0.00000	0.30103	0.47712	0.60206	0.69897	1.00000

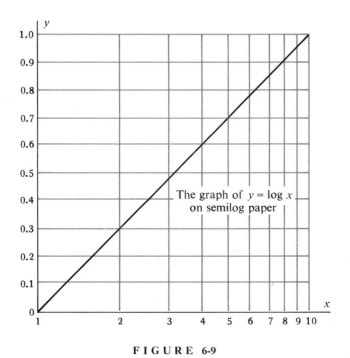

The graph of $y = \log x$ on semilog paper

FIGURE 6-9

167

Example 2. | Draw the graph of $y = 2 \log x + 3$ on semilog paper with the x axis in logarithmic scale.

Solution: A table of values and the graph appear below.

x	1	2	5	10
y	3	3.602	4.397	5

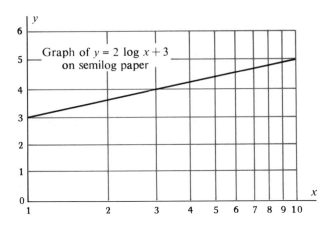

F I G U R E   6-10

Analysis: The function crosses the y axis at $y = 3$, and for a one unit increase in x ($\log 10 - \log 1$), y increases by two units. Therefore, $b = 3$ and $m = 2$.

Example 3. | Find the equation of the form $y = m \log x + b$ that passes through the points $A(1, 4)$ and $B(10, 7)$.

Solution: We can solve for m and b by the method of elimination or we can plot the points on semilog paper to find the values of m and b.

e_1: $4 = m \log 1 + b$
e_2: $7 = m \log 10 + b$

Because $\log 1$ is equal to zero, we obtain $b = 4$. Then substituting the value of b into e_2 we have

$$7 = m \log 10 + 4$$

$$3 = m \log 10$$

$$m = \frac{3}{\log 10}$$

$$m = 3$$

The desired function is $y = 3 \log x + 4$.

Next we obtain this function graphically using semilog paper. Plotting the two given points on semilog paper and drawing a straight line through them gives the following graph.

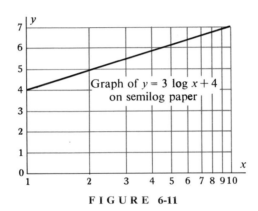

Graph of $y = 3 \log x + 4$ on semilog paper

F I G U R E 6-11

From the fact that the graph crosses the y axis at $y = 4$, we conclude that $b = 4$. Also, since a one unit increase in x ($\log 10 - \log 1$) results in a 3 unit increase in y, we see that the slope is 3. Therefore, $m = 3$. The desired equation is $y = 3 \log x + 4$, as we found before by the method of elimination.

Consider the equation $y = ab^x$, where a and b are positive constants. This equation is equivalent to $\log y = \log a + x \log b$. This means that $y = ab^x$ graphs as a straight line on semilog paper with the y axis in logarithmic scale. Furthermore, a equals the vertical intercept and $\log b$ equals the slope of the line.

Example 4.   Draw the graph of $y = 5(2^x)$ on semilog paper with the y axis in logarithmic scale.

Solution:

x	0	1	2	3
y	5	10	20	40

169

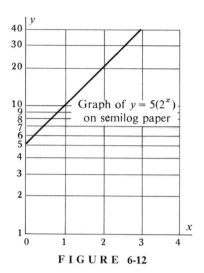

FIGURE 6-12

Analysis: (a) The vertical intercept is 5; therefore, $a = 5$.

(b) The slope is given by $\dfrac{\log 40 - \log 5}{3} = \dfrac{1.6021 - 0.6990}{3}$,

$\log b = 0.301$

Therefore,

$b = 2$

Finally, we illustrate the use of log-log paper. Consider the power function $y = ax^b$ with a, b constant and a, x positive. If we take the logarithm to the base 10 of both sides, we obtain $\log y = \log a + b \log x$. Log-log paper is constructed in such a way that both axes are in logarithmic scale. (See Fig. 6-13.) It follows that any power function of the type described above graphs as a straight line on log-log paper. Furthermore, a equals the vertical intercept and b equals the slope of the line.

Example 5. Draw the graph of $y = 2(x^{1.5})$ on log-log paper.

Solution: A table of values and the graph appear below.

x	1	2	3
y	2	5.65	10.1039

170

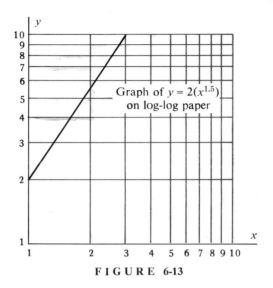

FIGURE 6-13

Analysis: (a) The vertical intercept is 2; therefore, $a = 2$.

(b) The slope is given by $b = \dfrac{\log 10.10 - \log 2}{\log 3 - \log 1}$

$$b = \frac{1.0167 - 0.301}{0.47712}$$

$$b = 1.5$$

A mathematical equation or model can be found to describe approximately certain classes of empirical data as follows:

1. If the data graph approximately as a straight line on semilog paper with the x axis in logarithmic scale, then the data can be described by a function of the form $y = m \log x + b$, a log function.

2. If the data graph approximately as a straight line on semilog paper with the y axis in logarithmic scale, then the data can be described by a function of the form $y = ab^x$, an exponential function.

3. If the data graph approximately as a straight line on log-log paper, then the data can be described by a function of the type $y = ax^b$, a power function.

The parameters a, b, and m can be estimated using the method of least squares discussed in Sec. 1-8. The appropriate procedure for each of these important cases is described below.

1. Estimation of m and b. Fit a straight line to ordered pairs of the form

log x_i, y_i, i.e., make a logarithmic transformation on x. In this case m and b are estimated directly by the least-squares procedure, with $y = m \log x + b$ as the proposed model.

2. Estimation of a and b in $y = ab^x$. Fit a straight line to ordered pairs of the form x_i, log y_i, i.e., make a logarithmic transformation on y. In this case log a and log b are estimated by the least-squares procedure. Then take antilogs to obtain estimates of a and b based on $y = ab^x$, which implies log $y = \log a + x \log b$.

3. Estimation of a and b in $y = ax^b$. Fit a straight line to ordered pairs of the form log x_i, log y_i, i.e., make a logarithmic transformation on both x and y. In this case, b and log a are estimated by the least-squares procedure. Then take the antilog of a to obtain the estimate of a based on $y = ax^b$, which implies log $y = \log a + b \log x$.

PROBLEMS

1. Graph the following functions on semilog paper:
   (a) $y = 2 \log x + 2$ (c) $y = \log (2x)$
   (b) $y = 3 \log x + 2$ (d) $y = \log (2x) + 3$

2. Find the equation of the form $y = m \log x + b$ that passes through the points $(1, 2)$ and $(10, 4)$. Use semilog paper.

3. Find the equation of the form $y = m \log x + b$ that passes through the points $(1, 5)$ and $(10, 6)$. Use semilog paper.

4. Graph the following functions on semilog paper:
   (a) $y = 3^x$ (c) $y = 3(4)^x$
   (b) $y = 2e^x$ (d) $y = 2(\frac{1}{2})^x$

5. Determine the function of the form $y = ab^x$ that passes through the points $(0, 3)$ and $(1, 6)$. Use semilog paper.

6. Determine the function of the form $y = ab^x$ that passes through the points $(0, 2)$ and $(4, 3)$. Use semilog paper.

7. Graph the following functions on log-log paper:
   (a) $y = x^3$ (c) $y = 0.5x^{2.5}$
   (b) $y = 3x^{1/2}$ (d) $y = 2x^{1/3}$

8. Determine the function of the form $y = ax^b$ that passes through the points $(1, 1)$ and $(10, 10)$. Use log-log paper.

9. You are given the following figures for cost in thousands of dollars and production in hundreds of units. Find the equation of the form $y = ab^x$ that corresponds to this information.

x	0	1	2	3	4	5
y	1	2	4	8	16	32

x is in hundreds of units.
y is in thousands of dollars.

10. Given the following:

x	1	2	3	4	5	6	7	8
y	0.77	1.50	2.34	3.21	4.11	5.03	5.95	6.90

(a) Complete the table:

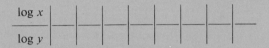

log *x*								
log *y*								

(b) Prepare a scatter diagram for the transformed data on ordinary graph paper.

(c) Prepare a scatter diagram on log-log paper for the given data.

(d) Fit $\log y = a + b \log x$ by the method of least squares.

(e) Use the result of (d) to fit $y = cx^d$ to the given data, and compare the resulting function graphically with the scatter diagram of (b).

11. The general linear homogeneous constant elasticity of substitution (*CES*) production function can be put in the following form[1]:

$$\frac{V}{L} = \left(\frac{1}{1-\delta}\right)^{1/(1+P)} \gamma^{P/(1+P)} W^{1/(1+P)} \tag{1}$$

where V = output (value added in current dollars)
  L = labor input (production man-hours worked)
  W = wage rate (wage bill/man-hours)
  γ = efficiency parameter
  P = substitution parameter
  δ = distribution parameter

(a) Express (1) in the form

$$\frac{V}{L} = AW^b \tag{2}$$

and identify A and b.

(b) Express (2) in logarithms by taking the logarithm of both sides.

(c) Describe a procedure for estimating A and b.

12. Given Fig. 6-14.

---

1. Christos C. Paraskevopoulos, "Impact of Regional Wage Differentials," *Growth and Change* IV, 2: 40–41.

(a) What type of function would best fit these data, i.e., linear, exponential, or logarithmic?

(b) What is the general form of this function?

(c) On what kind of paper would these data graph approximately as a straight line?

Life insurance sales in the U.S. in 1972 totaled $212 billion, up from $189.2 billion in 1971, the Life Insurance Institute reports.

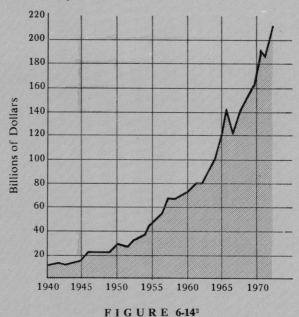

F I G U R E   6-14[2]

13. Plot the data of Prob. 9 of Sec. 6-6 on semilog paper using y as the ratio scale.

14. Use the plot of Prob. 13 to fit $y = ab^x$ to these data, and compare your result with the result of Prob. 9 of Sec. 6-6.

15. What functional relationship between money supply and time for the period 1965 to 1969 is indicated by Fig. 6-15?

---

2. *Wall Street Journal:* June 15, 1973, p. 1.

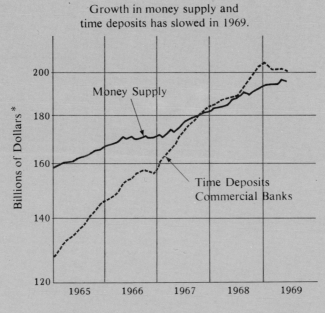

Growth in money supply and time deposits has slowed in 1969.

*Ratio scale seasonally adjusted

F I G U R E 6-15[3]

16. Use the graph in Prob. 15 to estimate a and b in the function money supply $= ab^{time}$.

17. Consider the hypothetical sales data in Table 6-1.

TABLE 6-1

Year	Sales
1	1,120,000
2	1,254,300
3	1,404,900
4	1,573,600
5	1,762,400
6	1,973,800

(a) Form a scatter diagram for these data on arithmetic paper.
(b) Form a scatter diagram for these data on semilog paper using log y versus x.

3. *Business Conditions:* June 1969, p. 3.

(c) Perform a logarithmic transformation on $S = a(1 + r)^z$.

(d) Fit a straight line to the scatter diagram of (b) by eye. Use your fitted line to estimate $1 + r$ and a.

(e) Fit a straight line to the scatter diagram of (b) using the least-squares procedure. Use this fitted line to estimate $1 + r$ and a.

(f) Using the estimated values of $1 + r$, a, $1 + \hat{r}$, and $\hat{a}$, plot the function $\hat{S} = \hat{a}(1 + \hat{r})^z$ on the scatter diagram of (a).

(g) Calculate the residuals $S_i - \hat{S}_i$, $i = 1, 2, \ldots, 6$, and compute $\sum_{i=1}^{6} (S_i - \hat{S}_i)^2$.

SEVEN

Mathematics of finance

In this chapter we define the important mathematical concept of a sequence and then discuss in detail two special kinds of sequences, arithmetic progressions and geometric progressions. Geometric progressions are then applied to compound interest and present value problems in the field of finance. The chapter ends with a discussion of annuities.

7-1 SEQUENCES

In Chap. 1 we introduced the concept of a function. In this section we will discuss a special class of functions called sequences.

DEFINITION 7.1.   *A sequence of real numbers is a real-valued function whose domain is the set of positive integers.*

In this text the term sequence will be understood to mean a sequence of real numbers.

Example 1. | Discuss the following sequence:

x	$f(x)$
1	1
2	1/2
3	1/3
.	.
.	.
.	.
n	$1/n$
.	.
.	.
.	.

Note that the function values or terms of the sequence are not necessarily positive integers.

Solution: This function is a sequence since its domain is the set of positive integers, 1, 2, 3, . . . , n, ... The functional form is given by $f(n) = 1/n$. The range of this function is 1, 1/2, 1/3, . . . , 1/n, ...

Example 1 stresses the idea that a sequence is a special case of the more general notion of a function. Ordinarily, however, one does not use the tabular format of Example 1 to display a given sequence. For example, consider a typical sequence:

x	1	2	3	$\cdots$	n	$\cdots$
$f(x)$	$f(1)$	$f(2)$	$f(3)$	$\cdots$	$f(n)$	$\cdots$

If we denote $f(n)$ by a_n, all of the above information is contained in the listing $a_1, a_2, a_3, . . . , a_n, ...$ This conventional notation for sequences will generally be used in this text.

Example 2. Discuss the sequence 0, 1/2, 2/3, . . . , $1 - 1/n$, ...

Solution: The nth term of this sequence is $f(n) = a_n = 1 - 1/n$.

$$f(1) = a_1 = 1 - 1/1 = 1 - 1 = 0$$
$$f(2) = a_2 = 1 - 1/2 = 1/2, \text{ etc.}$$

There are times when one is interested in finding the sum of the first n terms of a sequence. This process, viewed as a function of n, generates a new sequence, called the *sequence of partial sums*.

Example 3. Form the first five terms of the sequence of partial sums for the given sequence 1, 4, 7, 10, 13, 16, ...

Solution: Let $a_1 = 1$, $a_2 = 4$, etc. Define $s_n = a_1 + a_2 + \cdots + a_n$. Then

$$s_1 = 1$$
$$s_2 = 1 + 4 = 5$$
$$s_3 = 1 + 4 + 7 = 12$$
$$s_4 = 1 + 4 + 7 + 10 = s_3 + 10 = 22$$
$$s_5 = 1 + 4 + 7 + 10 + 13 = s_4 + 13 = 35$$

The sequence of partial sums is 1, 5, 12, 22, 35, ...

PROBLEMS

1. Write out the first five terms of the following sequences:
    (a) $a_n = 2 + 4/n$
    (b) $a_n = n^2$
    (c) $a_n = \sqrt{n}$
    (d) $a_n = \log n$
    (e) $a_n = \ln n$

(f) $a_n = 2^n$
(g) $a_n = e^n$
(h) $a_n = e^{-n}$

2. Plot the graph of $y = f(x)$, where $x = 1, 2, 3, 4, 5, 6$ and $f(x) = 2 + (x - 1)3$.

3. Plot the graph of $y = f(x)$, where $x = 1, 2, 3, 4, 5, 6$ and $f(x) = (1.06)^x$.

4. Write the first six terms of the sequence $1, 2, \ldots, n!, \ldots$, where $n!$ denotes n factorial and by definition $n! = n(n - 1)(n - 2) \cdots 2(1)$.

5. Write the first six terms of $n!/n$, where $n! = n(n - 1)(n - 2) \cdots 2(1)$.

6. Write the first five terms of the following sequence: $a_1 = 2$ and $a_n = 2 + (n - 1)3, n = 1, 2, 3, \ldots$.

7. Write the first five terms of the following sequence: $a_1 = a$ and $a_n = a + (n - 1)d, n = 1, 2, 3, \ldots$.

8. Form the first five terms of the sequence of partial sums for:
   (a) the sequence in Prob. 6
   (b) the sequence in Prob. 7

9. Show that the sequence with $a_1 = a, a_n = a_{n-1} + d, n = 2, 3, \ldots$ is the same sequence as the one defined in Prob. 7.

10. Show that the nth term of the sequence of partial sums for the sequence $a, a + d, \ldots, a + (n - 1)d, \ldots$ is equal to $na + d(1 + 2 + 3 + \cdots + n - 1)$.

11. Write the first five terms of the following sequence: $a_1 = 2$ and $a_n = 3a_{n-1}, n = 2, 3, \ldots$. Note that $a_n = 2(3)^{n-1}$.

12. Write the first five terms of the following sequence: $a_1 = a$ and $a_n = ra_{n-1}, n = 2, 3, \ldots$. Note that $a_n = ar^{n-1}$.

13. Show that the nth term of the sequence of partial sums for the sequence $a, ar, \ldots, ar^{n-1}, \ldots$ is given by $s_n = a(1 + r + r^2 + \cdots + r^{n-1})$.

14. Form the first five terms of the sequence of partial sums for the sequence $a, b, c, d, e, \ldots$.

15. Form the first three terms of the sequence of partial sums for the sequence $a_n = (1.06)^{-n}, n = 0, 1, 2, \ldots$.

7-2   ARITHMETIC AND GEOMETRIC PROGRESSIONS

In the previous section we introduced the notion of a sequence and pointed out that a sequence is a special case of a function. In this section we single out two special kinds of sequences for more detailed investigation. These two special cases are called arithmetic and geometric progressions.

DEFINITION 7.2.   *An arithmetic progression is a sequence of the form a, $a + d, a + 2d, \ldots, a + (n - 1)d, \ldots$, where d is called the common difference.* For example, $1, 3, 5, 7, \ldots$ is an arithmetic progression with $a = 1$ and $d = 2$.

An arithmetic progression has the distinctive property that the kth term can be obtained by adding d, the common difference, to the $k - 1$st term.

In the previous section we also introduced the concept of a sequence of partial sums. In the case of an arithmetic progression it is possible to obtain a formula for the nth term of the sequence of partial sums. The desired formula is

$$s_n = \sum_{k=1}^{n} a + (k - 1)d = na + \frac{n(n - 1)\,d}{2}$$

Proof:

$$s_n = a + (a + d) + (a + 2d) + \cdots + [a + (n - 1)d]$$

Reversing the order of the terms,

$$s_n = [a + (n - 1)d] + \cdots + (a + 2d) + (a + d) + a$$

Combining these two expressions for s_n gives $2s_n = n[2a + (n - 1)d]$. Therefore,

$$s_n = na + \frac{n(n - 1)d}{2} \tag{1}$$

This formula for the sum of the first n terms of an arithmetic progression is given in terms of a, n, and d. The right-hand side can also be expressed in terms of a_1, n, and a_n, where $a_n = a + (n - 1)d$ and $a_1 = a$.

$$s_n = \frac{n}{2}[2a + (n - 1)d]$$

$$= \frac{n}{2}[a + a + (n - 1)d]$$

$$= \frac{n}{2}(a_1 + a_n) \tag{2}$$

Example 1.   Compute the sum of the first ten terms of the arithmetic progression 1, 3, 5, . . . in two ways.

Solution: $a = 1, n = 10, d = 3 - 1 = 5 - 3 = 2$.

$$s_{10} = 10a + \frac{10(9)d}{2} \qquad \textit{from (1)}$$

$$s_{10} = 10 + 45(2)$$

$$s_{10} = 100$$

or

$$a_{10} = a + 9d \qquad \textit{from (2)}$$

$$a_{10} = 19$$

$$s_{10} = \frac{10}{2}(1 + 19)$$

$$s_{10} = 100$$

Next we define the term *geometric progression.*

DEFINITION 7.3.   A *geometric progression is a sequence of the form a,* $ar, ar^2, ar^3, \ldots, ar^{n-1}, \ldots,$ *where r is called the common ratio.*

A geometric progression has the distinctive property that the kth term can be obtained by multiplying the $k - 1$st term by r, the common ratio. An example of a geometric progression is

$$1, 2, 4, 8, \ldots, 256, \qquad \text{where } a = 1 \text{ and } r = 2$$

Geometric progressions are used extensively in the remaining sections of this chapter in connection with the mathematics of finance. An understanding of geometric progressions is basic to the study of the implications of investing money at compound interest.

As with arithmetic progressions, it is possible to develop a formula for the sum of the first n terms of a geometric progression. In this case we seek a formula for $s_n = a + ar + ar^2 + \cdots + ar^{n-1}$ (nth partial sum). The correct formula is $s_n = a(r^n - 1)/(r - 1)$.

Proof:

$$s_n = a + ar + ar^2 + \cdots + ar^{n-1}$$

$$rs_n = ar + ar^2 + \cdots + ar^n \qquad \textit{multiplying both sides by r}$$

$$rs_n - s_n = ar^n - a$$

$$(r - 1)s_n = a(r^n - 1)$$

$$\therefore s_n = \frac{a(r^n - 1)}{r - 1} \tag{3}$$

Example 2.   Compute $1 + 2 + 4 + 8 + \cdots + 128 + 256$.

Solution: This is the sum of the first nine terms of a geometric progression with $a = 1$ and $r = 2$. Applying (3) we have

$$s_9 = \frac{1(2^9 - 1)}{2 - 1}$$

$$s_9 = 511$$

Formula (3) is very important and is used later in this chapter to obtain the formula for the amount of an annuity.

PROBLEMS

1. $4, 7, 10, \ldots, a_n, \ldots$ is an arithmetic progression. Determine the following quantities:
   - (a)   the common difference, d
   - (b) $a_4, a_{10},$ and a_{20}
   - (c)   the sum of the first 20 terms
2. $a_1, a_2, a_3, \ldots$ is an arithmetic progression with $a_5 = 40$ and $a_{11} = 80$.

Determine the common difference, d. [*Hint:* Use some elementary algebra.]

3. Find the sum of the first 100 positive integers using a result from this section.

4. $2, 6, 18, \ldots, a_n, \ldots$ is a geometric progression. Determine the following quantities.
   (a) the common ratio, r
   (b) a_2, a_4, and a_6
   (c) the sum of the first six terms

5. $a_1, a_2, a_3, \ldots$ is a geometric progression with $a_4 = 30$ and $a_8 = 480$. Determine the common ratio, r.

6. Find the sum of the first eight terms of the geometric progression $1, 2, 4, 8, \ldots$.

7. Graph the following functions on the same coordinate system.
   (a) $f(x) = 1 + (x - 1)2$, $x = 1, 2, 3, 4, 5$, i.e., the first five terms of the arithmetic progression with $a = 1$ and $d = 2$
   (b) $g(x) = 2^{x-1}$, $x = 1, 2, 3, 4, 5$, i.e., the first five terms of the geometric progression with $a = 1$ and $r = 2$
   (c) Do the points of the graph in (a) lie along a straight line?

8. Consider the geometric progression with $a_n = 3(2)^{n-1}$.
   (a) Write the first six terms of this progression.
   (b) Discuss the sequence $b_1, b_2, \ldots, b_n, \ldots$, where $b_n = \log a_n$.
   (c) Do the six points of the graph of $f(x) = b_x$, $x = 1, 2, \ldots, 6$, lie along a straight line? If so, what is its slope?

9. Let $x_1, x_2, \ldots, x_n$ be the first n terms of an arithmetic progression. Give a formula for $\bar{x} = (1/n) \sum_{i=1}^{n} x_i$, where $\bar{x}$ is called the mean or arithmetic average of $(x_1, x_2, \ldots, x_n)$.

10. Use the result of Prob. 9 to find the mean of $\frac{1}{2}, 1, \frac{3}{2}, 2, \frac{5}{2}, 3, \frac{7}{2}$.

11. Write the first four terms of the geometric progression with
    (a) $a = 1$ and $r = 1.08$
    (b) $a = 100$ and $r = 1 + i$

12. Write the first four terms of the geometric progression with $a = 1$ and $r = 1/1.08$.

13. Find the fourth partial sum of the geometric progression with $a = 1000$ and $r = 1.06$, i.e., the fourth term in the sequence of partial sums.

14. Show that $\sum_{k=1}^{n} a[(1 + i)^{k-1}] = a \left(\dfrac{(1 + i)^n - 1}{i} \right)$.

15. Use the concept of area to prove $\sum_{k=1}^{n} a + (k - 1)d = (n/2)(a_1 + a_n)$, where $a_1 = a$ and $a_n = a + (n - 1)d$.

7-3   COMPOUND INTEREST

The concept of compound interest is familiar to most readers. Assume that $1,000.00 is deposited in a bank and left for one year. The interest rate is 6% per year. Figure 7-1 illustrates the principal on deposit at the end of Year 1. At the end of Year 1 the accumulated amount is $1060.00. If this principal were allowed to remain deposited for an

$1000 $1000 + $60

Year 1

P $P + Pi$

F I G U R E 7-1

additional year under the same conditions, we would have Fig. 7-2, where V_n denotes the value of the original principal at the end of Year n.

$1000 $1000 + $60 $1060 + $1060(0.06)

Year 1   Year 2

$V_0 = P$ $V_1 = P + Pi$ $V_2 = (P + Pi) + (P + Pi)i$

F I G U R E 7-2

Note that the interest at the end of Year 2 is paid on the amount on deposit at the beginning of the period, which is equivalent to the amount at the end of the previous period.

This process is called compound interest because the interest is *converted* to principal; that is, in the next period one earns interest on the interest. In this case the number of conversions is two.

Example 1. | Show that $(P + Pi) + (P + Pi)i = P(1 + i)^2$.

Solution:

$$(P + Pi) + (P + Pi)i$$
$$= (P + Pi)(1 + i) \qquad \text{taking out the common factor } P + Pi$$
$$= P(1 + i)(1 + i)$$
$$= P(1 + i)^2$$

We can see from the above example that the value of the original principal at the end of the second year is given by the formula $V_2 = P(1 + i)^2$.

Example 2. | Use this formula to compute the amount that would result if $1000.00 were deposited at 6% for two years.

Solution:

$$V_2 = P(1 + i)^2$$
$$= 1000(1 + 0.06)^2$$
$$= 1000(1.1236)$$
$$= \$1123.60$$

The formula $V_2 = P(1 + i)^2$ suggests the following formula for

183

the amount on deposit at the end of n years. The amount, V_n, on deposit after n years at compound interest i is given by

$$V_n = P(1 + i)^n$$

Proof: Let $V_n =$ amount on deposit after n years. Then $V_{n+1} = V_n + V_n i$ by definition of compound interest. Simplified,

$$V_{n+1} = V_n(1 + i)$$

This means that the progression P, V_1, V_2, . . . , V_n is a geometric progression. Explicitly, we have

$$P, P(1 + i), P(1 + i)^2, P(1 + i)^3, \ldots, P(1 + i)^n$$

$$\therefore V_n = P(1 + i)^n$$

The geometric progression written above has $n + 1$ terms and n conversions. Furthermore, the $n + 1$st term gives V_n, the amount on deposit at the end of n years.

Example 3. | Apply the formula $V_n = P(1 + i)^n$. Find the amount on deposit after four years if $P = \$2000$ and $i = 0.06$.

Solution:

$$V_4 = \$2000(1 + 0.06)^4$$

$$= \$2000(1.06)^4$$

$$= \$2000(1.2625)$$

$$= \$2535$$

If the number of years in Example 3 were 20, the calculation $(1.06)^{20}$ would be tedious. One could multiply 1.06×1.06 twenty times, use logs, or use a calculator that has an exponential key. The first two options are time-consuming and can be inaccurate. The third option may not be available. In light of these difficulties, we suggest the use of Table A-4 in the Appendix. This table provides the compound interest of \$1 for $n = 1$ through 50 periods.

To use this table for values of P other than \$1 simply multiply the table entry by P, i.e., this table gives values of $(1 + i)^n$.

Example 4. | Find the amount on deposit if \$1000 is deposited at an interest rate of 8% for 20 years.

Solution:

$$V_{20} = 1000(1 + 0.08)^{20}$$

$$= 1000(4.6610) \qquad \textit{from Table A-4}$$

$$= \$4661$$

In all of the previous examples the interest was compounded annually. What would happen if interest were compounded, or converted to principal, before the year end, i.e., semi-annually, quarterly, or daily? The following example illustrates what has to be done to handle this type of problem.

Example 5. | Calculate the amount on deposit at the end of one year if $1.00 is deposited at an interest rate of 8% compounded semi-annually.

Solution:

$1.000 $1.0400 $1.0816

|————————————————|————————————————|

180 days   360 days

$1.00(0.08) \dfrac{180}{360}$ $1.040(0.08) \dfrac{180}{360}$

F I G U R E 7-3

Note that at the first conversion at the end of 180 days, or one-half of a year,

Interest $= 1.0000(0.08)(\tfrac{1}{2})$

$= 1.0000(0.04)$

The amount at the end of the first period is given by

$$\text{Amount} = 1\left(1 + \frac{i}{2}\right)^1$$

At the end of the first year (360 days) the amount is $1.0816. The same result could have been obtained from Table A-4 using $i = 0.04$ and $n = 2$.

In general, to compute the amount on deposit, P, when interest is compounded k times per year at i percent per year for n years, we use Table A-4 and the following formula:

$$V_n = P\left(1 + \frac{i}{k}\right)^{kn}$$

Example 6. | Calculate the amount on deposit if interest on $1000 is compounded quarterly for ten years at 8% per year.

Solution:

$$V_{10} = 1000\left(1 + \frac{0.08}{4}\right)^{4(10)}, \qquad k = 4, \; n = 10$$

$$= 1000(1.02)^{40}$$

$$= \$2208$$

It is interesting to note that if we had compounded annually, rather than quarterly, the amount would have been $2,158.90. After the calculus has been introduced, it will be shown that if we compounded instantaneously or continuously, the amount would be

Amount $= Pe^{in}$

or, in this case,

$$\text{Amount} = \$1000e^{(0.08)10}$$

$$= \$1000e^{0.8}$$

$$= \$1000(2.23) \qquad \textit{using Table A-3}$$

$$= \$2230$$

In summary, if we had invested \$1000 at 8% at the end of ten years we would have

TABLE 7-1

Compounding	Amount
annually	\$2158.90
quarterly	2208.00
instantaneously	2230.00

PROBLEMS

1. Compute the amount that would result if \$3000, deposited at 4%, were compounded annually for five years.

2. Given that one deposits \$2000 at a rate of 6% compounded annually for ten years.
   (a) Find the amount on deposit by using the formula for V_n.
   (b) Find the amount on deposit by using logarithms.
   Note: One would expect the answers to (a) and (b) to be the same. This will not be the case because of truncation errors in the tables.

3. Given that $a = 100$ and $r = (1 + 0.08)$, write the first five terms of the corresponding geometric progression.

4. Given the geometric progression 200, 208, 216.32, 224.97, 233.97, ...
   (a) What is a?
   (b) What is r?
   (c) Interpreting this as a compound interest problem, what is the interest rate?

5. Calculate the amount on deposit if interest on \$2000 is compounded semi-annually for 12 years at 8% per year.

6. Complete Table 7-2 for $P = \$1000$, $n = 1$, and $i = 0.08$.

TABLE 7-2

Compounding	V_n
$k = 1$ (annually)	
$k = 2$ (semi-annually)	
$k = 4$ (quarterly)	

7. Given that $(1.00666)^{12} = 1.0829995$ and $(1.0002222)^{360} = 1.083277$, extend the table of Prob. 6 to:
   (a) $k = 12$ (compounding monthly)
   (b) $k = 360$ (compounding daily)

8. Given that $e^{0.08} = 1.083287$, extend the table in Prob. 6 assuming instantaneous compounding.

9. What would be the result of Example 5 if one compounded quarterly?

10. Complete the following table. Use compound interest and $P = \$1.00$. Assume annual compounding.

n	1	2	3	4	5
$i = 0.04$ V_n					
$i = 0.08$ V_n					

11. Plot the data of Prob. 10 on a single coordinate system with time as the horizontal axis.

12. A competing bank is paying interest compounded semi-annually. Assume that you are currently paying 8% compounded annually, and this is the maximum amount that can be paid by law. What rate, compounded semi-annually, would yield the same return as 8% compounded annually?

13. A certain bank is currently paying 4% per year on $2,000,000. A branch manager who graduated from college the previous year suggests to top management that they convert to a semi-annual compounding policy. Playing the role of a member of the higher echelon,
    (a) Evaluate the extra interest cost that would result if this suggestion were implemented.
    (b) Would you accept or reject the suggestion?

7-4 PRESENT VALUE

As we saw in the previous section, if one were to put $1.00 in the bank at the beginning of the year, by year end he would have more than $1.00 as the interest converted to principal. The amount that results, V_n, is determined by the interest rate and the length of time that the money is on deposit.

Example 1. | Using the formula $V_n = P(1 + i)^n$ with $P = \$1.00$, $n = 1$, and $i = 0.08$ (compounding annually), solve for V_1.

Solution:

$$V_1 = \$1.00(1 + 0.08)^1$$

$$= \$1.00(1.08)$$

$$= \$1.08$$

In this section we would like to answer the following question— What is the worth now (i.e., *present value*) of a given amount that is to be received in the future, given a specific discount rate? By *discount*

187

rate we mean a rate at which we discount the worth of a dollar because it is not received at this moment.

Example 2. | Given a discount rate of 0.08, what would be the current worth of $1.08 to be received one year from now?

Solution: Using $V_n = P(1 + i)^n$ and solving for P, we have

$$P = \frac{V_n}{(1 + i)^n}$$

$$= \frac{1.08}{1.08}$$

$$= 1.00$$

In general, P_n will denote the present value of an amount V to be received n periods from now using a discount rate i. The formula for present value is

$$P_n = \frac{V}{(1 + i)^n}$$

Using laws of exponents and writing the right-hand side as a product, we have

$$P_n = V(1 + i)^{-n}$$

Example 3. | Using a discount rate of 6%, calculate the present value of $2000 that is to be received two years from now.

Solution:

$$P_2 = \$2000(1 + 0.06)^{-2}$$

$$= \$2000(0.8900)$$

$$= \$1780$$

Note that in the above example one is faced with evaluating $(1.06)^{-2}$ or $1/(1.06)^2$. This can easily be done longhand. However, if n were equal to 14, one would be forced to use logarithms or some type of calculator. Because these calculations occur often, Table A-5 in the Appendix lists present values of $1 for $n = 1$ through 50 periods. To use this table for values of V other than $1.00, simply multiply the table entry by V, i.e., this table gives values of $(1 + i)^{-n}$.

Example 4. | Using a discount rate of 6%, find the present value of $10,000 that is to be received five years from now.

Solution:

$$P_n = V(1 + i)^{-n}$$

$$P_5 = \$10,000(1.06)^{-5}$$

$$= \$10,000(0.7474) \qquad using\ Table\ A\text{-}5$$

$$= \$7473$$

In all of the above examples the discount rate assumed annual discounting. As in the previous section, we have the formula

$$P_n = V\left(1 + \frac{i}{k}\right)^{-kn}$$

where k is the number of times per year that P is discounted.

Example 5. Using a discount rate of 8% discounted quarterly, find the present value of $10,000 that is to be received five years from now.

Solution:

$$P_n = V\left(1 + \frac{i}{k}\right)^{-kn}$$

$$V_5 = \$10,000(1.02)^{-4(5)}$$

$$= \$10,000(1.02)^{-20}$$

$$= \$10,000(0.6730)$$

$$= \$6730$$

In some cases one may know the values of P_n and V and wish to solve for i, such as in the purchase of an item bought now at P_n for the purpose of resale at price V at a time n periods from now.

Example 6. Given that one can purchase now for $15,000 an item he expects to be able to sell for $18,000 four years from now. Solve for i assuming annual discounting.

Solution:

$$P_n = V(1 + i)^{-n}$$

$$\$15,000 = \$18,000(1 + i)^{-4}$$

$$\frac{\$15,000}{\$18,000} = \frac{1}{(1 + i)^4}$$

$$(1 + i)^4 = \frac{18}{15}$$

$$1 + i = \sqrt[4]{1.2}$$

$$1 + i = 1.0466$$

$$i = 0.0466$$

PROBLEMS

1. Using an annual discount rate of 0.08, find the present value of $100 that is to be received three years from now.
2. Given that one is going to receive $2000 upon return home four years from now. Assume an annual discount rate of 6%.
    (a) Find the present value using the formula for P_n.
    (b) Find the present value using logarithms.

Note: The results of *a* and *b* will differ because of truncation errors in the tables.

3. Given that $a = 100$, $r = 1/1.06$ in a geometric progression. Write the first five terms of this geometric progression.

4. Given the geometric progression 1.0000, 0.9434, 0.8900, 0.8396, ...
    (a) What is *a*?
    (b) What is *r*?
    (c) Interpreting this as a present value problem, what is the discount rate?

5. Find the present value of $10,000 to be received three years from now discounted semi-annually at 8% per year.

6. Complete Table 7-3 for $V = \$1000$, $n = 1$, and $i = 0.08$.

TABLE 7-3

Discounting	P_n
$k = 1$ (annually)	
$k = 2$ (semi-annually)	
$k = 4$ (quarterly)	

7. Redo Example 6 of this section assuming quarterly discounting. [*Hint:* $\sqrt[16]{1.2} = 1.01146$.]

8. Complete the following table for $V = \$1.00$.

	n	1	2	3	4	5
$i = 0.04$	P_n					
$i = 0.08$	P_n					

9. Plot the data of Prob. 8 on a single coordinate system with time as the horizontal axis.

10. One can purchase a building that he expects to resell at $120,000 five years from now. The cost of the building is $110,000.
    (a) Solve for *i* assuming annual discounting.
    (b) Would this be a wise decision?

7-5   ANNUITIES

In Sec. 7-3 we looked at compound interest and how a *single* amount deposited can grow as the interest becomes principal. In this section we will do something quite similar, except that, rather than a single deposit, we will look at an amount being deposited each term (i.e., year). By definition, an annuity is a series of payments or receipts of a fixed amount for a specified number of years. Note that the payments will be made at the end of the period rather than at the beginning of the period.

Example 1.

How much would one have on deposit if he were to make payments of $1000 a year for four years (i.e., a four-year annuity)? The interest being paid is 6%.

Solution:

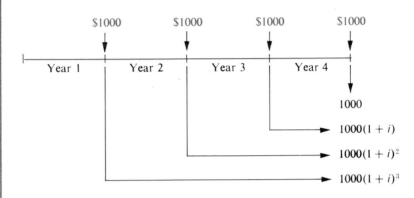

F I G U R E 7-4

Sum = $1000 + $1000(1.06) + $1000(1.06)² + $1000(1.06)³

$\qquad$ = 1000 + 1000(1.06) + 1000(1.1236) + 1000(1.1910)

$\qquad$ = 1000.00 + 1060.00 + 1123.60 + 1191.00

$\qquad$ = $4374.60

The solution was obtained by using Table A-4. We could have made use of the formula developed in Sec. 7-2 for the first *n* terms of a geometric progression,

$$s_n = \frac{a(r^n - 1)}{r - 1}$$

where $\quad$ a = first term in the progression

$\qquad\quad$ r = common ratio

$\qquad\quad$ n = number of terms

Example 2.

Use the formula for the *n*th partial sum of a geometric progression to solve the problem posed in Example 1.

Solution: $\quad$ We have the following progression:

$\qquad$ 1000, 1000(1.06), 1000(1.06)², 1000(1.06)³, . . .

The sum of these first four terms is

$$s_4 = \frac{1000(1.06^4 - 1)}{1.06 - 1}$$

191

$$= \frac{1000(1.2625 - 1)}{0.06}$$

$$= \frac{1000(0.2625)}{0.06}$$

$$= \$4374.60$$

Using the formula for the nth partial sum of a geometric progression, we would like to develop a formula for the *amount of an annuity* with payments or receipts of R dollars and an interest rate i.

Let $r = 1 + i$. Then we have

$$S_n = \frac{R[(1 + i)^n - 1]}{1 + i - 1}$$

$$= R\left[\frac{(1 + i)^n - 1}{i}\right]$$

Next, let $s_{\overline{n}|i} = \frac{(1 + i)^n - 1}{i}$. Then $S_n = Rs_{\overline{n}|i}$. The values of $s_{\overline{n}|i}$ are tabulated in Table A-6.

The quantity $s_{\overline{n}|i}$ is the amount of an annuity of \$1.00, i.e., the special case $R = 1$.

Example 3. Redo Example 1 using the above formula and Table A-6.

Solution: $i = 0.06$, $n = 4$, and $R = 1000$.

$$S_n = Rs_{\overline{n}|i}$$

$$S_4 = 1000s_{\overline{4}|0.06}$$

$$= 1000(4.3746)$$

$$= \$4374.60, \qquad \textit{as expected}$$

Thus far we have been concerned with the worth of a sequence of payments at some time in the future. As a businessman, you may also be interested in the present value of a sequence of receipts to be received at year end for n years.

Example 4. What is the present value of receipts of \$1000 to be received at year end for four years? Assume a discount rate of 6%.

Solution:

Present value $= 1000(1.06)^{-1} + 1000(1.06)^{-2} + 1000(1.06)^{-3} + 1000(1.06)^{-4}$

$$= 1000(0.9434) + 1000(0.8900) + 1000(0.8396) + 1000(0.7921)$$

$$= 1000(0.9434 + 0.8900 + 0.8396 + 0.7921)$$

$$= 1000(3.4651)$$

$$= \$3465.10$$

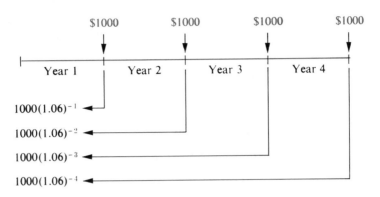

FIGURE 7-5

The present value of an annuity of $1000 to be received over a period of four years is $3465.10.

In the previous problem we saw that to calculate the present value of an annuity we simply multiplied the sum of the first four terms of a geometric progression by $R = 1000$. In general, we will denote these sums by $a_{\overline{n}|i}$, where n is the number of years and i is the appropriate discount rate. We then have the following formula for the *present value of an annuity*.

$$A_n = Ra_{\overline{n}|i}$$

A table of values of $a_{\overline{n}|i}$ is provided in Table A-7. Note that the entry in column 3 of this table for $n = 4$ is the same as the sum of the first four entries in column 3 of Table A-5. There will be a slight discrepancy due to truncation.

Example 5.   Use Table A-7 to find the present value of an annuity of $10,000 that is to be received for five years. Use an 8% discount rate.

Solution:

$$A_n = Ra_{\overline{n}|i}$$
$$A_5 = \$10,000(3.9927)$$
$$A_5 = \$39,927$$

In many applications, the receipts in the sequence, sometimes referred to as the cash flow, are not all equal. One may receive $2000 for the first three years and $1000 for the next three years (Fig. 7-6).

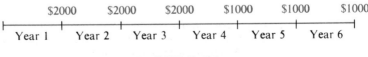

FIGURE 7-6

193

Clearly, we can use our formula to evaluate the present value of the receipts of the first three years. It is simply

$$A_n = Ra_{\overline{n}|i}$$

$$A_3 = 2000(2.5771) \qquad \textit{assuming 8\% as the discount rate}$$

$$A_3 = \$5154.20$$

Evaluating the flow over the last three years, we have for the present value of the last three receipts

$$\$1000[(1.08)^{-4} + (1.08)^{-5} + (1.08)^{-6}]$$

$$= 1000(0.7350 + 0.6806 + 0.6302)$$

$$= 1000 (2.0458)$$

$$= \$2045.80$$

The same result could have been obtained as follows:

$$\$1000[a_{\overline{6}|0.08} - a_{\overline{3}|0.08}]$$

$$= 1000(4.6229 - 2.5771)$$

$$= 1000(2.0458)$$

$$= \$2045.80$$

Combining these two sums, we see that the present value of all six payments, A_6, is given by

$$A_6 = 2000a_{\overline{3}|0.08} + 1000(a_{\overline{6}|0.08} - a_{\overline{3}|0.08})$$

$$= 5154.20 + 2045.80$$

$$= \$7200$$

The following is a summary of the formulas in the last three sections of this chapter.

Compound interest	$V_n = P(1 + i)^n$
Present value	$P_n = V(1 + i)^{-n}$
Amount of an annuity	$S_n = Rs_{\overline{n}|i}$
Present value of an annuity	$A_n = Ra_{\overline{n}|i}$

Values for $(1 + i)^n$, $(1 + i)^{-n}$, $s_{\overline{n}|i}$, and $a_{\overline{n}|i}$ can be found in Tables A-4 through A-7, respectively, in Appendix A.

PROBLEMS

1. How much would one have on deposit after three years if he made annual payments of $10,000? Assume an 8% interest rate.
   (a) Arrive at the solution intuitively.

(b) Arrive at the solution using the formula for the partial sum of a geometric series.

(c) Arrive at the solution using the formula for the amount of an annuity.

2. How much would one have on deposit at the end of 15 years given that he deposited $1200 at the end of each year? Use a discount rate of 6%.

3. If one wants to have $10,000 at the end of ten years, how much must he deposit annually? Assume an interest rate of 6%.

4. What is the present value of receipts of $10,000 received at year end for three years? Assume a discount rate of 10%.
   (a) Arrive at a solution intuitively.
   (b) Arrive at a solution using the formula for the present value of an annuity.

5. What is the present value of receipts of $2000 received for 15 years? Assume a discount rate of 12%.

6. Given that one can purchase a machine for $10,000. Assume a discount rate of 12% and a flow of five years. How much must the annual receipts be in order to give a 12% return on the money invested in the machine?

7. Find the present value of an annuity of $10,000 for three years followed by an annuity of $5000 for three additional years. Assume a discount rate of 10%.

8. One can purchase a machine for $28,300. It is anticipated that this will result in a cash flow of $5000 a year for the next 12 years. What is the rate of return on this investment?

Problems 9–12 are based on the following symbols and formulas from the following tables:

$$S^n = (1 + i)^n \qquad\qquad A\text{-}4 \quad (compound\ interest\ of\ \$1)$$

$$V^n = (1 + i)^{-n} \qquad\qquad A\text{-}5 \quad (present\ value\ of\ \$1)$$

$$s_{\overline{n}|i} = \frac{(1 + i)^n - 1}{i} \qquad A\text{-}6 \quad (amount\ of\ an\ annuity)$$

$$a_{\overline{n}|i} = \frac{1 - (1 + i)^{-n}}{i} \qquad A\text{-}7 \quad (present\ value\ of\ an\ annuity)$$

9. Show that $V^n = 1/S^n$ \quad (*A-5 in terms of A-4*).
10. Show that $s_{\overline{n}|i} = (S^n - 1)/i$ \quad (*A-6 in terms of A-4*).
11. Show that $a_{\overline{n}|i} = (1 - V^n)/i$ \quad (*A-7 in terms of A-5*).
12. Show that $a_{\overline{n}|i} = (S^n - 1)/iS^n$ \quad (*A-7 in terms of A-6*).

REFERENCES

Hart, William L. *Mathematics of Investment*. Lexington, Mass.: D. C. Heath & Co., 1958.

Johnson, Robert W. *Financial Management*, fourth ed. Boston: Allyn and Bacon, Inc., 1971.

Kent, Frederick C., and Kent, Maude E. *Compound Interest and Annuity Tables*. New York: McGraw-Hill Book Co., Inc., 1954.

Spiegel, Murray R. *Mathematical Handbook of Formulas and Tables*. New York: McGraw-Hill Book Co., Inc., 1968.

Weston, Fred J., and Brigham, Eugene F. *Managerial Finance*. New York: Holt, Rinehart and Winston, Inc., 1972.

EIGHT

Introduction to differential calculus

8-1   PRE-CALCULUS GRAPHING

Differential calculus deals with the problem of finding the *instantaneous* or *point* rate of change of nonlinear functions. Geometrically speaking, it deals with the problem of finding the slope of the *tangent line* to a curve at a given point on the curve. The notions of point rate of change and tangent line will be defined later in this chapter.

This section is designed to give the reader some additional graphing experience with nonlinear functions. A familiarity with the graphs of elementary functions helps the student to gain intuitive insight into some of the rather subtle concepts of the calculus.

We begin by discussing the graphs of some functions of the form $y = ax^3 + bx^2 + cx + d$, where a, b, c, and d are constants.

First, assume $a = b = 0$ (linear case). Then $y = cx + d$, which graphs as a straight line with slope c and y intercept d. For functions of this type, y increases at a constant rate, decreases at a constant rate, or remains constant as x increases.

Next, assume $a = 0$ (quadratic case). Then $y = bx^2 + cx + d$ is a nonlinear function. The graph of this function is called a *parabola*. Some examples of this type of function are $y = 3x^2$, $y = x^2 - 2x + 7$, $y = -3x^2$, and $x^2 + 3x - 2y + 6 = 0$.

197

Example 1. | Graph and discuss the function $y = x^2$ (quadratic).

Solution:

x	-2	-1	0	1	2
y	4	1	0	1	4

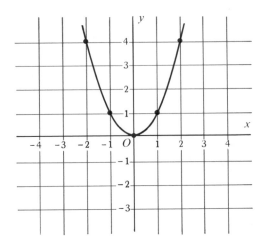

FIGURE 8-1

Discussion: $b = 1$, $c = 0$, and $d = 0$. For positive values of x, y increases at an increasing rate as x increases. The graph is a parabola opening upward with *vertex* at the origin.

Example 2. | Graph and discuss the function $y = x^2 + 3x$ (quadratic).

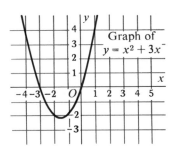

Graph of
$y = x^2 + 3x^-$

FIGURE 8-2

Discussion: $b = 1$, $c = 3$, and $d = 0$. The graph is a parabola opening upward with vertex at $x = -\frac{3}{2}$ and $y = -\frac{9}{4}$. For $x < -\frac{3}{2}$, y decreases at a decreasing rate. For $x > -\frac{3}{2}$, y increases at an increasing rate as x increases. This function is concave upward for all values of x. The concept of concavity is developed in Sec. 10-2.

Example 3. | Graph and discuss the function $y = -x^2 + 3x + 2$ (quadratic).

Solution:

x	-1	0	1	2	3
y	-2	2	4	4	2

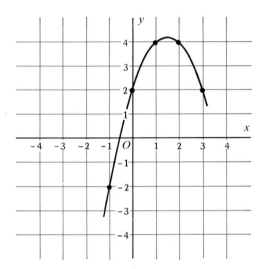

F I G U R E   8-3

Discussion: $b = -1$, $c = 3$, and $d = 2$. The graph is a parabola opening downward with vertex at $x = \frac{3}{2}$ and $y = 4\frac{1}{4}$.

Finally, we return to the general case under consideration, $y = ax^3 + bx^2 + cx + d$ (cubic case).

Example 4. | Graph and discuss the function $y = x^3$ (cubic).

Solution:

x	-2	-1	0	1	2	3
y	-8	-1	0	1	8	27

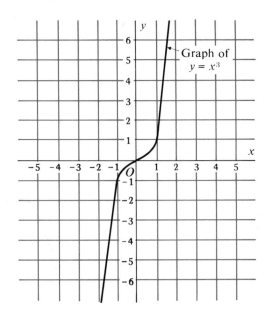

FIGURE 8-4

Discussion: $a = 1, b = c = d = 0$. For $x > 0$, y increases at an increasing rate. For $x < 0$, y increases at a decreasing rate as x increases. This function is concave upward for $x > 0$ and concave downward for $x < 0$.

Example 5. | Graph and discuss the function $y = x^3 + 2x^2$ (cubic).

Solution:

x	-3	-2	$-4/3$	-1	0	1
y	-9	0	$32/27$	1	0	3

Discussion: $a = 1$, $b = 2$, and $c = d = 0$. This function has a relative maximum at $x = -\frac{4}{3}$ and a relative minimum at $x = 0$. The graph is concave downward for $x < -\frac{2}{3}$ and concave upward for $x > -\frac{2}{3}$. The point $x = -\frac{2}{3}$, $y = \frac{16}{27}$ is an inflection point. The concepts of *relative maximum* and *relative minimum* are defined in Sec. 10-1. The term *inflection point* is defined in Sec. 10-2.

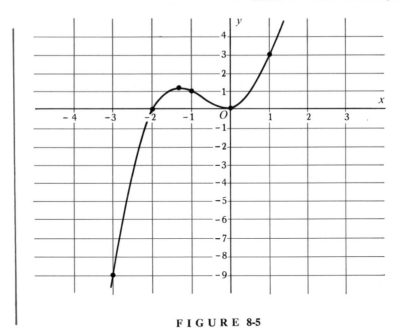

F I G U R E 8-5

The graph of $y = a/(x - b) + c$, where a, b, and c are constants, is called a *hyperbola*.

Example 6.   Graph and discuss the function $y = 2/(x - 3)$.

Solution:

x	3	3.01	4	5	7	2.99	2	1	0	−1
y	—	200	2	1	0.5	−200	−2	−1	−2/3	−0.5

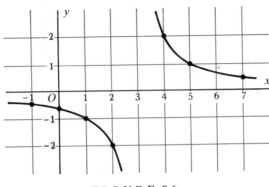

F I G U R E 8-6

201

Discussion: $a = 2$, $b = 3$, and $c = 0$. The vertical line $x = 3$ has a special relationship to the graph of this function. It is called a *vertical asymptote*. It is possible to find points on the graph that are arbitrarily close to this vertical asymptote by choosing x close, but not equal, to 3. Note that y is undefined for $x = 3$. The horizontal line $y = 0$ has a similar relationship to the graph. It is called a *horizontal asymptote*.

Example 7.   Express $(x - 3)(y - 4) = 2$ in the form $y = a/(x - b) + c$.

Solution:

$$y - 4 = \frac{2}{x - 3}$$

$$y = \frac{2}{x - 3} + 4$$

Example 8.   Graph and discuss the function of Example 7.

Solution:

x	-1	1	2	3	4	5	7
y	3.5	3	2	—	6	5	4.5

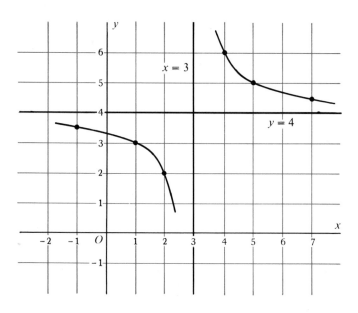

F I G U R E 8-7

Discussion: $a = 2$, $b = 3$, and $c = 4$. The line $x = 3$ is a vertical asymptote. The line $y = 4$ is a horizontal asymptote. y is undefined at $x = 3$.

PROBLEMS

1. Graph the following straight lines:
   (a) $y = 2x - 3$
   (b) $y = -\frac{1}{2}x + 4$
   (c) $2x + 3y - 6 = 0$
2. Graph the following functions of the form
   $y = bx^2 + cx + d$ (quadratic):
   (a) $y = 3x^2$
   (b) $y = x^2 - 3x$
   (c) $y = x^2 + 3x$
   (d) $y = x^2 + 3x + 4$
3. Find the function of the form $y = bx^2 + cx + d$ whose graph passes through the following triple of points: $A(0, 3)$, $B(1, 3)$, and $C(2, -1)$.
4. Graph the following functions of the form
   $y = ax^3 + bx^2 + cx + d$ (cubic):
   (a) $y = -x^3$
   (b) $y = x^3 - 2x^2$
   (c) $y = x^3 + 2x^2 + 2$
   (d) $y = x^3 + 6x$
   (e) $y = x^3 - 6x$
   (f) $y = -x^3 + 6x$
5. Find the function of the form $y = ax^3 + bx^2 + cx + d$ whose graph passes through the following four points: $A(0, 2)$, $B(1, 0)$, $C(2, 8)$, and $D(-1, 2)$.
6. Graph the following functions of the form $y = a/(x - b) + c$:
   (a) $y = 2/x$
   (b) $y = 2/(x + 3)$
   (c) $y = 2/x + 4$
   (d) $y = -2/x + 4$

8-2 RATE OF CHANGE OF A FUNCTION

In this section we begin the study of differential calculus. The notion of *derivative* is the central concept of this chapter. It is defined analytically and interpreted geometrically. The geometric interpretation of the derivative will help the reader gain intuitive insights into this important mathematical concept.

Historically, the derivative has been applied in many areas of study such as physics, engineering, economics, etc. In keeping with the purpose of this text we illustrate the use of the derivative through business and economic applications.

We will begin this section by defining the concept of the *average rate of change of a function between two points.*

DEFINITION 8.1.   *Let $y = f(x)$ and let $A = (x_1, y_1)$ and $B = (x_2, y_2)$ be two points on the graph of $y = f(x)$. Then the average rate of change of*

203

$f(x)$ between A and B is defined to be the ratio $R_f(A, B) = (y_2 - y_1)/(x_2 - x_1)$.

Example 1.

Let $f(x) = x^2 + 3x - 3$, $A = (1, 1)$, and $B = (2, 7)$. Find $R_f(A, B)$.

Solution:

$x_1 = 1$, $x_2 = 2$, $y_1 = 1$, and $y_2 = 7$
$R_f(A, B) = (7 - 1)/(2 - 1)$
$\qquad\quad = 6/1$
$\qquad\quad = 6$

Recall the definition of the slope of a straight line. We see immediately that $R_f(A, B)$ is the slope of the line that passes through the points A and B. This statement is illustrated in Fig. 8-8.

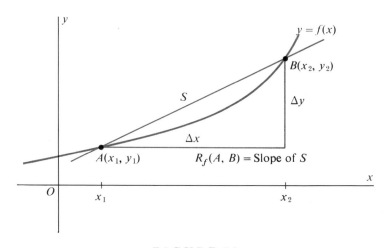

FIGURE 8-8

Expressions such as $x_2 - x_1$, $y_2 - y_1$, etc. occur so often in the study of calculus that a common symbol is used to denote all such differences.

DEFINITION 8.2.   *Let q_1 and q_2 be any pair of real numbers. Then $\Delta q = q_2 - q_1$, where the symbol Δ is the Greek letter delta.*

Using the symbolism introduced above, we have for $y = f(x)$ and $A = (x_1, y_1)$ and $B = (x_2, y_2)$ that $R_f(A, B) = (\Delta y)/(\Delta x)$.

Example 2.

Find the equation of the line passing through the points in Example 1.

Solution: Starting with the form $y = mx + b$ and using the fact that $m = R_f(A, B)$, we have, from Example 1, $y = 6x + b$. Using the point $A = (1, 1)$ to find b gives $1 = 6(1) + b$, or $b = -5$. Therefore, $y = 6x - 5$ is the desired equation.

DEFINITION 8.3.   *Consider the sequence of points B_1, B_2, B_3, . . .   on the graph of $y = f(x)$, as shown in Fig. 8-9. From the diagram it appears that the numbers $R_f(A, B_1)$, $R_f(A, B_2)$, . . .   are all distinct. Now it often happens in such a situation that although these average rates are all different, they get numerically close to some fixed number as the points B_i get closer and closer to the fixed point A. If such a number does exist, it is called the "instantaneous" or "point" or simply the rate of change of $f(x)$ at A.*

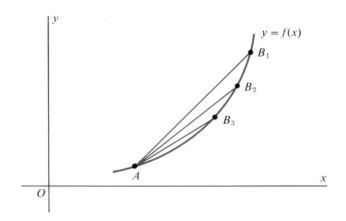

FIGURE 8-9

The problem of determining *the* rate of change of a function (in contrast to an average rate of change) involves the study of the behavior of the ratio $\Delta y/\Delta x$ as the points B_i get closer and closer to A, or equivalently as Δx gets closer and closer to zero. The somewhat imprecise terminology of "getting closer and closer to" will be explained further in the next section.

We use the notation $R_f(A)$, in contrast to $R_f(A, B)$, to denote *the* rate of change of $f(x)$ at the point A.

PROBLEMS

1. Find the average rate of change, $R_f(A, B)$, where $f(x) = 2x^2 - 4x + 2$ and the points A and B are given as follows:
    (a) $A = (-1, 8)$ and $B = (3, 8)$
    (b) $A = (-1, 8)$ and $B = (2, 2)$
    (c) $A = (-1, 8)$ and $B = (1, 0)$
    (d) $A = (-1, 8)$ and $B = (0, 2)$

2. Find an equation for the line which passes through the points given in Prob. 1, part (c).

3. Plot a large graph of $y = x^2$ between $x = 1$ and $x = 2$.

4. Plot the points A, B_1, B_2, B_3, and B_4 on the graph of Prob. 3, where $A = (1, 1)$ and $B_n = (1 + 1/n, [1 + 1/n]^2)$.

5. Draw the straight lines between A and B_1, between A and B_2, between A and B_3, and between A and B_4 on the graph of Probs. 3 and 4.

6. Compute $R_f(A, B_n)$ for $f(x) = x^2$ and A and B_n as in Prob. 4. Do this for $n = 1, 2, 3,$ and 4.

7. Compute $R_f(A, B_n)$ in general (i.e., for any positive integer n). A and B_n are given in Prob. 4, and $f(x) = x^2$.

8. Discuss the behavior of $R_f(A, B_n)$ as n gets very large. Use the result obtained in Prob. 7.

9. Using the result of Prob. 8, try to predict the *point* rate of change of $f(x) = x^2$ at $A = (1, 1)$.

Marginal cost, as it is used in economics, is the change in cost, ΔC, that results from producing one more unit of output. It is the per unit change in cost. Similarly, *marginal revenue* is the per unit change in revenue.

10. Let $C = f(x)$ and $R = g(x)$ be cost and revenue functions, respectively, where x is the level of output.
    (a) Express the marginal cost of the $x + 1$th unit of output using functional notation.
    (b) Let $A = (x, f(x))$ and $B = (x + 1, f(x + 1))$. Show that the marginal cost of the $x + 1$th unit is equal to $R_f(A, B)$.

11. (a) Complete Table 8-1 adapted from hypothetical data by Campbell R. McConnell.[1]

TABLE 8-1

X	C	MC	MR	R	P
0	100				
1	190	90	131	131	−59
2	270	80	131	262	−8
3	340				
4	400				
5	470				
6	550				
7	640				
8	750				
9	880				
10	1030	150			

where X = output MR = price = \$131
C = total cost R = total revenue
MC = marginal cost of xth unit P = profit (or loss,
MR = marginal revenue of xth unit   if negative)

1. Campbell R. McConnell, *Economics*. New York: McGraw-Hill Book Co., Inc., 1966, p. 460.

(b)   At what level would you produce to maximize profit? How are marginal cost and marginal revenue related at this level of output?

12. (a)   Use the hypothetical cost function $C = x^3 - 3x^2 + 3x + 1$ and price = \$76 to construct a table like the one in Prob. 11(a).

(b)   At what level would you produce to maximize profit? How are marginal cost and marginal revenue related at this level of output? Do you think that profit is always maximized when marginal cost equals marginal revenue?

8-3   THE LIMIT CONCEPT

In this section we give a definition of the symbolic statement $\lim_{x \to a} f(x) = L$. This is a complete sentence and is read *as x approaches a, f(x) approaches the limit L*. It should be noted that both a and L are constants. A typical example is $\lim_{x \to 2} f(x) = 4$. No attempt will be made to relate the limit concept to the ratio $\Delta y / \Delta x$ until Sec. 8-4.

DEFINITION 8.4(a).   (*Informal Version*) $\lim_{x \to a} f(x) = L$ *if the values of f(x) get closer and closer to L as x gets close to a.*

Example 1.   Find $\lim_{x \to 2} x^2$.

Solution: Form Table 8-2.

TABLE 8-2

x	$f(x)$
1.9	3.61
1.99	3.9601
1.999	3.996001

Based on the values of this table and Definition 8.4(a), we suspect that $\lim_{x \to 2} x^2 = 4$.

DEFINITION 8.4(b).   (*Modified Version*) $\lim_{x \to a} f(x) = L$ *if (f(x) − L) gets closer and closer to zero as (x − a) gets close to zero.*

Example 2.   Interpret the solution of Example 1 in terms of the modified version of Definition 8.4(b).

Solution:

TABLE 8-3

x	$f(x)$	$x - 2$	$f(x) - 4$
1.9	3.61	−0.1	$3.61 - 4 = -0.39$
1.99	3.9601	−0.01	−0.0399
1.999	3.996001	−0.001	−0.00399

DEFINITION 8.4(c).   (*Mathematical Version*) $\lim_{x \to a} f(x) = L$ *if given any positive real number ϵ no matter how small, there is always another positive number δ depending on the choice of ϵ such that $|x - a| < \delta$ (see note) insures that $|f(x) - L| < \epsilon$.*

The reader should study the three versions of Definition 8.4 from time to time until he is convinced that they all express the same idea. Mathematicians prefer version 8.4(c) because it enables them to give more convincing arguments for theorems about limits.

Note: $|x| = \quad x$ if $x \geq 0$
$\qquad\qquad -x$ if $x < 0$

For example, $|3| = 3, |0| = 0$, and $|-3| = -(-3) = 3$. In other words, $|x|$, read absolute value of x, is always nonnegative.

We now state without proof an important theorem about limits.

THEOREM 8.1.   *If $\lim_{x \to a} f(x)$ and $\lim_{x \to a} g(x)$ both exist, then*

A. $\lim_{x \to a} [f(x) + g(x)] = \lim_{x \to a} f(x) + \lim_{x \to a} g(x)$
B. $\lim_{x \to a} f(x)g(x) = \lim_{x \to a} f(x) \lim_{x \to a} g(x)$
C. $\lim_{x \to a} cf(x) = c \lim_{x \to a} f(x)$, where c is a constant

This theorem can be summarized by the statement that the *limit of a sum* is the *sum of the limits*; the *limit of a product* is the *product of the limits*; and *any constant* can be *taken outside* the *limit symbol*. This theorem is of fundamental importance in the study of calculus.

PROBLEMS

1. Let $f(x) = x^2$. Complete the following table:

x	2.9	2.99	2.999
$f(x)$			

Using the completed table as evidence, what value would you give for $\lim_{x \to 3} x^2$?

2. Complete the table below.

x	$x - 3$	$f(x) = x^2$
3.1		
3.01		
3.001		

Using the completed table as evidence, what value would you give for $\lim_{x \to 3} x^2$?

3. Using the information given in Prob. 2, complete the table below.

x	$x - 3$	$f(x) - L$
3.1		
3.01		
3.001		

4. Complete the table below for $f(x) = x^2 + 2x$.

x	$f(x)$
1.1	
1.01	
1.001	

    What value would you give for $\lim_{x \to 1} (x^2 + 2x)$?

5. Complete the following table for $\lim_{x \to 1} (x^2 + 2x) = 3$, where $a = 1$ and $L = 3$.

x	$f(x)$	$(x - a)$	$(f(x) - L)$
1.1			
1.01			
1.001			

6. Describe the statement $\lim_{x \to 1} (x^2 + 2x) = 3$ in words. Use the modified version of Definition 8.4(b).

7. Set up a table which could be used as evidence for the statement $\lim_{x \to 4} x^2 = 16$.

8. Show that $\lim_{x \to a} (x + b) = a + b$.

9. Use Theorem 8.1 and the result of Prob. 8 to show that $\lim_{x \to a} x^2 = a^2$.

10. Find $\lim_{x \to 3} (x^2 + 3x + 6)$.

11. Find $\lim_{x \to 0} (x^2 - 2x + 3)$.

12. Find $\lim_{\Delta x \to 0} [3a^2 + 3a(\Delta x) + (\Delta x)^2]$.

8-4 DEFINITION OF THE DERIVATIVE

Combining the symbolism of Sec. 8-3 with the definition of the rate of change of a function given in Definition 8-1, we can set forth the following statement. The *rate of change* of $f(x)$ at A is given by $\lim_{\Delta x \to 0} (\Delta y)/(\Delta x)$, where A, Δx, and Δy are as shown in Fig. 8-10.

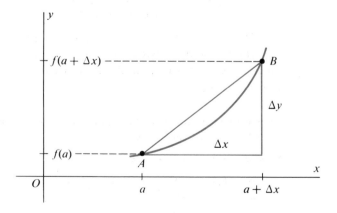

FIGURE 8-10

DEFINITION 8.5. *The derivative of the function $y = f(x)$ at $x = a$ is defined to be* $\lim_{\Delta x \to 0} \dfrac{f(a + \Delta x) - f(a)}{\Delta x}$. *This limit is denoted by the symbol $f'(a)$.*

A function $y = f(x)$ is said to be *differentiable* at $x = a$ if the derivative of $f(x)$ exists at $x = a$. A function $y = f(x)$ is said to be *differentiable on an interval* $a < x < b$ if $f(x)$ is differentiable at each point of this interval.

The reader should gain considerable insight into the concept of the derivative by studying the following numerical example.

For $y = 3x^2 + 4x + 5$, we can form the following table, where $a = 2$ and Δx takes on the values 1, 0.5, 0.01, and 0.001.

TABLE 8-4

Δx	$a = x_1$	$x_2 = x_1 + \Delta x$	$y_1 = f(x_1)$	$y_2 = f(x_2)$	Δy	$\Delta y / \Delta x$
1	2	3	25	44	19	19
0.5	2	2.5	25	33.75	8.75	17.5
0.01	2	2.01	25	25.1603	0.1603	16.03
0.001	2	2.001	25	25.016003	0.016003	16.003

Analysis: (from top to bottom using the data from Table 8-4)

    (a) Δx approaches zero.
    (b) x_1 is fixed.
    (c) x_2 approaches x_1.
    (d) y_1 is fixed at $f(2)$.
    (e) y_2 approaches y_1.
    (f) Δy approaches zero.
    (g) $\Delta y / \Delta x$ does not change much from the third entry on and appears to approach 16.

The fact that the ratio $\Delta y / \Delta x$ seems to approach a definite number even though both Δx and Δy are approaching zero is of utmost significance. This number is called the derivative of the function at $x = a$ and is denoted by $f'(a)$.

Example 1.   Show without the use of a table that the derivative of the function $y = 3x^2 + 4x + 5$ at $x = 2$ is in fact 16.

Solution: $f(x) = 3x^2 + 4x + 5$ and $a = 2$.

$$\frac{\Delta y}{\Delta x} = \frac{f(a + \Delta x) - f(a)}{\Delta x} = \frac{f(2 + \Delta x) - f(2)}{\Delta x}$$

$$= \frac{3(2 + \Delta x)^2 + 4(2 + \Delta x) + 5 - [3(4) + 4(2) + 5]}{\Delta x}$$

$$= \frac{3(4 + 4\,\Delta x + \Delta x\,\Delta x) + 8 + 4\,\Delta x + 5 - (12 + 8 + 5)}{\Delta x}$$

$$= \frac{12\,\Delta x + 3\,\Delta x\,\Delta x + 4\,\Delta x}{\Delta x}$$

$$\frac{\Delta y}{\Delta x} = 16 + 3\,\Delta x$$

By definition, the derivative in this case is given by $f'(2) = \lim_{\Delta x \to 0} (16 + 3\,\Delta x)$. Now it should be intuitively clear that this limit, and hence $f'(2)$, equals 16.

PROBLEMS

1. Complete the following table for $y = 2x^2 + 3x + 5$.

$a = x_1$	x_2	Δx	y_1	y_2	Δy	$\Delta y/\Delta x$
2	3					
2	2.4					
2	2.02					
2	2.001					

2. Based on the completed table of Prob. 1, what value would you give for $f'(2)$, where $f(x) = 2x^2 + 3x + 5$?

3. Use the method of Example 1 of this section to show that if $f(x) = 2x^2 + 3x + 5$, then $f'(2) = 11$.

4. Repeat Prob. 1 using $y = g(x)$, where $g(x) = x^3 + 2x$, $a = x_1 = 3$, and $x_2 = 4, 3.3, 2.99$, and 3.001.

5. Using the results of Prob. 4, what value would you give for $g'(3)$?

6. Using the method of Example 1 of this section, show that if $g(x) = x^3 + 2x$, then $g'(3) = 29$. [*Hint:* $(a + b)^3 = a^3 + 3a^2b + 3ab^2 + b^3$.]

7. Given $h(x) = x^2 + 3x + 4$, find
   (a) $h'(4)$
   (b) $h'(a)$

8. Complete the following table for $y = \sqrt{x}$:

$a = x_1$	x_2	Δx	y_1	y_2	Δy	$\Delta y/\Delta x$
4	5					
4	3.4					
4	4.1					

[*Hint:* Use logs if necessary.]

9. Using the results of Prob. 8, what value would you give for $f'(4)$ if $f(x) = \sqrt{x}$?

8-5 INTERPRETATIONS OF THE DERIVATIVE

In Sec. 8-2 the notation $R_f(A, B)$ was introduced to denote the average rate of change of $f(x)$ between A and B. We are now ready to interpret the derivative in terms of the average rate of change of a function. Consider the function pictured below.

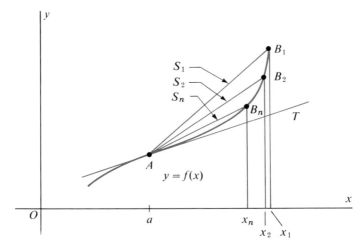

F I G U R E 8-11

Now $R_f(A, B_i) = (\Delta y)/(\Delta x)$ gives the slope of the straight line passing through A and B_i ($i = 1, 2, 3, \ldots, n$). These lines are called *secant lines*. By definition of the derivative, $\lim_{\Delta x \to 0} (\Delta y)/(\Delta x) = f'(a)$. Also, as Δx approaches zero, the points B_i approach the point A. These two statements taken together mean that $f'(a)$ gives the limit of the average rates of change of $y = f(x)$ between A and B_i as B_i approaches A along the graph of the function. This limit is called simply the rate of change of the function at A and is denoted in this text by $R_f(A)$. In summary we have for $y = f(x)$:

RATE OF CHANGE INTERPRETATION OF THE DERIVATIVE

$$R_f(A) = \lim_{B \to A} R_f(A, B)$$

$$= \lim_{\Delta x \to 0} \frac{f(a + \Delta x) - f(a)}{\Delta x}$$

$$= f'(a)$$

Interpreting the derivative geometrically, we see that it gives the slope of the straight line that touches the curve at $A = (a, f(a))$ and occupies the limiting position of the secant lines. The line just described is called the *tangent line* to the curve at A. It is shown in Fig. 8-11 as T. Summarizing these statements we have:

GEOMETRIC INTERPRETATION OF THE DERIVATIVE

Slope of tangent line at $A = \lim_{\Delta x \to 0}$ (slope of secant line)

$$= \lim_{\Delta x \to 0} \frac{f(a + \Delta x) - f(a)}{\Delta x}$$

$$= f'(a)$$

Finally, the two interpretations discussed above are summarized by the following statement. The point rate of change of $y = f(x)$ at the point A equals the slope of the tangent line to the graph of $y = f(x)$ at the point A.

PROBLEMS

1. Consider the function $y = x^2 + 1$.
   (a) Compute the slopes of the secant lines that pass through the point (2, 5) and the points on the graph of $y = x^2 + 1$ with x coordinates 4, 3, 2.5, and 2.1, respectively.
   (b) Sketch all 4 secant lines of (a) on the same coordinate system.

2. In Prob. 1, use the derivative to find the slope of the tangent line to the given curve at the point (2, 5).

$$\left[Hint: \quad f'(x) = \lim_{\Delta x \to 0} \frac{(x + \Delta x)^2 + 1 - (x^2 + 1)}{\Delta x}. \right]$$

   Sketch the tangent line on the coordinate system of Prob. 1(b).

3. Consider the function $y = x^2 + 2$.
   (a) Sketch the curve.
   (b) Compute the slopes of the secant lines that pass through the point (1, 3) and the points on the graph of $y = x^2 + 2$ with x coordinates 3, 2, 1.5, and 1.1, respectively.
   (c) Sketch all 4 secant lines of part (b) on the same coordinate system.

4. Use the derivative to find the slope of the tangent line to the curve $y = x^2 + 2$ at the point (1, 3).

5. Given the equation $y = 6x + 2$.
   (a) Sketch the graph of the equation.
   (b) Compute the slopes of the secant lines that pass through the point (1, 8) and the points on the graph of $y = 6x + 2$ with x coordinates 4, 3, and 2, respectively.

(c)   What can you say about the slopes of the 3 secant lines calculated in (b)?

(d)   Under what conditions do you think this would happen?

6.   Given that $f(x) = x^3$, $A(1, 1)$, and $B = (2, 8)$, find
(a) $R_s(A, B)$
(b) $R_t(A)$ [*Hint:* $(a + b)^3 = a^3 + 3a^2b + 3ab^2 + b^3$.]

7.   Consider a function $f(x)$ with the following geometric properties:
(a)   The slope of the tangent line at A is 4.
(b)   The slope of the secant line passing through A and B is 5. What is the average rate of change of $f(x)$ between A and B? Why?

8.   What is *the* rate of change of $f(x)$ at A for the function described in Prob. 7? Why?

In economics we have the following definition for arc elasticity of demand:

$$\text{elasticity} = \frac{\text{percentage change in quantity demanded}}{\text{percentage change in price}}$$

9.   Given the following for a given commodity:

TABLE 8-5

Price	Quantity demanded
$1.00	10
0.90	12

(a)   Calculate the percentage change in quantity demanded.
(b)   Calculate the percentage change in price.
(c)   Calculate elasticity.
(d)   In general, if the formula for elasticity yields a value greater than one, then demand is said to be elastic. Is demand elastic in this case?
(e)   Did you have any trouble doing the calculations in (a) or (b)? Your answer to (e) should have been yes. In order to calculate a percentage one needs to work from a base. In calculating the percentage change in quantity, we have 2/?, where one could use 10, 12, or $(10 + 12)/2$ in the denominator. The same applies to the calculation of the percentage change in price. This problem is not encountered when calculating the point elasticity using the calculus.

10.   Let the demand law be $x = f(P)$, where $x =$ quantity demanded and $P =$ price. Formulate the definition of elasticity given above using increments and/or functional notation. Use original price and original quantity as the basis of comparison for calculating the percentage change.

11.   Show that the definition of elasticity given above can be expressed symbolically as $e_d = \dfrac{\Delta x}{\Delta P} \cdot \dfrac{P}{x}$.

12.   Let $\Delta P \to 0$ in $e_d = \dfrac{\Delta x}{\Delta P} \dfrac{P}{x}$ of Prob. 11 to obtain

$$e_d = \frac{P}{x} \lim_{\Delta P \to 0} \frac{\Delta x}{\Delta P}$$

13. Let $A = (P, x)$ and $B = (P + \Delta P, x + \Delta x)$, where $x = f(P)$ denotes a demand law. Show that elasticity of demand, e_d, is given by the following formula: $e_d = (P/x)R_f(A, B)$. In economics this quantity is called *arc* elasticity of demand.

14. Use the result of Prob. 13 and let $B \to A$ to obtain $e_d = (P/x)R_f(A)$. In economics this quantity is called *point* elasticity of demand.

8-6 THE DERIVATIVE AS A NEW FUNCTION

It is recalled that a real-valued function $y = f(x)$ associates with each element $x = a$ of the domain a real number that is denoted by $f(a)$. The process of finding the derivative of a function at $x = a$ associates with a another real number called $f'(a)$. Given a function $y = f(x)$, we can define a *new* function by associating with each x the unique real number $\lim_{\Delta x \to 0} \dfrac{f(x + \Delta x) - f(x)}{\Delta x}$ if it exists. This new function is denoted by $f'(x)$ or by y'.

The notation

$$\frac{dy}{dx}, \frac{dy}{du}, \frac{dy}{dt}, \cdots$$

depending on the choice of the independent variable is also in common use.

Example 1. Given the function $f(x) = 2x^2$, find the new function $f'(x)$.

Solution: Using x instead of a, we have

$$f(x + \Delta x) - f(x) = 2(x + \Delta x)^2 - 2x^2$$
$$f(x + \Delta x) - f(x) = 2[x^2 + 2x\,\Delta x + (\Delta x)^2] - 2x^2$$
$$f(x + \Delta x) - f(x) = 2x^2 + 4x\,\Delta x + 2(\Delta x)^2 - 2x^2$$
$$f(x + \Delta x) - f(x) = \Delta x(4x + 2\,\Delta x)$$
$$\frac{f(x + \Delta x) - f(x)}{\Delta x} = 4x + 2\,\Delta x$$

Therefore, the new function $f'(x) = \lim_{\Delta x \to 0} \dfrac{f(x + \Delta x) - f(x)}{\Delta x}$ is found as follows:

$$f'(x) = \lim_{\Delta x \to 0} (4x + 2\,\Delta x)$$

$$f'(x) = 4x$$

The function $f'(x) = \lim_{\Delta x \to 0} \dfrac{f(x + \Delta x) - f(x)}{\Delta x}$ is called the *derivative of $f(x)$ with respect to x.* In Example 1 we found that the derivative of $2x^2$ is $4x$. In the next few sections, short-cut formulas are given for finding the derivative of certain important functions.

215

The next example contains numerical evidence for the fact that the derivative of the exponential function $f(x) = e^x$ is also e^x.

Example 2. Find an approximate value for the derivative of $f(x) = e^x$ at $x = 0, 0.2, 0.4, 0.6, 0.8,$ and 1.0.

Solution: Choosing $\Delta x = 0.01$ and using a table of exponentials, we have

TABLE 8-6

$x = a$	Δx	$y_1 = f(a)$	$y_2 = f(a + \Delta x)$	Δy	$\Delta y / \Delta x$
0	0.01	1	1.0101	0.0101	1.01
0.2	0.01	1.2214	1.2337	0.0123	1.23
0.4	0.01	1.4918	1.5068	0.0150	1.50
0.6	0.01	1.8221	1.8404	0.0183	1.83
0.8	0.01	2.2255	2.2479	0.0224	2.24
1.0	0.01	2.7183	2.7456	0.0273	2.73

Analysis: For emphasis we repeat columns one, three, and six. Note that the same value of Δx is used each time to obtain a single approximation for the different values of x.

TABLE 8-7

a	$y = e^a$	$\Delta y / \Delta x$
0	1	1.01
0.2	1.2214	1.23
0.4	1.4918	1.50
0.6	1.8221	1.83
0.8	2.2255	2.24
1.0	2.7183	2.73

Remark: Column three gives an approximate value for the derivative of $y = e^x$ at $x = 0, 0.2, 0.4, 0.6, 0.8,$ and 1.0. Column two gives the value of $y = e^x$ itself at these x values. The fact that the corresponding entries in these two columns are nearly equal suggests that the derivative of $y = e^x$ is e^x. The reader will find in Sec. 8-8 that this is indeed the case.

PROBLEMS

1. Given the function $f(x) = x^2 + 3x + 4$, find
   (a) $f'(x)$
   (b) $f'(a)$
   (c) $f'(4)$

2. Using the function given in Prob. 1, find
   (a) The slope of the tangent to $y = f(x)$ at the point $(1, 8)$.
   (b) The slope of the secant line passing through $(1, 8)$ and $(2, 14)$.

3. Find an equation for the tangent line in Prob. 2(a).

4. Find $\dfrac{dy}{dx}$ for the following functions:

   (a) $y = 4$ (d) $y = x^3$
   (b) $y = x$ (e) $y = x^4$
   (c) $y = x^2$

   [*Hint:* $(x + \Delta x)^4 = (x + \Delta x)(x + \Delta x)^3$ and $(a + b)^3$
   $= a^3 + 3a^2b + 3ab^2 + b^3$.]

5. Find $\dfrac{dy}{du}$ for the following functions:

   (a) $y = u^2$ (c) $y = u^2 + 2u$
   (b) $y = u + 3$ (d) $y = 4 - u^2$

6. Given that $y = f(x)$, list two symbols that have the same meaning as y'.

7. Given that $w = g(u)$, list two symbols that have the same meaning as w'.

8. Given that $f'(a) = \lim_{\Delta x \to 0} \dfrac{(-2 + \Delta x)^3 - (-2)^3}{\Delta x}$, find $f(x)$ and a.

9. From Prob. 14 of Sec. 8-5 we have $e_d = (P/x)R_f(A)$, where $x = f(P)$, $A = (P, x)$, and e_d denotes the point elasticity of demand at P. Using derivative notation, rewrite this formula for point elasticity.

10. Obtain $e_d = \dfrac{P}{x}\left(\dfrac{dx}{dP}\right)$ from Prob. 12 of Sec. 8-5.

11. Find $f'(3)$ by definition if $f(x) = x^2 - 4x + 3$.

8-7 THE POWER RULE AND SOME PROPERTIES OF THE DERIVATIVE

In Sec. 8-6 we defined the derivative of $y = f(x)$ to be

$$\lim_{\Delta x \to 0} \frac{f(x + \Delta x) - f(x)}{\Delta x}$$

and this definition was used to find the derivative either exactly or approximately for some specific functions. We remind the student at this point that, in practice, the procedure for determining the derivative of a function is usually not as lengthy as is indicated by the previous section. This is because there exist many *differentiation formulas* that are quite easy to apply. Some of these will be given in this section.

For reasons that will become clear in Chap. 9, these formulas will be stated in terms of u rather than x.

The first formula that follows directly from the definition of the derivative is

$$\frac{d}{du}(c) = 0 \qquad \textit{where c is any constant} \qquad \text{D-1}$$

217

One of the most useful differentiation formulas is the so-called *power rule:*

$$\frac{d}{du}(u^n) = nu^{n-1} \qquad\qquad \text{D-2}$$

Formula D-2 is valid for any constant *n*. Before giving a proof of D-2 for *n*, a positive integer, we include several examples to illustrate its use.

Example 1. | Differentiate $y = u^3$ with respect to *u*.

Solution:

$$y = u^3$$

$$\frac{dy}{du} = 3u^2$$

Example 2. | Differentiate $y = u^3$ with respect to *u* using the definition of the derivative.

Solution: Let $y = u^3$.

$$\Delta y = (u + \Delta u)^3 - u^3$$
$$\Delta y = u^3 + 3u^2\,\Delta u + 3u(\Delta u)^2 + (\Delta u)^3 - u^3$$
$$\Delta y = \Delta u[3u^2 + 3u\,\Delta u + (\Delta u)^2]$$

$$\frac{\Delta y}{\Delta u} = 3u^2 + 3u\,\Delta u + (\Delta u)^2$$

$\text{Limit}_{\Delta u \to 0} \dfrac{\Delta y}{\Delta u} = 3u^2$. Therefore,

$$\frac{dy}{du} = 3u^2 \qquad\qquad \textit{as was found in Example 1 using the power rule}$$

Example 3. | Differentiate $y = \sqrt{u^3}$ by the power rule.

Solution: First of all, from algebra we have $\sqrt{u^3} = u^{3/2}$.

$$y = u^{3/2}$$

$$\frac{dy}{du} = \frac{3}{2}u^{1/2} = \frac{3}{2}\sqrt{u}$$

Example 4. | Differentiate $y = \dfrac{1}{u^4}$ with respect to *u*.

Solution: First of all, $y = u^{-4}$.

$$\frac{dy}{du} = -4u^{-4-1}$$

$$= -4u^{-5}$$

$$= -\frac{4}{u^5} \qquad\qquad \textit{by laws of exponents}$$

The proof of the power rule for the special case where *n* is a positive whole number is not difficult and this proof will follow.

Proof: Let $y = u^n$, where n is a positive integer. Then

$$\Delta y = (u + \Delta u)^n - u^n$$

$$\Delta y = u^n + nu^{n+1}\Delta u + k_2 u^{n-2}(\Delta u)^2 + k_3 u^{n-3}(\Delta u)^3 + \cdots$$
$$\qquad\qquad + (\Delta u)^n - u^n \qquad \text{\textit{by the binomial theorem of algebra}}^2$$

$$\Delta y = \Delta u\,[nu^{n-1} + k_2 u^{n-2}\,\Delta u + k_3 u^{n-3}(\Delta u)^2 + \cdots + (\Delta u)^{n-1}]$$

$$\frac{\Delta y}{\Delta u} = nu^{n-1} + k_2 u^{n-2}\,\Delta u + k_3 u^{n-3}(\Delta u)^2 + \cdots + (\Delta u)^{n-1}$$

$\text{Limit}_{\Delta u \to 0} \dfrac{\Delta y}{\Delta u} = nu^{n-1}$ as was to be proved. Therefore,

$$\frac{dy}{du} = nu^{n-1}$$

We emphasize the fact that even though we have proven this result for n, a positive integer, the power rule is valid for *any* real number. This fact is proven in more extensive books on calculus.

The theorem that follows from the definition of the derivative and limit, Theorem 8.1, is extremely important. A proof of Theorem 8.2(B) can be found in Sec. 9-3. The proof of part (A) is left as an exercise in the problems of Sec. 9-3.

THEOREM 8.2.   *Let $f(u)$ and $g(u)$ be differentiable functions and c be a constant. Then*

A. $\dfrac{d}{du}\,cf(u) = c\dfrac{d}{du}\,f(u)$

B. $\dfrac{d}{du}\,[f(u) + g(u)] = \dfrac{d}{du}\,f(u) + \dfrac{d}{du}\,g(u)$

In words, Theorem 8.2(A) states that a constant can be taken "outside" the derivative symbol. Furthermore, by repeated application of Theorem 8.2(B), we see that the derivative of a finite sum of functions equals the sum of the derivatives of these functions. Finally, we caution the reader that the derivative of a product of functions *does not equal* the product of the derivatives.

Example 5. | Differentiate the two functions $y = 3u^4$ and $y = 3$.

---

2. The binomial theorem. For any positive integer n,

$$(a + b)^n = k_0 a^n + k_1 a^{n-1} b + k_2 a^{n-2} b^2 + \cdots + k_j a^{n-j} b^j + \cdots + nab^{n-1} + b^n$$

where

$$k_j = \frac{n!}{j!(n-j)!} \qquad \text{and} \qquad j! = j(j-1)(j-2)\cdots 2\cdot 1$$

Solution:

$$y = 3u^4$$

$$\frac{dy}{du} = 3\frac{d}{du}(u^4) \qquad \text{\textit{by Theorem 8.2(A)}}$$

$$= 3(4)u^3 \qquad \text{\textit{by D-2}}$$
$$= 12u^3$$

If

$$y = 3$$

then

$$\frac{dy}{du} = 0 \qquad \text{\textit{by D-1}}$$

Note that a constant by itself is treated differently than a constant times a function.

Example 6.   Find the derivative of $y = 4u$ with respect to u.

Solution: Write $y = 4u$ as $y = 4u^1$. By Theorem 8.2(A) and D-2, we have

$$\frac{dy}{du} = 4(1)u^0$$

$$= 4(1)(1) \qquad \text{\textit{since} } u^0 = 1$$

Therefore,

$$\frac{dy}{du} = 4$$

Example 7.   Differentiate $y = 5u^2 + 5u - 7$ with respect to u.

Solution:

$$y = 5u^2 + 5u - 7$$

$$\frac{dy}{du} = 10u + 5 \qquad \text{\textit{by Theorem 8.2(A), (B), D-1, and D-2}}$$

PROBLEMS

1. Find the derivative of $y = 3u^2 - 2u$ by definition.

2. Find the derivative of the two functions $f(u) = 3u^2$, $g(u) = -2u$.

3. Relate the results of Probs. 1 and 2 to Theorem 8.2.

4. Let $y = f(u) = u^3$.

    (a)   Find $\dfrac{dy}{du}$ by the power rule.

    (b)   Use the result in (a) to find $f'(-2)$.

5. Use the appropriate formula to find $\dfrac{dy}{du}$ for the following functions:

   (a) $y = 4$

   (b) $y = u$

   (c) $y = u^2$

   (d) $y = u^4$

   (e) $y = u^5$

   (f) $y = u^{1/3}$

6. Find $\dfrac{dy}{du}$ for the following functions:

   (a) $y = u^{1/2}$

   (b) $y = \sqrt{u}$

   (c) $y = u^{1/3}$

   (d) $y = \sqrt[3]{u}$

   (e) $y = u^{-1/3}$

   (f) $y = \dfrac{1}{\sqrt[3]{u}}$

7. State the power rule for $w = z^k$.

8. Find $\dfrac{dy}{du}$ for the following functions:

   (a) $y = 3u^2$

   (b) $y = 2u + 4$

   (c) $y = u^2 + 10u + 13$

   (d) $y = 4u^{3/2} - 2\sqrt{u}$

9. Find $\dfrac{dy}{du}$ for the following functions:

   (a) $y = 6u^4$

   (b) $y = 5u + 8$

   (c) $y = 4u^2 - 8u + 10$

   (d) $y = 2u^2 + 2u + \sqrt[4]{u}$

10. Find $\dfrac{dy}{du}$ for the following power functions:

    (a) $y = 2u^4$

    (b) $y = 1.3u^{2.7}$

    (c) $y = -0.8u^{-1.4}$

8-8 DIFFERENTIATION OF EXPONENTIAL AND LOGARITHMIC FUNCTIONS

Next we learn how to differentiate $y = \log_a u$.

$$\frac{d}{du}(\log_a u) = \frac{1}{u} \log_a(e) \qquad\qquad \text{D-3}$$

where e is the base of the natural log system. [Recall $e = 2.7183$ to four decimal places.]

Proof:

$$\Delta y = \log_a(u + \Delta u) - \log_a u$$

$$\Delta y = \log_a \frac{u + \Delta u}{u}$$

and

$$\frac{\Delta y}{\Delta u} = \frac{1}{\Delta u} \log_a \left(1 + \frac{\Delta u}{u}\right)$$

$$\frac{\Delta y}{\Delta u} = \log_a \left(1 + \frac{\Delta u}{u} \right)^{1/\Delta u} \qquad \textit{using a property of logs}$$

Now to find the limit of $(\Delta y)/(\Delta u)$ as $\Delta u \to 0$ is by no means a trivial matter in this case. Some progress can be made by the following procedure.

Starting again with $\dfrac{\Delta y}{\Delta u} = \dfrac{1}{\Delta u} \log_a \left(1 + \dfrac{\Delta u}{u} \right)$ and writing $\dfrac{1}{\Delta u} \log_a$

$\left(1 + \dfrac{\Delta u}{u} \right)$ as $\dfrac{u}{u \, \Delta u} \log_a \left(1 + \dfrac{\Delta u}{u} \right)$ leads to $\dfrac{\Delta y}{\Delta u} = \dfrac{1}{u} \log_a \left(1 + \dfrac{\Delta u}{u} \right)^{u/\Delta u}$

Writing $\dfrac{\Delta u}{u} = h$ gives $\dfrac{\Delta y}{\Delta u} = \dfrac{1}{u} \log_a (1 + h)^{1/h}$ since h approaches zero as Δu approaches zero. The converse of this is also true. It follows that the derivative is given by $\dfrac{dy}{du} = \lim_{h \to 0} \dfrac{1}{u} \log_a (1 + h)^{1/h}$. This limit is known to exist and it is denoted by e, the base of the natural log system. In symbols, $e = \lim_{h \to 0} (1 + h)^{1/h}$. The numerical value of this limit correct to four decimal places is $\lim_{h \to 0} (1 + h)^{1/h} = 2.7183$.

Continuing now with the expression for $\dfrac{dy}{du}$, we have

$$\frac{dy}{du} = \frac{1}{u} \lim_{h \to 0} \log_a (1 + h)^{1/h} \qquad \textit{by Theorem 8.1(C) of Sec. 8-3}$$

$$\frac{dy}{du} = \frac{1}{u} \log_a \left[\lim_{h \to 0} (1 + h)^{1/h} \right]$$

$$\frac{dy}{du} = \frac{1}{u} \log_a (e) \qquad \textit{by definition of e}$$

Example 1. Find $\dfrac{dy}{du}$ if $y = \log_2 u$.

Solution:

$$\frac{dy}{du} = \frac{1}{u} \log_2 e$$

Example 2. Find $\dfrac{dy}{du}$ if $y = \log_{10} u$.

Solution:

$$\frac{dy}{du} = \frac{1}{u} \log_{10} e$$

$$= \frac{1}{u} (0.43425)$$

Example 3. Find $\dfrac{dy}{du}$ if $y = \ln u$.

Solution:

$$y = \ln u = \log_e u$$

$$\frac{dy}{du} = \frac{1}{u} \log_e e$$

$$\frac{dy}{du} = \frac{1}{u}$$

We note from Example 3 that the derivative of $y = \ln u$ is simply $\frac{dy}{du} = \frac{1}{u}$. This explains the term "natural" as applied to the natural log system. It is "natural" in the sense that of all the bases a that could be used for a log system, the base e gives the simplest possible derivative formula for $y = \log_a u$,

$$\frac{d}{du}(\ln u) = \frac{1}{u} \qquad\qquad \text{D-4}$$

Finally, we state without proof the formula for the derivative of an exponential function.

$$\frac{d}{du}(a^u) = a^u \ln a \qquad\qquad \text{D-5}$$

Example 4.   Find $\frac{dy}{du}$ if $y = 2^u$.

Solution:

$$\frac{dy}{du} = 2^u \ln 2$$

Example 5.   Find $\frac{dy}{du}$ if $y = 10^u$.

Solution:

$$\frac{dy}{du} = 10^u \ln 10$$

$$= 10^u(2.30259)$$

Example 6.   Find $\frac{dy}{du}$ if $y = e^u$.

Solution:

$$\frac{dy}{du} = e^u \ln e$$

$$\frac{dy}{du} = e^u(1)$$

$$\frac{dy}{du} = e^u$$

We note from Example 6 that the derivative of $y = e^u$ is simply e^u,

$$\frac{d}{du}(e^u) = e^u \qquad\qquad \text{D-6}$$

223

The simplicity of D-6 explains the expression "*the* exponential function" that is used to denote the function e^u.

In particular $\dfrac{d}{dx}(e^x) = e^x$. The reader should check Table 8-7 and the associated remarks of Sec. 8-6 for some numerical evidence of this fact.

PROBLEMS

1. Find $\dfrac{dy}{du}$ for the following functions:

   (a) $y = \log_3 u$ (c) $y = 2^u$
   (b) $y = \log_5 u$ (d) $y = 10^u$

2. Find $\dfrac{dy}{dz}$ for the following functions:

   (a) $y = \ln z$ (c) $y = \log z$
   (b) $y = 4^z$ (d) $y = e^z$

3. Use a property of logarithms to write the following in a different form:

   (a) $\log (1 + h)^h$ (c) $\log_a \left(1 + \dfrac{1}{h}\right)^{1/h}$

   (b) $\ln \left(1 + \dfrac{1}{h}\right)^{1/h}$ (d) $\log_a \left(1 + \dfrac{\Delta u}{u}\right)^{u/\Delta u}$

4. Use logarithms to compute the following:

   (a) $\left(1 + \dfrac{1}{2}\right)^2$ (c) $\left(1 + \dfrac{1}{100}\right)^{100}$

   (b) $\left(1 + \dfrac{1}{10}\right)^{10}$ (d) $\left(1 + \dfrac{1}{1000}\right)^{1000}$

5. Compare your answers for Prob. 4 with the value 2.7183 given for $\lim_{h \to 0} (1 + h)^{1/h}$.

6. Find $\dfrac{dy}{dx}$ for the following functions:

   (a) $y = e^x + \ln x$ (c) $y = x^2 + \log x$
   (b) $y = x^2 + 2x$ (d) $y = \sqrt{x} + 3x + 2$

7. Find $\dfrac{dy}{dx}$ for the following functions:

   (a) $y = 2^x + \log_2 x$ (c) $y = x^{-3} + \ln x$
   (b) $y = x^3 + 3^x$ (d) $y = 2x^{-5/2} - x^{3/2} + 4^x$

The compound interest formula for compounding k times per year at i percent for n years is

$$V_n = P\left(1 + \dfrac{i}{k}\right)^{kn}$$

8. Show that $V_n = P[(1 + i/k)^{k/i}]^{ni}$.

9. Express V_n of Prob. 8 in terms of h, where $h = i/k$, and observe that h approaches zero as k approaches infinity.
10. Use the result of Prob. 9 to show that for continuous compounding

$$V_n = Pe^{ni}$$

11. Find $\dfrac{dy}{du}$ for the following exponential functions:

   (a) $y = 100(1.06)^u$
   (b) $y = 50(1 + 0.08)^u$
   (c) $y = a(1 + r)^u$, where a and r are constants

8-9 GEOMETRIC AND ECONOMIC APPLICATIONS OF THE DERIVATIVE

In Sec. 8-2 we used the notation $R_f(A, B)$ to denote the average rate of change of $y = f(x)$ between two points A and B on the graph of $y = f(x)$ and the notation $R_f(A)$ to denote the rate of change of $y = f(x)$ at the single point A. In terms of limit notation, $R_f(A) = \lim_{B \to A} R_f(A, B)$.

Interpreted geometrically, $R_f(A, B)$ is the slope of the secant line passing through the points A and B whereas $R_f(A)$ is the slope of the tangent to the graph of $y = f(x)$ at A. It should also be recalled that $R_f(A) = f'(a)$, where a is the x coordinate of A.

The notation $f'(a)$ has been used to denote the derivative of $y = f(x)$ evaluated at $x = a$. An alternate notation, which is also useful, is

$$f'(a) = \frac{dy}{dx}\bigg|_{x=a}$$

Example 1. | Find an equation of the line that is tangent to the curve $y = 3x^2$ at the point $A = (2, 12)$.

Solution: The slope $m = R_f(A)$ is given by $f'(2)$.

$$y = 3x^2$$

$$\frac{dy}{dx} = 6x$$

$$f'(2) = \frac{dy}{dx}\bigg|_{x=2} = 6(2) = 12$$

$$m = 12$$

Writing the equation of the tangent line in the form $y = mx + b$, where m is the slope and b is the y intercept, we have

$$y = 12x + b$$
$$12 = 12(2) + b$$
$$b = -12$$

Therefore, $y = 12x - 12$ is an equation of the tangent line.

So far in this section, we have examined the geometric interpretation of the derivative. The derivative can also be interpreted as the *instantaneous* or *point* rate of change of the dependent variable with respect to the independent variable.

Instantaneous rates of change are important in applications of mathematics to economics and business administration.

Examples of this are the concepts of marginal cost and marginal revenue.

In an article entitled "Computer Graphics for Decision Making," Irvin M. Miller writes:

To solve business problems requiring executive decisions, one must define the total problem and then assign a mathematical equation to each aspect of the problem. A composite of all equations yields a mathematical model representing the problem confronting the executive.

Mr. Miller also includes a list of eleven typical parameters used to phrase business problems.

Of these eleven parameters, the following have particular significance in this text: marginal cost (*MC*), marginal revenue (*MR*), total cost, and total revenue.[3]

Let $C = f(x)$ be a total cost function. Then the first derivative, $f'(x)$, is called the *marginal cost function*. We use the notation *MC* to denote the marginal cost function that is derived from the total cost function $C = f(x)$. In symbols, we have $MC = f'(x)$. The marginal cost at a particular point $x = a$ will be denoted by $MC \mid_{x=a}$.

Example 2.

Given the total cost function $C = 10(2^x)$, find the marginal cost function and the marginal cost at $x = 1$.

Solution:

$$C = 10(2^x)$$
$$MC = 10(2^x) \ln 2$$
$$MC = 10(2^x)0.69315$$

The marginal cost function is $6.9315(2^x)$.
Marginal cost at $x = 1$ is given by $6.9315(2^1) = 13.863$.

PROBLEMS

1. Find an equation of the line tangent to the curve $y = 2x^2$ at point *A* (3, 18).

2. Find an equation of the line tangent to the curve $y = 2^x$ at point *A* (1, 2).

3. Find an equation of the line tangent to the curve $y = \ln x$ at the point $A(1, 0)$.

---

3. Irvin M. Miller, "Computer Graphics for Decision Making," *Harvard Business Review*, 47, p. 124.

4. Given the total cost function $C = 3^x$, find the marginal cost function and the marginal cost at $x = 1$.

5. Given the total cost function $C = x^3$, find the marginal cost function and the marginal cost at $x = 4$.

The remaining problems in this set are based on the concept of elasticity. We quote Michael J. Brennan, *Preface to Econometrics*, for a definition and a brief description of this concept[4]:

One extremely important measure employed in economic theory is elasticity. Textbooks on economic theory define *price elasticity* of demand as the percentage change in the quantity of a good demanded in response to a percentage change in its price.

He then defines *elasticity of the function $f(x)$* as $e = \dfrac{dy}{dx} \cdot \dfrac{x}{y}$.

6. Consider the demand function $y = 100 - 15x$, where x denotes the price and y denotes the quantity demanded. Determine the elasticity at $x = 2$, $x = 4$, and at $x = 6$.

7. Determine the elasticity of $f(x) = 24/x^4$.

8. Show that if $y = A/x^n$, where A and n are constants, then the elasticity, e, is given by $e = -n$.

Typically, one expects *demand*, x, for a product to decrease as the price, P, increases. Some demand laws frequently encountered in the literature are listed below.

$$x = \frac{a - P}{b} \tag{1}$$

$$x = \frac{a}{P + c} - b \tag{2}$$

$$x = \sqrt{\frac{a - P}{b}}, \qquad \textit{where a, b, and c are positive constants} \tag{3}$$

9. The above demand laws (1)–(3) are given in the form $x = f(P)$. For each of these demand laws express P as a function of x, i.e., in the form $P = g(x)$.

10. Illustrate (1) graphically with $a = 10$ and $b = 1$. Label the vertical axis P and the horizontal axis x.

11. By definition, the total revenue R received from x units of a product sold at price P is given by the formula $R = Px$. Using the results of Prob. 9, determine the total revenue as a function of x for each of the demand laws (1)–(3).

12. Determine MR, the marginal function, for demand laws (1) and (2), where $MR = \dfrac{dR}{dx}$.

---

4. Michael J. Brennan, *Preface to Econometrics*. Cincinnati, Ohio: South-Western Publishing Co., 1960, pp. 134–139.

Consider the following types of cost functions:

$$C = ax + b \qquad\qquad linear \qquad\qquad\qquad (1)$$

$$C = ax^2 + bx + c \qquad\qquad quadratic \qquad\qquad (2)$$

$$C = ax^3 - bx^2 + cx + d \qquad cubic \qquad\qquad\qquad (3)$$

$$C = ae^{bx} \qquad\qquad\qquad exponential \qquad\qquad (4)$$

where a, b, c, and d are positive constants.

13. Let $a = 1$, $b = 3$, $c = 3$, and $d = 1$ in (3) of Prob. 12.
    (a) Graph the resulting cost function, labelling the vertical axis C.

    (b) Find the marginal cost function, $MC = \dfrac{dC}{dx}$.

    (c) Graph the marginal cost function of (b), labelling the vertical axis MC.

14. Find $MC = \dfrac{dC}{dx}$ for the cost functions (1), (2), and (3). If price is denoted by P and output is denoted by x, then elasticity of demand, e_d, is given by the formula

$$e_d = \frac{dx}{dP} \cdot \frac{P}{x}$$

15. Obtain a formula for elasticity of demand, e_d, for Demand Law 1, $x = (a - P)/b$.

NINE

Additional differentiation techniques and applications

9-1 THE BEHAVIOR OF THE DEPENDENT VARIABLE IN A DIFFERENTIABLE FUNCTION

The first part of this chapter is devoted to the study of additional differentiation techniques. The proofs of some of the important formulas in this chapter are based on the fact that for a differentiable function $y = f(x)$, Δy approaches zero as Δx approaches zero. This theorem is stated and proved next.

THEOREM 9.1. *Let $y = f(x)$ be a function that is differentiable at $x = a$. Then $\lim_{\Delta x \to 0} [f(a + \Delta x) - f(a)] = 0$, i.e., $\lim_{\Delta x \to 0} \Delta y = 0$.*

Before giving a proof of this important theorem, we give a numerical example to illustrate it.

Example 1. Let $y = f(x) = x^2$. Determine the value of Δy at $x = 2$ for $\Delta x = 0.1$, $\Delta x = 0.01$, and $\Delta x = 0.001$.

Solution:

$$y = x^2$$

$$\frac{dy}{dx} = 2x$$

At $x = 2$,

$$\frac{dy}{dx} = 2(2)$$

$$= 4$$

Hence, by direct calculation we see that $y = x^2$ is differentiable at $x = 2$. Sample calculation for $\Delta x = 0.01$:

$$f(2 + 0.01) = f(2.01)$$
$$= (2.01)^2$$
$$= 4.0401$$
$$f(2) = 4$$

Therefore, $\Delta y = 0.0401$ when $\Delta x = 0.01$.
In a similar manner the reader can calculate Δy for $\Delta x = 0.1$ and 0.001.

x	Δx	Δy
2	0.1	0.41
2	0.01	0.0401
2	0.001	0.004001

Note that Δy tends toward zero as Δx takes on values 0.1, 0.01, and 0.001, respectively.

Proof of Theorem 9.1:   Let $y = f(x)$ be differentiable at $x = a$.

Consider the identity $\Delta y = \dfrac{\Delta x}{\Delta x} \Delta y$, $\Delta x \neq 0$. Applying Theorem 8.1(B), we have $\lim_{\Delta x \to 0} \Delta y = \lim_{\Delta x \to 0} \Delta x \lim_{\Delta x \to 0} \dfrac{\Delta y}{\Delta x}$ at $x = a$. Since $f(x)$ is differentiable at $x = a$, $\lim_{\Delta x \to 0} \dfrac{\Delta y}{\Delta x}$ exists and equals the real number $f'(a)$. Therefore, $\lim_{\Delta x \to 0} \Delta y = \lim_{\Delta x \to 0} \Delta x f'(a)$
$$= 0 f'(a)$$
$$= 0$$

A function with the property that $\lim_{\Delta x \to 0} [f(a + \Delta x) - f(a)] = 0$ is said to be *continuous* at $x = a$. In words, a function $y = f(x)$ is continuous at $x = a$ if "small" deviations in x from $x = a$ result in "small" deviations in y from $y = f(a)$. Continuity at $x = a$ can also be described briefly by the statement that $f(x)$ is continuous at $x = a$ if a is in the domain of f and $\lim_{x \to a} f(x) = f(a)$. A function is called *continuous on an interval $a < x < b$* if $f(x)$ is continuous at each point of this interval. The concept of a continuous function is illustrated graphically below.

In terms of the concept of continuity, Theorem 9.1 asserts that if $y = f(x)$ is differentiable at $x = a$, then $y = f(x)$ is also continuous at $x = a$. This is equivalent to the statement that $y = f(x)$ is differentiable at $x = a$ *only if* $y = f(x)$ is continuous at $x = a$. In other words, continuity is a prerequisite, so to speak, for differentiability.

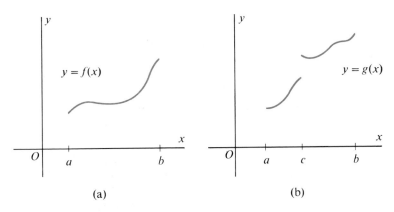

(a)   (b)

This function is continuous on   This function fails to be contin-
the interval $a < x < b$.   uous at $x = c$.

FIGURE 9-1

It is possible for a function to be continuous at a point, but fail to
be differentiable at that point. A simple example of this point is fur-
nished by the function $y = |x|$, where $|x|$ is called the absolute value of
x. A graph of $y = |x|$ is shown below.

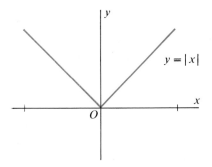

FIGURE 9-2

This function is continuous at $x = 0$, but fails to have a derivative at
$x = 0$.

Example 2. | Let $y = f(u(x))$, where $u(x)$ is differentiable at $x = a$ and $f(x)$ is differentiable
at $u(a)$. Show that Δy approaches zero as Δx approaches zero at $x = a$.

Solution: By Theorem 9.1, Δu approaches zero as Δx approaches zero.
But $y = f(u)$. Therefore, again by Theorem 9.1, Δy approaches zero as Δu
approaches zero. Combining these two statements, we have the result: Δy
approaches zero as Δx approaches zero at $x = a$.

PROBLEMS

1. Let $y = x^3$. Determine the value of Δy at $x = 1$ for the following values of Δx:

   (a) $\Delta x = 0.1$ (c) $\Delta x = 0.001$
   (b) $\Delta x = 0.01$ (d) $\Delta x = 0.0001$

2. Repeat Prob. 1 if $x = 1$ is changed to $x = 2$.

3. Are the results of Probs. 1 and 2 to be expected? Why?

4. Let $f(x) = x^2$. Find $y = f(g(x))$ for the following functions:

   (a) $g(x) = x$ (d) $g(x) = 2 - x^3$
   (b) $g(x) = x^2$ (e) $g(x) = e^x$
   (c) $g(x) = x^2 + 4$ (f) $g(x) = 2^x$

5. Let $f(x) = e^x$. Find $y = f(g(x))$ for the following functions:

   (a) $g(x) = x$ (c) $g(x) = x^2 + 4$
   (b) $g(x) = x^2$ (d) $g(x) = -x^2$

6. Let $f(x) = \ln x$, $g(x) = x^2$, and $y = f(g(x))$. Compute Δy at $x = 1$ for the following values of Δx:

   (a) $\Delta x = 1$ (c) $\Delta x = 0.1$
   (b) $\Delta x = 0.2$ (d) $\Delta x = 0.01$

9-2   THE CHAIN RULE

In many cases where a function is defined by a formula, some simpler combination of xs occurs within the main formula. For example, suppose $y = 2^{(x^2)}$. In this case the main formula is $y = 2^u$, where $u = x^2$. If we agree to write 2^u as $f(u)$, then it follows that $y = f(u)$ or, better still, $y = f(u(x))$. Functions of this type are called *composite functions*. Recall Example 2 of Sec. 9-1.

Example 1.   Given that $f(u) = \ln u$, $u(x) = 2^x$, and $y = f(u(x))$, write out y directly in terms of x.

Solution: $y = \ln u$, $u = 2^x$. Therefore, $y = \ln (2^x)$.

An important theorem of calculus called the *chain rule* states that if $y = f(u(x))$, where f and u are differentiable functions, then the derivative of y with respect to x equals the derivative of y with respect to u times the derivative of u with respect to x.

THEOREM 9.2.   *If $y = f(u(x))$, where f and u are differentiable functions, then*

$$\frac{dy}{dx} = \frac{dy}{du}\frac{du}{dx} \qquad\qquad \text{D-7}$$

Before giving the proof of this theorem, we examine its geometric interpretation.

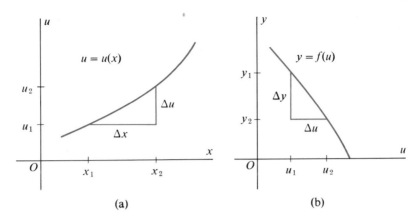

FIGURE 9-3

Since $y = f(u(x))$, a change, Δx, induces a change, Δu, in the function $u = u(x)$. This change in u, in turn, induces a change, Δy, in the function $y = f(u)$. Figure 9-3 should help the reader visualize these statements.

Proof of the chain rule:
Consider the identity

$$\frac{\Delta y}{\Delta x} = \frac{\Delta y}{\Delta x} \frac{\Delta u}{\Delta u}$$

$$= \frac{\Delta y}{\Delta u} \frac{\Delta u}{\Delta x} \qquad \text{algebra of fractions}$$

Taking limits, we have

$$\lim_{\Delta x \to 0} \frac{\Delta y}{\Delta x} = \lim_{\Delta x \to 0} \frac{\Delta y}{\Delta u} \frac{\Delta u}{\Delta x}$$

$$\lim_{\Delta x \to 0} \frac{\Delta y}{\Delta x} = \lim_{\Delta x \to 0} \frac{\Delta y}{\Delta u} \lim_{\Delta x \to 0} \frac{\Delta u}{\Delta x} \qquad \text{by limit Theorem 8.1(B)}$$

$$\frac{dy}{dx} = \lim_{\Delta u \to 0} \frac{\Delta y}{\Delta u} \lim_{\Delta x \to 0} \frac{\Delta u}{\Delta x} \qquad \begin{array}{l} \text{since } \Delta u \text{ approaches zero as } \Delta x \\ \text{approaches zero by Theorem} \\ \text{9.1 and Example 2, Sec. 9-1} \end{array}$$

Therefore,

$$\frac{dy}{dx} = \frac{dy}{du} \frac{du}{dx} \qquad \text{by definition of the derivative}$$

Example 2. | Use the chain rule to find $\dfrac{dy}{dx}$ if $y = (x^2)^{10}$.

Solution: Let $u = x^2$. Then $y = u^{10}$.

233

$$\frac{dy}{dx} = \frac{dy}{du} \cdot \frac{du}{dx} \qquad\qquad \textit{chain rule}$$

$$= 10u^9(2x)$$
$$= 10(x^2)^9(2x) = 10x^{18}(2x) = 20x^{19}$$

Example 3.   Let $y = (x^2)^{10}$. Find $\dfrac{dy}{dx}$ *without* using the chain rule.

Solution:

$$y = (x^2)^{10}$$
$$y = x^{20}$$

$$\frac{dy}{dx} = 20x^{19} \qquad \textit{by D-2}$$

The reader should compare this result with the result in Example 2.

Example 4.   Use the chain rule to find $\dfrac{dy}{dx}$ if $y = e^{bx}$; b is a constant.

Solution: Let $u = bx$. Then $y = e^u$.

$$\frac{dy}{dx} = \frac{dy}{du} \cdot \frac{du}{dx}$$

$$= e^u \frac{d(bx)}{dx}$$

$$= e^{bx}(b)$$

$$\frac{dy}{dx} = be^{bx}$$

Example 5.   Let $y = e^{bx}$. Find $\dfrac{dy}{dx}$ *without* using the chain rule.

Solution:

$$y = e^{bx}$$
$$y = (e^b)^x \qquad\qquad \textit{by E-4}$$
$$y = a^x \qquad\qquad \textit{where } a = e^b$$

$$\frac{dy}{dx} = a^x \ln a \qquad\qquad \textit{by D-5}$$

$$\frac{dy}{dx} = (e^b)^x \ln e^b$$

$$\frac{dy}{dx} = be^{bx} \qquad\qquad \textit{since } \ln e^b = b, \textit{ by definition}$$

$$\frac{dy}{dx} = be^{bx} \qquad\qquad \textit{as found in Example 4}$$

Several examples of functions that cannot be differentiated without using the chain rule are included in Sec. 9-4.

PROBLEMS

1. Use the chain rule to find $\dfrac{dy}{dx}$ for the following functions:

    (a) $y = (x^3)^4$ (c) $y = (\sqrt{x})^6$
    (b) $y = (x^3)^{10}$ (d) $y = (\sqrt[3]{x})^9$

2. Find $\dfrac{dy}{dx}$ for the functions given in Prob. 1 above *without* using the chain rule.

3. Use the chain rule to find $\dfrac{dy}{dx}$ for the following functions:

    (a) $y = e^{2x}$ (c) $y = 2^{4x}$
    (b) $y = e^{5x}$ (d) $y = 3^{5x}$

4. Find $\dfrac{dy}{dx}$ for the functions given in Prob. 3 above *without* using the chain rule.

5. Use the chain rule to find $\dfrac{dy}{dx}$ for the following functions:

    (a) $y = e^{x^2}$ (c) 3^{x^3}
    (b) $y = e^{-x^2}$ (d) $2^{\sqrt{x}}$

6. Use the chain rule to find $\dfrac{dy}{dx}$ for the following functions:

    (a) $y = \ln(x^2)$ (c) $y = \log(x^3)$
    (b) $y = \ln(\sqrt{x})$ (d) $y = \log(x^{3/2})$

7. Find $\dfrac{dy}{dx}$ for the following functions:

    (a) $y = e^{x^2 + 3x}$ (c) $y = (x^3 + 2)^3$
    (b) $y = \ln(x^2 + 4x + 7)$ (d) $y = e^{3x} + \sqrt{x^2 + 4}$

8. Find $\dfrac{dy}{dx}$ for the following functions:

    (a) $y = 2^{x^2} - 3x$ (c) $y = (x^4 - x)^2$
    (b) $y = \log(x^2 - 3x + 2)$ (d) $y = \ln(5x) + \sqrt[3]{x^3 + 8}$

9. Let $f(x) = x^2$ and $u = e^x$.
    (a) Draw the graph of $u = e^x$ from $x = 0$ to $x = 2$.
    (b) Draw the graph of $y = f(u) = u^2$ from $u = 0$ to $u = 10$.
    (c) Show Δx, Δu, and Δy on your graphs. [*Hint:*   See Figure 9-3.]

9-3 SOME GENERAL DIFFERENTIATION FORMULAS

The following general formulas are basic for finding derivatives. The letter c denotes a constant and the letters u and v denote differentiable functions of x.

$$\frac{d}{dx}(cu) = c\frac{du}{dx}$$ D-8

$$\frac{d}{dx}(u + v) = \frac{du}{dx} + \frac{dv}{dx}$$ D-9

$$\frac{d}{dx}(uv) = u\frac{dv}{dx} + v\frac{du}{dx}$$ D-10

$$\frac{d}{dx}\left(\frac{u}{v}\right) = \frac{v\frac{du}{dx} - u\frac{dv}{dx}}{v^2}$$ D-11

According to D-1, the derivative of a constant by itself is zero. In contrast, by D-8 the derivative of a constant times a differentiable function equals the constant times the derivative of the function. In other words, a constant "can be taken outside" of the derivative symbol. We leave the proof of D-8 as an exercise.

Example 1. Find $\frac{dy}{dx}$ if $y = 3x^2$.

Solution:

$$\frac{dy}{dx} = \frac{d}{dx}(3x^2)$$

$$= 3\frac{d}{dx}(x^2) \qquad \text{by D-8}$$

$$= 3(2x) \qquad \text{by D-2}$$

$$= 6x$$

Formula D-9, Theorem 8.1(B), is proven as follows:

Proof:

$$\Delta y = u(x + \Delta x) + v(x + \Delta x) - [u(x) + v(x)]$$
$$\Delta y = u(x + \Delta x) - u(x) + v(x + \Delta x) - v(x)$$
$$\frac{\Delta y}{\Delta x} = \frac{u(x + \Delta x) - u(x)}{\Delta x} + \frac{v(x + \Delta x) - v(x)}{\Delta x}$$
$$\lim_{\Delta x \to 0}\frac{\Delta y}{\Delta x} = \lim_{\Delta x \to 0}\left[\frac{u(x + \Delta x) - u(x)}{\Delta x} + \frac{v(x + \Delta x) - v(x)}{\Delta x}\right]$$
$$= \lim_{\Delta x \to 0}\frac{u(x + \Delta x) - u(x)}{\Delta x} + \lim_{\Delta x \to 0}\frac{v(x + \Delta x) - v(x)}{\Delta x}$$

by Theorem 8.1(A)

$$\frac{dy}{dx} = \frac{du}{dx} + \frac{dv}{dx}$$ *by definition of the derivative*

Example 2. Find the derivative of $y = 4x^3 + x^2$.

Solution: Let $u = 4x^3$ and $v = x^2$. Then $y = u + v$.

$$\frac{dy}{dx} = \frac{du}{dx} + \frac{dv}{dx}$$

$$\frac{dy}{dx} = \frac{d}{dx}(4x^3) + \frac{d}{dx}(x^2) \qquad by\ D\text{-}9$$

$$= 4\frac{d(x^3)}{dx} + \frac{d}{dx}(x^2) \qquad by\ D\text{-}8$$

$$\frac{dy}{dx} = 4(3x^2) + 2x$$

$$\frac{dy}{dx} = 12x^2 + 2x$$

The next example illustrates the fact that a finite sum of functions is differentiated by finding the sum of the derivatives of the individual functions.

Example 3. Find $\frac{dy}{dx}$ if $y = u + v + w$, where w is also a differentiable function of x.

Solution:

$$\frac{dy}{dx} = \frac{d}{dx}(u + v + w)$$

$$= \frac{d}{dx}[(u + v) + w] \qquad by\ A\text{-}3\ (Associative\ Law)$$

$$= \frac{d}{dx}(u + v) + \frac{d}{dx}(w) \qquad by\ D\text{-}9$$

$$\frac{dy}{dx} = \frac{du}{dx} + \frac{dv}{dx} + \frac{dw}{dx} \qquad by\ D\text{-}9$$

Example 4. Find $\frac{dy}{dx}$ if $y = x^4 + x^3 + x^2$.

Solution: Let $u = x^4$, $v = x^3$, and $w = x^2$. Then

$$y = u + v + w \qquad and \qquad \frac{dy}{dx} = \frac{du}{dx} + \frac{dv}{dx} + \frac{dw}{dx}$$

It follows that

$$\frac{dy}{dx} = \frac{d}{dx}(x^4) + \frac{d}{dx}(x^3) + \frac{d}{dx}(x^2)$$

$$\frac{dy}{dx} = 4x^3 + 3x^2 + 2x$$

The proof of the formula for the derivative of a product is as follows:

Proof: Let $y = u(x)v(x)$ or, more briefly, $y = uv$.

$$\Delta y = (u + \Delta u)(v + \Delta v) - uv$$
$$= uv + u\,\Delta v + v\,\Delta u + \Delta u\,\Delta v - uv$$
$$\Delta y = u\,\Delta v + v\,\Delta u + \Delta u\,\Delta v$$

$$\frac{\Delta y}{\Delta x} = u \frac{\Delta v}{\Delta x} + v \frac{\Delta u}{\Delta x} + \Delta u \frac{\Delta v}{\Delta x}$$

$$\lim_{\Delta x \to 0} \frac{\Delta y}{\Delta x} = \lim_{\Delta x \to 0} \left(u \frac{\Delta v}{\Delta x} \right) + \lim_{\Delta x \to 0} \left(v \frac{\Delta u}{\Delta x} \right) + \lim_{\Delta x \to 0} \left(\Delta u \frac{\Delta v}{\Delta x} \right)$$

recalling that the limit of a sum is the sum of the limits.

$$\frac{dy}{dx} = u \lim_{\Delta x \to 0} \frac{\Delta v}{\Delta x} + v \lim_{\Delta x \to 0} \frac{\Delta u}{\Delta x} + \lim_{\Delta x \to 0} \Delta u \lim_{\Delta x \to 0} \frac{\Delta v}{\Delta x}$$

$$\frac{dy}{dx} = u \frac{dv}{dx} + v \frac{du}{dx} + \left(\lim_{\Delta x \to 0} \Delta u \right) \frac{dv}{dx}$$

Since $u(x)$ is differentiable, it follows that $\lim_{\Delta x \to 0} \Delta u = 0$. Recall Example 2 of Sec. 9-1.

Hence, the term $(\lim_{\Delta x \to 0} \Delta u) \dfrac{dv}{dx}$ equals zero, leaving

$$\frac{dy}{dx} = u \frac{dv}{dx} + v \frac{du}{dx}$$

Example 5. Find $\dfrac{dy}{dx}$ if $y = (x^2 + 3)(x^3)$.

Solution: Let $u = x^2 + 3$, $v = x^3$. Then $y = uv$ and $\dfrac{dy}{dx} = u \dfrac{dv}{dx} + v \dfrac{du}{dx}$.

$$\frac{dy}{dx} = (x^2 + 3) \frac{d}{dx}(x^3) + x^3 \frac{d}{dx}(x^2 + 3)$$

$$\frac{dy}{dx} = (x^2 + 3)3x^2 + x^3(2x) \qquad\qquad \text{by D-2, D-7, and D-9}$$

$$\frac{dy}{dx} = 3x^4 + 9x^2 + 2x^4$$

$$\frac{dy}{dx} = 5x^4 + 9x^2$$

Example 6. Find $\dfrac{dy}{dx}$ if $y = xe^x$.

Solution: $y = xe^x$. Let $u = x$, $v = e^x$. Then $y = uv$.

$$\frac{dy}{dx} = u \frac{dv}{dx} + v \frac{du}{dx}$$

$$= x \frac{de^x}{dx} + e^x \frac{d(x)}{dx}$$

$$\frac{dy}{dx} = xe^x + e^x(1) \qquad\qquad \text{by D-6 and D-2}$$

The proof of the formula for the derivative of a quotient is left as an exercise. The following two examples illustrate its use.

Example 7. Find $\dfrac{dy}{dx}$ if $y = \dfrac{x^2}{x^3 + x}$.

Solution: Let $u = x^2$ and $v = x^3 + x$. Then by D-11,

$$\frac{dy}{dx} = \frac{v\dfrac{du}{dx} - u\dfrac{dv}{dx}}{v^2}$$

$$\frac{dy}{dx} = \frac{(x^3 + x)\dfrac{d}{dx}(x^2) - x^2\dfrac{d}{dx}(x^3 + x)}{(x^3 + x)^2}$$

$$= \frac{(x^3 + x)2x - x^2(3x^2 + 1)}{(x^3 + x)^2}$$

$$\frac{dy}{dx} = \frac{2x^4 + 2x^2 - 3x^4 - x^2}{(x^3 + x)^2}$$

$$= \frac{-x^4 + x^2}{(x^3 + x)^2}$$

$$= \frac{x^2(-x^2 + 1)}{x^2(x^2 + 1)^2}$$

$$\frac{dy}{dx} = \frac{1 - x^2}{(x^2 + 1)^2}$$

Example 8. Find $\dfrac{dy}{dx}$ if $y = \dfrac{2^x}{x^2}$.

Solution: Let $u = 2^x$, $v = x^2$.

$$\frac{dy}{dx} = \frac{x^2\dfrac{d}{dx}(2^x) - 2^x\dfrac{d}{dx}(x^2)}{(x^2)^2} \qquad by\ D\text{-}11$$

$$= \frac{x^2 2^x \ln 2 - 2^x 2x}{x^4} \qquad by\ D\text{-}2\ and\ D\text{-}5$$

$$\frac{dy}{dx} = \frac{2^x x(x \ln 2 - 2)}{x^4}$$

$$\frac{dy}{dx} = \frac{2^x(x \ln 2 - 2)}{x^3}$$

PROBLEMS

1. Prove formula D-8.

2. Find $\dfrac{dy}{dx}$ for the following functions:

   (a) $y = 6x^3$ (d) $y = 6(2)^x$
   (b) $y = 3 \log x$ (e) $y = 5e^x$
   (c) $y = 5 \ln x$ (f) $y = 10(3)^x$

3. Find $\dfrac{dy}{dx}$ for the following functions; a, c, and h are constants.

(a) $y = 2x^h$ (c) $y = he^x$
(b) $y = cx^h$ (d) $y = c(a)^x$

4. Differentiate the following functions with respect to x.

(a) $f(x) = 3x^2 + 6$ (d) $f(x) = 2x + 5^x$
(b) $f(x) = 5x^3 + 6x^2 + 6$ (e) $f(x) = x^3 + \ln x$
(c) $f(x) = 4x + e^x$ (f) $f(x) = x^4 + 3x^2 + 5 \log x$

5. Use the product formula to find $\dfrac{dy}{dx}$ for the following functions:

(a) $y = (x^2)(6x)$ (d) $y = x \ln x$
(b) $y = x^3 e^x$ (e) $y = x^2 \log x$
(c) $y = 5(6x^2)$ (f) $y = x^5 (5)^x$

6. Prove formula D-11.

7. Use the quotient formula to differentiate the following functions with respect to x.

(a) $f(x) = \dfrac{3x^2 + 6x}{4}$ (d) $f(x) = \dfrac{\ln x}{3x}$

(b) $f(x) = \dfrac{x^3}{2x^2}$ (e) $f(x) = \dfrac{\log x}{x^2}$

(c) $f(x) = \dfrac{e^x + 4}{4}$ (f) $f(x) = \dfrac{5^x}{6x^3}$

8. Do Prob. 7 without using the quotient formula.

9. Complete Table 9-1.

TABLE 9-1

$f(x)$ (function)	$f'(x)$ (derivative)	$f'(1)$ (derivative evaluated at $x = 1$)
$4\sqrt{x}$		
$2e^{3x}$		
$e^x + e^{-x}$		
$e^x + e^{-2x}$		
$(\ln x)/e^x$		

9-4 SUMMARY OF DIFFERENTIATION TECHNIQUES

Formulas D-1 through D-6 enable us to differentiate some of the most common functions that occur in the application of differential calculus to business and economics.

The following is a complete list of the differentiation formulas used in this text.

Formulas D-8 through D-11 enable us to differentiate sums, products, and quotients of the specific functions covered by D-1 through D-6. The reader will encounter repeated use of D-7, the chain rule.

We now give several illustrative examples, each of which requires two or more of the following formulas for its solution.

D-1 $\dfrac{d}{du}(c) = 0$ *Derivative of a constant*

D-2 $\dfrac{d}{du}(u^n) = nu^{n-1}$ *Power rule*

D-3 $\dfrac{d}{du}(\log_a u) = \dfrac{1}{u}\log_a e$

D-4 $\dfrac{d}{du}(\ln u) = \dfrac{1}{u}$

D-5 $\dfrac{d}{du}(a^u) = a^u \ln a$

D-6 $\dfrac{d}{du}(e^u) = e^u$

D-7 $\dfrac{dy}{dx} = \dfrac{dy}{du}\dfrac{du}{dx}$ *Chain rule*

D-8 $\dfrac{d}{dx}(cu) = c\dfrac{du}{dx}$ *Derivative of a constant times a function*

D-9 $\dfrac{d}{dx}(u+v) = \dfrac{du}{dx} + \dfrac{dv}{dx}$ *Derivative of a sum*

D-10 $\dfrac{d}{dx}(uv) = u\dfrac{dv}{dx} + v\dfrac{du}{dx}$ *Derivative of a product*

D-11 $\dfrac{d}{dx}\left(\dfrac{u}{v}\right) = \dfrac{v\dfrac{du}{dx} - u\dfrac{dv}{dx}}{v^2}$ *Derivative of a quotient*

Example 1.   Find $\dfrac{dy}{dx}$ if $y = \ln x^2$.

Solution: Let $u = x^2$. Then $y = \ln u$.

$\dfrac{dy}{dx} = \dfrac{1}{u}\dfrac{du}{dx}$ *D-4 and chain rule*

$\dfrac{dy}{dx} = \dfrac{1}{x^2}\dfrac{d}{dx}(x^2)$ *substitution*

$$\frac{dy}{dx} = \frac{2x}{x^2} = \frac{2}{x} \qquad D\text{-}2$$

Example 2.   Find $\dfrac{dy}{dx}$ if $y = \sqrt{4 - x^2}$.

Solution: $y = (4 - x^2)^{1/2}$. Let $u = 4 - x^2$. Then $y = u^{1/2}$.

$$\frac{dy}{dx} = \frac{1}{2} u^{-1/2} \frac{du}{dx} \qquad\qquad \textit{D-2 and chain rule}$$

$$\frac{dy}{dx} = \frac{1}{2\sqrt{4 - x^2}} \frac{d}{dx}(4 - x^2) \qquad \textit{substitution, law of exponents}$$

$$\frac{dy}{dx} = \frac{-x}{\sqrt{4 - x^2}} \qquad\qquad \textit{D-1, D-2, D-9}$$

Example 3.   Find $\dfrac{dy}{dx}$ if $y = e^{2x} + x^2$.

Solution:

$$y = e^{2x} + x^2$$

$$\frac{dy}{dx} = \frac{d(e^{2x})}{dx} + \frac{d(x^2)}{dx} \qquad \textit{by D-9}$$

$$\frac{dy}{dx} = 2e^{2x} + 2x$$

$$\frac{dy}{dx} = 2(e^{2x} + x)$$

Example 4.   Find $\dfrac{dy}{dx}$ if $y = 2^{\sqrt{3x+7}}$.

Solution: Let $u = \sqrt{3x + 7}$, then $y = 2^u$.

$$\frac{dy}{dx} = 2^u \ln 2 \frac{du}{dx} \qquad\qquad \textit{D-5 and chain rule}$$

Let $z = 3x + 7$. Then $u = z^{1/2}$ and

$$\frac{du}{dx} = \frac{1}{2} z^{-1/2} \frac{dz}{dx}$$

$$\frac{du}{dx} = \frac{1}{2}(3x + 7)^{-1/2}(3) \qquad \textit{D-2 and chain rule}$$

$$\frac{du}{dx} = \frac{3}{2\sqrt{3x + 7}}$$

$$\frac{dy}{dx} = 2^{\sqrt{3x+7}} \ln 2 \frac{3}{2\sqrt{3x + 7}} \qquad \textit{substitution}$$

Example 5.   Find $\dfrac{dy}{dx}$ if $y = 2(x^2 + 4)$.

Solution:

$$y = 2(x^2 + 4)$$

$$\frac{dy}{dx} = 2\frac{d}{dx}(x^2 + 4) \qquad D\text{-}8$$

$$\frac{dy}{dx} = 2(2x + 0) \qquad D\text{-}1,\ D\text{-}2,\ D\text{-}9$$

$$\frac{dy}{dx} = 4x$$

Example 6. Find $\dfrac{dy}{dx}$ if $y = x^3 e^{2x}$.

Solution: Let $u = x^3$ and $v = e^{2x}$. Then $y = uv$.

$$\frac{dy}{dx} = u\frac{dv}{dx} + v\frac{du}{dx} \qquad D\text{-}10$$

$$\frac{dy}{dx} = x^3\frac{d}{dx}(e^{2x}) + e^{2x}\frac{d}{dx}(x^3) \qquad \text{substitution}$$

$$\frac{dy}{dx} = x^3 e^{2x}2 + e^{2x}3x^2 \qquad D\text{-}2,\ D\text{-}6, \text{and chain rule}$$

$$\frac{dy}{dx} = x^2 e^{2x}(2x + 3)$$

Example 7. Find $\dfrac{dy}{dx}$ if $y = \dfrac{3x^2}{\log_4 x^3}$.

Solution: Let $u = 3x^2$ and $v = \log_4 x^3$.

$$\frac{dy}{dx} = \frac{\log_4 x^3 \dfrac{d}{dx}(3x^2) - 3x^2 \dfrac{d}{dx}(\log_4 x^3)}{(\log_4 x^3)^2} \qquad D\text{-}11$$

Let $z = x^3$. Then

$$\frac{dv}{dx} = \frac{d}{dx}\log_4 z$$

$$= \frac{1}{z}(\log_4 e)\frac{dz}{dx}$$

$$\frac{dv}{dx} = \frac{1}{x^3}\log_4 e \cdot 3x^2$$

$$\frac{d}{dx}(\log_4 x^3) = \frac{3}{x}\log_4 e$$

$$\frac{dy}{dx} = \frac{\log_4 x^3 6x - 3x^2(3/x)\log_4 e}{(\log_4 x^3)^2} \qquad \text{substitution and } D\text{-}2$$

$$\frac{dy}{dx} = \frac{3x(2\log_4 x^3 - 3\log_4 e)}{(\log_4 x^3)^2}$$

243

PROBLEMS

Find the derivatives of the following functions:

1. $y = x^2 + 6x$
2. $y = (x^2 + 4)^5$
3. $y = x^3 + 4$
4. $y = e^{3x}$
5. $y = e^{x^2} + 4x$
6. $y = \ln x^3$ (use chain rule)
7. $y = \ln x^3$ (do not use chain rule)
8. $y = \ln e^x$
9. $y = 6^{\sqrt{2x^2 + 5}}$
10. $y = \dfrac{x + 3}{(x^2 + 4x + 2)^2}$
11. $y = 6(x^2 + 3)^2$
12. $y = e^{3x^2}/5x^3$
13. $y = x/(1 + 2x)$
14. $y = (x + 3)\sqrt{x^2 + 4}$
15. $y = \sqrt{(x + 2)/(x - 3)}$
16. $y = (ax + b)^n$
17. $y = ax^2 + bx + c$
18. $y = (e^{3x} - e^{-3x})/2$

Indicate the derivatives of the following functions in simplified form:

19. $y = [f(x)]^2$
20. $y = f(x)e^{g(x)}$
21. Complete Table 9-2.

TABLE 9-2

Function	$\dfrac{dy}{dx}\Big|_{x=1}$	$\dfrac{dy}{dx}\Big|_{x=2}$
$y = 3$		
$y = \dfrac{x^2}{2}$		
$y = x^{1/3}$		
$y = 2^x$		
$y = e^x$		
$y = xe^x$		
$y = \ln x$		
$y = \log x^2$		
$y = x^2 \ln 2x$		
$y = 2 + 3e^{-4x}$		

9-5 APPLICATIONS OF THE DERIVATIVE

We will begin this section with two examples that require the use of some of the differentiation formulas given in this chapter.

Example 1. Find an equation of the line that is tangent to the curve $y = x^2 + 3x - 3$ at the point $A = (1, 1)$.

Solution: The slope $m = R_f(A)$ is given by $f'(1)$.

$$y = x^2 + 3x - 3$$

$$\frac{dy}{dx} = 2x + 3$$

$$f'(1) = \frac{dy}{dx}\Big|_{x=1} = 2(1) + 3 = 5$$

$$m = 5$$

If we write the equation of the tangent line in the form $y = mx + b$, where m is the slope and b is the y intercept, we have

$$y = 5x + b$$
$$1 = 5(1) + b$$
$$b = -4$$

Therefore, $y = 5x - 4$ is an equation of the line in question.

Example 2. Find an equation of the line tangent to the curve $y = \ln x^2$ at $x = 2$.

Solution: Start with $y = mx + b$ and determine the value of m. We find that m equals $\dfrac{dy}{dx}\Big|_{x=2}$

$$y = \ln x^2$$

$$\frac{dy}{dx} = \frac{1}{x^2} 2x = \frac{2}{x}$$

$$\frac{dy}{dx}\Big|_{x=2} = \frac{2}{2} = 1$$

Therefore, $y = 1x + b$. To solve for b we must substitute values for x and y. If we remember that the tangent line at $x = 2$ touches the curve at the point of tangency, we can get the corresponding y value from the original function $y = \ln x^2$. This gives $y = \ln 2^2$ or $\ln 4$, which is 1.3863.

Solving for b gives

$$y = 1x + b$$
$$1.3863 = 1(2) + b$$
$$b = 1.3863 - 2$$
$$b = -0.6137$$

Therefore, an equation of the tangent line at $x = 2$ is $y = x - 0.6137$.

An important application of calculus to economics is the so-called *marginalist approach* to profit maximization. Using the *marginalist approach* one seeks to maximize the profit of a firm by producing at the level where the rate of change of revenue is equal to the rate of change of cost. These rates are called *marginal revenue* and *marginal cost*. Using calculus notation, we have

$$\text{Marginal revenue} = MR = \frac{dR}{dx}$$

$$\text{Marginal cost} \quad = MC = \frac{dC}{dx}$$

where C = total cost
        R = total revenue
        x = quantity produced

The marginalist approach is discussed in more detail in the next chapter, and the remainder of this section deals with marginal cost and marginal revenue functions.

Example 3.   Given the cost function $C = 2500 + 0.6x$, find the marginal cost of this function at $x = 50$ and at $x = 100$.

Solution:

$$C = 2500 + 0.6x$$

$$MC = \frac{dC}{dx} = 0.6$$

$$\left.\frac{dC}{dx}\right|_{x=50} = 0.6$$

$$\left.\frac{dC}{dx}\right|_{x=100} = 0.6$$

Note that the marginal cost remains constant for all values of x. This is the case because C is a linear function of x.

Example 4.   Given the nonlinear cost function $C = 2500 + 0.6x + \dfrac{1000}{x}$, $45 < x < 1000$, find the marginal cost at $x = 50$ and at $x = 100$.

Solution:

$$C = 2500 + 0.6x + 1000x^{-1}$$

$$\frac{dC}{dx} = 0.6 - 1000x^{-2}$$

$$\frac{dC}{dx} = 0.6 - \frac{1000}{x^2}$$

$$\left.\frac{dC}{dx}\right|_{x=50} = 0.6 - \frac{1000}{2500} = 0.6 - 0.4$$

$$MC\,|_{x=50} = 0.2 \qquad\qquad \textit{by definition of marginal}$$

$$\left.\frac{dC}{dx}\right|_{x=100} = 0.6 - \frac{1000}{10,000} = 0.6 - 0.1 \qquad \textit{cost}$$

$$MC\,|_{x=100} = 0.5 \qquad\qquad \textit{by definition of marginal}$$
$$\textit{cost}$$

Note that the marginal cost varies with the level of production. This dependence of marginal cost on the level of production is typical of nonlinear cost functions.

Two important demand laws are $p = a - bx$ and $p = a/(x + b) - c$, where p denotes price per unit of x and a, b, and c are constants. The revenue functions, which correspond to these demand laws, are $R = ax - bx^2$ and $R = (ax)/(x + b) - cx$, respectively. This follows from the relationship $R = px$.

The following example illustrates the use of the quotient formula to compute the marginal revenue function for one of these functions.

Example 5.   Find the marginal revenue function that corresponds to $R = ax/(x + b) - cx$.

Solution:

$$MR = \frac{(x + b)a - ax(1)}{(x + b)^2} - c$$

$$MR = \frac{a}{x + b} - \frac{ax}{(x + b)^2} - c$$

PROBLEMS

1. Find an equation of the line that is tangent to the curve $y = x^2 - 3x + 3$ at the point $A = (1, 1)$.

2. Find an equation of the line tangent to the curve $y = e^{x^2}$ at $x = 1$.

3. Given the cost function $C = 2500 + 0.4x + (1000/x)$, find the marginal cost at $x = 60$ and at $x = 80$.

4. Find the marginal revenue function that corresponds to the following total revenue functions:
   (a) $R = 3x$ (c) $R = 0.4\sqrt{x}$
   (b) $R = 5x$ (d) $R = 1.3 \ln (x + 1)$

5. Given the total cost function $C = 10 + e^x + \ln x$, find the marginal cost function.

6. Given the cost function $C = x + 6$ and the revenue function $R = 6x - x^2$, find the break-even point or points.

7. Using the functions given in Prob. 6, find the x value for which marginal revenue equals marginal cost.

8. Using the functions given in Prob. 6, find the profit function, where profit = total revenue − total cost.

247

9. Using the profit function of Prob. 8, compute and compare the profits at $x = 2.3$, $x = 2.5$, and $x = 2.6$. Interpret your results with respect to Prob. 7 and the marginalist approach described in this section.

10. Given the total cost function $C = 2x^2 + x + 3$.
    (a) Find the marginal cost function.
    (b) Find the average cost function, i.e., C/x.

11. Find the marginal revenue function that corresponds to the demand law $p = a - bx$.

9-6 DEFINITION AND APPLICATION OF DIFFERENTIALS

In many problems involving functions of the type $y = f(x)$, we are interested in finding the change, Δy, in the dependent variable, y, which results from a small change, Δx, in the independent variable, x. The derivative provides an easy method of approximating this change. To see this we start with the identity

$$\Delta y = \frac{\Delta y}{\Delta x}\, \Delta x \qquad (1)$$

and recall that

$$f'(x) = \lim_{\Delta x \to 0} \frac{\Delta y}{\Delta x}$$

by definition of the derivative. This means that the ratio $\Delta y / \Delta x$ is approximately equal to $f'(x)$ for small values of Δx. Using this approximation in (1) gives

$$\Delta y \approx f'(x)\, \Delta x \qquad (2)$$

where the symbol $\approx$ denotes the expression "is approximately equal to."

A strict equality can be obtained from (2) by introducing a slack variable q,

$$\Delta y = f'(x)\, \Delta x + q \qquad (3)$$

DEFINITION 9.1. *Let $y = f(x)$ be a differentiable function. Then* $dy = f'(x)\, \Delta x$.

If we examine the above definition more closely, we see that $\Delta y = dy + q$, where q is a small quantity if Δx is small. Therefore, the differential, dy, is an approximation for the desired quantity Δy, i.e., Δy equals (approximately) $f'(x)\, \Delta x$ for small Δx. Furthermore, dy is usually easier to calculate than Δy.

Example 1.   Given the linear cost function $C = 2500 + 0.72x$. Calculate both the exact change ΔC and the approximate change dC that result if the production level is changed from $x = 50$ to $x = 100$.

Solution: $C = 2500 + 0.72x$. Evaluating C at $x = 50$ and at $x = 100$, we have

$$C|_{x=50} = 2500 + 36 = 2536$$
$$C|_{x=100} = 2500 + 72 = 2572$$

Therefore, $\Delta C = 2572 - 2536$ and $\Delta C = \$36$.

By definition, $dC = \dfrac{dC}{dx}\bigg|_{x=50}$ times Δx, where $\Delta x = 100 - 50$.

Therefore,

$$dC = (0.72)(50)$$
$$dC = \$36$$

We note that in this case $\Delta C = dC$. This is because linear cost functions have a constant rate of change.

Example 2.   Given the nonlinear cost function $C = 0.1x^2 + 1$, where C is in hundreds of dollars and x is in hundreds of units, calculate both the exact change, ΔC, and the approximate change, dC, that result if the production level is changed from 100 units to 200 units.

Solution:

$$C|_{x=1} = 0.1(1) + 1$$
$$= 1.1$$
$$C|_{x=2} = 0.1(4) + 1$$
$$= 1.4$$
$$\Delta C = 1.4 - 1.1 = 0.3$$
$$\Delta C = \$30$$

$$dC = \frac{dC}{dx}\bigg|_{x=1} \Delta x$$

$$= 0.2x|_{x=1}\,(2 - 1)$$
$$dC = 0.2, \qquad i.e.,\ dC = \$20$$

The fact that dC is not a very accurate approximation of the exact change is because the cost function is nonlinear and Δx is quite large. A smaller Δx is used in the next example.

Example 3.   Repeat Example 2, using a change in the production level of 10 units.

Solution: In this case, $\Delta x = 0.1$, since x is in hundreds of units.

$$\Delta C = 0.1(1.1)^2 + 1 - 1.1$$
$$= 1.121 - 1.1$$
$$\Delta C = 0.021 = \$2.10$$

$$dC = \frac{dC}{dx}\bigg|_{x=1} \Delta x$$

$$= 0.2x|_{x=1}\,(0.1)$$
$$= (0.2)(0.1)$$
$$dC = 0.02 \qquad i.e.,\ dC = \$2.00$$

To see that the approximation in Example 3 is indeed more accurate than the approximation in Example 2, we consider the percentage error involved. By *percentage error* we mean $(\Delta C - dC)/\Delta C$ times 100. The percentage error in Example 2 is 33 percent, whereas in Example 3 it is only 5 percent.

In Definition 9.1, we see that the *differential*, dy, of the dependent variable is defined to be the product of $f'(x)$ and Δx. The exact change in x, i.e., Δx, is called an increment. It is also customary to define the differential dx of the independent variable x to be equal to the increment Δx.

DEFINITION 9.2. *Let $y = f(x)$. Then $dx = \Delta x$.*

Combining Definition 9.1 and Definition 9.2, we can have

$$dy \div dx, \qquad dx = \Delta x \neq 0$$
$$= [f'(x) \, \Delta x] \div \Delta x$$
$$= f'(x)$$

In other words, the symbol $\dfrac{dy}{dx}$ can now be interpreted either as a single symbol denoting $f'(x)$ or as the fraction (the differential of y divided by the differential of x). This dual interpretation is made possible by the above definitions.

Example 4.

Transform the following derivatives into differential form.

(a) $\dfrac{dy}{dx} = 2e^{2x}$

(b) $\dfrac{dR}{dq} = 1 - 0.1q^2$

Solution:

(a) $dy = 2e^{2x} \, dx$
(b) $dR = (1 - 0.1q^2) \, dq$

PROBLEMS

1. Let $y = x^2 + 3x + 7$, $x_1 = 2$, $x_2 = 2.2$.
    (a) Compute Δy.
    (b) Compute dy.

2. Find the exact change in the function $y = x^2 - 4x$ as x changes from $x = 3$ to $x = 3.1$.

3. Use the differential, dy, to approximate the exact change found in Prob. 2.

4. Given the nonlinear cost function $C = 0.2x^2 + 2$, where C is in hundreds of dollars and x is in hundreds of units, compute the following:
    (a) The exact change, ΔC, that results if the production level is changed from 100 units to 105 units.

   (b) The approximate change, dC, if the production level is changed from $x = 100$ to $x = 105$.

5. Define dw, Δw, dz, and Δz for the differentiable function $w = g(z)$.

6. Find dy for the following functions:

   (a) $y = x^2 + 3x + 4$ **(d)** $y = \ln(4x)$

   (b) $y = \sqrt{x}$ **(e)** $y = x^{-1/2}$

   (c) $y = e^{3x}$ **(f)** $y = e^{x^2}$

7. Let $y = x^2 + 2x$.

   (a) Draw the graph of $y = x^2 + 2x$ from $x = 0$ to $x = 3$.

   (b) Plot the tangent to $y = x^2 + 2x$ at $x = 1$ on your graph in (a).

   (c) Locate $x_1 = 1$, $x_2 = 3$, y_1, and y_2 on your graph.

   (d) Identify Δx, dx, Δy, and dy on your graph for (c).

TEN

Max-min theory and applications

10-1 THE FIRST DERIVATIVE TEST FOR MAXIMA AND MINIMA

Consider the function $f(x) = x^2 - 3x + 6$. A look at Table 10-1 suggests that this function has a minimum value somewhere between $x = 1$ and $x = 2$. Table 10-2 indicates that this minimum value of $f(x)$ is between $x = 1.4$ and $x = 1.6$. As we will see, the first derivative test provides a powerful tool to determine the exact location of such a point.

In Sec. 8-6 it was pointed out that the derivative of a given function $y = f(x)$ determines a new function $f'(x)$. For the function $f(x) = x^2 - 3x + 6$, $f'(x) = 2x - 3$.

TABLE 10-1

x	$f(x)$
-1	10
0	6
1	4
2	4
3	6
4	10

TABLE 10-2

x	$f(x)$
1.0	4.0
1.4	3.76
1.5	3.75
1.6	3.76
2.0	4.0

TABLE 10-3

x	$f'(x)$
0	-3.0
1.0	-1.0
1.4	-0.2
1.5	0
1.6	0.2
2.0	1.0

Table 10-3 gives the value of $f'(x)$ at the indicated x values. We make two important observations about $f'(x)$:

1. It is zero at $x = 1.5$.

2. It changes from minus to plus at $x = 1.5$.

From the graphs of the original function $y = x^2 - 3x + 6$ and the derivative $y' = 2x - 3$ and from Table 10-3 we see that for $x < 1.5$, $f'(x)$ is negative. $f'(x)$ is positive for $x > 1.5$.

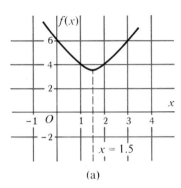
(a)

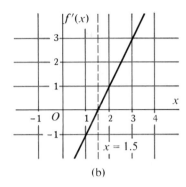
(b)

FIGURE 10-1

We are now ready to define the terms relative minimum, relative maximum and to state the so-called first derivative test for maxima and minima.

DEFINITION 10.1. *Let $y = f(x)$ be a function that is defined in some interval containing $x = a$. Then $f(x)$ is said to have a relative minimum [maximum] at $x = a$ if $f(x) \geq f(a)$ $[f(x) \leq f(a)]$ for all values of x sufficiently close to a. The term local is sometimes used instead of relative.*

If $f(x) \geq f(a)$ $[f(x) \leq f(a)]$ for all x in the domain of f, then $f(x)$ is said to possess an *absolute* or *global* minimum [maximum] at $x = a$.

Example 1. Discuss the maxima and minima of the function $y = f(x)$, as shown in Fig. 10-2.

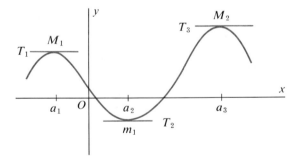

FIGURE 10-2

Solution: This function has relative maxima at $x = a_1$ and $x = a_3$. It has a relative minimum at $x = a_2$. It also has an absolute maximum at $x = a_3$ and an absolute minimum at $x = a_2$.

253

Before stating the first theorem about maxima and minima, we observe from Fig. 10-2 that at $x = a_1$, a_2, and a_3, the slope of the tangents T_1, T_2, and T_3 is zero. Since the slope of the tangent to a curve is given by the derivative, this means that $f'(a_1) = f'(a_2) = f'(a_3) = 0$.

THEOREM 10.1.   *Let $y = f(x)$ be a function that is differentiable on some interval containing $x = a$. Assume further that $f'(a) = 0$. Under these conditions, we have*

A.   *If $f'(x) < 0$ when $x < a$ and $f'(x) > 0$ when $x > a$, for x sufficiently close to a, then $y = f(x)$ has a relative minimum at $x = a$.*

B.   *If $f'(x) > 0$ when $x < a$ and $f'(x) < 0$ when $x > a$, for x sufficiently close to a, then $y = f(x)$ has a relative maximum at $x = a$.*

Example 2.   Use Theorem 10.1 to determine the exact location of the minimum value of $f(x) = x^2 - 3x + 6$.

Solution:

$$f(x) = x^2 - 3x + 6$$
$$f'(x) = 2x - 3$$

To find where $f'(x)$ is zero we set $2x - 3 = 0$. Solving for x gives

$$2x = 3$$
$$x = \tfrac{3}{2} = 1.5$$

We suspect from Table 10-2 of this section that $f(x)$ has a minimum at $x = 1.5$. To see that this is indeed the case, we apply Theorem 10.1(A). At

$$x = 1.4, f'(x) = 2(1.4) - 3$$
$$= 2.8 - 3$$
$$= -0.2 < 0$$

At

$$x = 1.6, f'(x) = 2(1.6) - 3$$
$$= 3.2 - 3 = 0.2 > 0$$

Therefore, $y = x^2 - 3x + 6$ has a minimum at $x = 1.5$.

Example 3.   Examine the function $f(x) = 2x^3 + 3x^2 - 36x + 6$ for possible maxima and minima and illustrate these points graphically.

Solution:

$$f(x) = 2x^3 + 3x^2 - 36x + 6$$
$$f'(x) = 6x^2 + 6x - 36$$
$$6x^2 + 6x - 36 = 0$$
$$6(x^2 + x - 6) = 0$$
$$6(x + 3)(x - 2) = 0$$

Hence, $f'(x) = 0$ if $x + 3 = 0$ or $x - 2 = 0$. This occurs for $x = -3$ and $x = 2$.

We know that $f'(2) = 0$. To see if $f(x)$ has a maximum or minimum at $x = 2$ we evaluate $f'(x)$ at $x = 1.9$ and at $x = 2.1$.

$$f'(1.9) = 6(1.9 + 3)(1.9 - 2)$$
$$= 6(4.9)(-0.1), \quad \text{which is negative}$$

For $x = 1.9 < 2$, $f'(x) < 0$

$$f'(2.1) = 6(2.1 + 3)(2.1 - 2)$$
$$= 6(5.1)(0.1), \quad \text{which is positive}$$

For $x = 2.1 > 2$, $f'(x) > 0$

Applying Theorem 10.1, we see that $y = 2x^3 + 3x^2 - 36x + 6$ has a minimum at $x = 2$.

Similar calculations show that for $x = -3.1$, $f'(x)$ is positive and for $x = -2.9$, $f'(x)$ is negative. Therefore, this function has a maximum at $x = -3$.

Substitution into $y = 2x^3 + 3x^2 - 36x + 6$ gives

$$y = 2(2)^3 + 3(2)^2 - 36(2) + 6$$
$$= 2(8) + 3(4) - 72 + 6$$
$$= 16 + 12 - 72 + 6$$
$$y = -38 \text{ when } x = 2, \qquad y = 87 \text{ when } x = -3$$

These results are summarized in Table 10-4 and Fig. 10-3.

TABLE 10-4

x	y	y'	Type
−3.1		+	
−3.0	87	0	MAX
−2.9		−	
1.9		−	
2.0	−38	0	MIN
2.1		+	

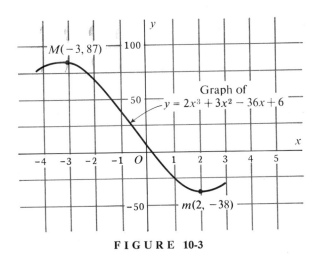

FIGURE 10-3

The next example illustrates the fact that a function may fail to have a maximum or minimum at $x = a$ even though $f'(a) = 0$.

Example 4.

Test $y = x^3 + 2$ for possible maxima and minima.

Solution:

$$f(x) = x^3 + 2$$
$$f'(x) = 3x^2$$

Set $f'(x) = 0$.

$$3x^2 = 0$$
$$x^2 = 0$$
$$x = 0$$

This is the only solution.

But for $x = 0.1$, $f'(x)$ is positive and for $x = -0.1$, $f'(x)$ is also positive. Therefore, $f(x) = x^3 + 2$ has neither a maximum nor a minimum at $x = 0$ since the first derivative does not change sign. The graph in Fig. 10-4 illustrates the reason.

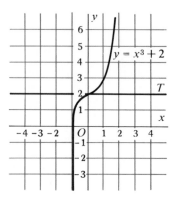

FIGURE 10-4

It is possible for a function to have a maximum or a minimum at a point where the function fails to be differentiable. In this case the derivative may be different from zero at all other points in the domain of the function. This situation is illustrated below for a function $f(x)$ that is continuous on the interval $a \leq x \leq b$, but fails to have a derivative at $x = c$.

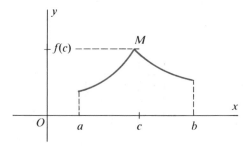

FIGURE 10-5

The above situation is *not covered* by the first and second derivative tests included in this chapter.

FIRST DERIVATIVE TEST (see Theorem 10.1)

Step 1: Find $f'(x)$.

Step 2: Solve the equation $f'(x) = 0$ for x. These values of x are candidates for maxima and minima. If $f'(x) = 0$ has no solution, there are no maxima or minima.

Step 3: Determine the sign of the first derivative slightly to the left and slightly to the right of each of the x values in Step 2.

Step 4: If the sign of the derivative is negative on the left and positive on the right, the function has a minimum. If the sign of the derivative is positive on the left and negative on the right, the function has a maximum.

Step 5: To find the y coordinate of the maximum or minimum point, substitute the x value of Step 2 into the expression $y = f(x)$.

PROBLEMS

1. Find the value or values of x that make $f'(x) = 0$ for the following functions:

    (a) $f(x) = x^2 - 3x$
    (b) $f(x) = x^2 + 3x + 4$
    (c) $f(x) = x^3 + 2x^2$

    (d) $f(x) = x^3 - 6x$
    (e) $f(x) = 2x^3 + 3x^2 - 36x + 4$
    (f) $f(x) = x^3 + 2x^2 - 3x + 7$

2. Sketch the graphs of $y = f(x)$ and $y = f'(x)$ if $f(x) = x^2 + 4x$ and determine the approximate location of all maxima and minima of $y = f(x)$ from your graphs. [*Hint:* Check the x intercepts of the graph of $y = f'(x)$.]

3. Using the function $f(x) = x^2 + 4x$ of Example 2,
    (a) Show that $f'(x) = 0$ at $x = -2$.
    (b) Calculate the sign of $f'(x)$ at $x = -3$ and $x = -1$.
    (c) Use the results of (a) and (b) and the first derivative test to determine if $y = x^2 + 4x$ has a maximum or a minimum at $x = -2$. Compare this result with Prob. 2.

4. Given the function $f(x) = 2x + 3$.
    (a) Find $f'(x)$.
    (b) Is $f'(x)$ ever zero?
    (c) Does this function have any maxima or minima? Why (based on calculus)?

5. Test the following functions for maxima and minima. Find both coordinates of all maximum and minimum points.
    (a) $f(x) = x^2 + 3x + 4$
    (b) $f(x) = x^3 + 2x^2 - 36x + 4$
    (c) $f(x) = e^{3x} - 3x$

6. Test the following functions for maxima and minima. Find both coordinates of all maximum and minimum points.
    (a) $f(x) = x^3 + 2x^2$
    (b) $f(x) = \frac{1}{4}x^4 + 3x^3 + 9x^2$
    (c) $f(x) = \ln x - 2x$
    (d) $f(x) = \ln x + 2x$

7. Given the function

$$f(x) = \begin{cases} x^2 & \text{if } 0 \le x \le 1 \\ 2 - x^2 & \text{if } 1 \le x \le 2 \end{cases}$$

(a) Draw the graph of this function. Is this function continuous?

(b) Determine $f'(x)$ at points other than $x = 1$. Draw the graph of $f'(x)$.

(c) Is $y = f'(x)$ a continuous function? Is $y = f(x)$ differentiable at $x = 1$?

(d) Determine the maximum and the minimum for the given function.

10-2 THE SECOND DERIVATIVE AND INFLECTION POINTS

In Sec. 8-6 it was pointed out that the derivative of $y = f(x)$ gives a new function called $f'(x)$. This new function can be interpreted geometrically as the slope of the tangent to $y = f(x)$ at each point or, in terms of rates, as the rate of change of $y = f(x)$ at each point. We are now ready to examine the derivative of the function $f'(x)$. This is called the second derivative of $y = f(x)$.

DEFINITION 10.2. *Let* $y = f(x)$. *Then the second derivative of* $y = f(x)$ *denoted by the symbol* $\dfrac{d^2y}{dx^2}$ *is defined to be* $\dfrac{d^2y}{dx^2} = \dfrac{d}{dx}[f'(x)]$.

Other common symbols for the second derivative are y'' and $f''(x)$. The second derivative gives the rate of change of the slope of the tangent line. If $f''(x)$ is positive on an interval, then the slope of the tangent line is increasing. This means that as x increases from left to right the tangent line rotates in a counterclockwise sense. The graph of a function that exhibits this property is said to be *concave upward*. If $f''(x)$ is negative then the slope of the tangent line is decreasing and as x increases from left to right the tangent line rotates in the clockwise sense. In this case the graph of $y = f(x)$ is said to be *concave downward*.

DEFINITION 10.3. *A point on the graph of* $y = f(x)$ *at which the curve changes from concave upward to concave downward or from concave downward to concave upward is called an inflection point.*

When the graph of $y = f(x)$ switches from concave upward to concave downward, the sign of the second derivative switches from positive to negative. If it switches from concave downward to concave upward, $f''(x)$ switches from negative to positive. Therefore, at an inflection point, the second derivative equals zero and switches sign.

Example 1. Test the function $y = x^3$ for concavity and inflection points. Illustrate graphically.

Solution:

$$f(x) = x^3$$
$$f'(x) = 3x^2$$
$$f''(x) = 6x$$

$f''(x) = 6x$ is negative for all $x < 0$, zero at $x = 0$, and positive for all $x > 0$. Therefore, the graph of $y = x^3$ is concave downward for all $x < 0$, concave upward for all $x > 0$, and has an inflection point at $(0, 0)$.

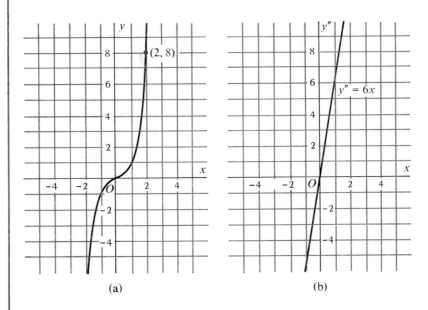

(a)   (b)

F I G U R E   10-6

Example 2.   Graph and discuss the function $y = x^3 - 3x^2 + 3x + 1$.

Solution:

$$y = x^3 - 3x^2 + 3x + 1$$
$$y' = 3x^2 - 6x + 3$$
$$y'' = 6x - 6$$

Let $y'' = 0$.
$$6x - 6 = 0$$
$$6x = 6$$
$$x = 1$$

Therefore, $x = 1$ is a *candidate* for an inflection point.

Furthermore, $y'' = 6x - 6$ is negative for $x < 1$ and positive for $x > 1$. This means that the graph of $y = x^3 - 3x^2 + 3x + 1$ has an inflection point at $(1, 2)$, is concave downward for all $x < 1$, and is concave upward for all $x > 1$.

Direct substitution gives the following table of values.

259

TABLE 10-5

x	y	$\Delta y/\Delta x$
-1	-6	
		7
0	1	
		1
1	2	
		1
2	3	
		7
3	10	

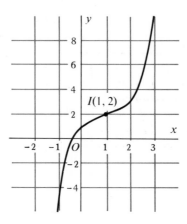

F I G U R E   10-7

It can be seen from the last column of Table 10-5 that this function is increasing at a decreasing rate for $x < 1$ and increasing at an increasing rate for $x > 1$.

TEST FOR INFLECTION POINTS

Step 1: Find $f''(x)$.

Step 2: Solve the equation $f''(x) = 0$ for x. These values of x are candidates for inflection points. If $f''(x) = 0$ has no solution there are no inflection points.

Step 3: If the sign of the second derivative is negative on the left and positive on the right of one of these x values, or vice versa, then the function has an inflection point there.

Step 4: To find the y coordinate of the inflection point, substitute into $y = f(x)$.

PROBLEMS

1. Find the first and second derivative of the following functions:

   (a) $y = x^2 + 4x - 7$ (c) $z = x^3 + 3x$
   (b) $y = x^{1/2} + x^{-1/4}$ (d) $y = 3 \ln x + 4 \log x$

2. Find the first and second derivative for the following functions:

   (a) $y = 2x^3 - 6x^2 + 3x - 8$ (c) $y = x^2 - 3x + 2$
   (b) $y = x^{3/4} + 2e^x + 3 \ln x$ (d) $y = x^4 - 8x^3 + 18x^2 + 10$

3. Determine the sign of the second derivative of $y = x^3 + x^2 + x + 1$ at $x = -2, -1, 0,$ and 2.

4. Use calculus to show that $y = x^4 - x$ is concave upward for all values of x.

5. Draw a graph of the function given in Prob. 4.

6. Does this function have any maximum or minimum points? If so, find them.

7. Use the four-step procedure given in this section to find the inflection points of the following functions:

   (a) $y = x^5$ (c) $y = x^3 + 3x^2$
   (b) $y = x^3 + 3x$ (d) $y = x^4 + 6x^2$

10-3 THE SECOND DERIVATIVE TEST FOR MAXIMA AND MINIMA

An important application of the second derivative is to determine if a function has a maximum or minimum at a point where the first derivative is zero.

THEOREM 10.2.   *Let $f''(x)$ be continuous at $x = a$.*

A.   *If $f'(a) = 0$ and $f''(a)$ is positive, then the graph of $y = f(x)$ is concave upward near $x = a$ and the function has a minimum at $x = a$.*

B.   *If $f'(a) = 0$ and $f''(a)$ is negative, then the graph of $y = f(x)$ is concave downward near $x = a$ and the function has a maximum at $x = a$.*

We will omit a proof of this theorem.

Example 1.   Use Theorem 10.2 to determine the maxima and minima of $y = 2x^3 + 3x^2 - 36x + 6$.

Solution:

$$y = 2x^3 + 3x^2 - 36x + 6$$
$$y' = 6x^2 + 6x - 36$$
$$y'' = 12x + 6$$
$$6x^2 + 6x - 36 = 0$$
$$6(x^2 + x - 6) = 0$$
$$6(x + 3)(x - 2) = 0$$

Therefore, the first derivative is zero at $x = 2$ and at $x = -3$. Also, when $x = 2$,

$$y'' = 30$$

261

which is positive, indicating a minimum at $x = 2$. At $x = -3$,

$$y'' = -30$$

which is negative, indicating a maximum at $x = -3$. [*Note:* These results are the same as in Example 3 of Sec. 10-1.]

Example 2.

Test the function $y = xe^x$ for maxima and minima. Use Theorem 10.2.

Solution:

$$\begin{aligned}
y &= xe^x \\
y' &= xe^x + e^x &\text{by D-10} \\
y' &= e^x(x + 1) \\
y'' &= e^x(1) + (x + 1)e^x \\
y'' &= e^x(x + 2) \\
y' &= 0 &\text{by setting the first derivative equal}
\end{aligned}$$

to zero

$$\begin{aligned}
e^x(x + 1) &= 0 \\
e^x &= 0 \quad \text{or} \quad x + 1 = 0
\end{aligned}$$

However, e^x is never zero. Therefore, the only value of x that makes the first derivative zero is $x = -1$. This means that $y = xe^x$ has at most one maximum or one minimum.

$$\begin{aligned}
y''|_{x=-1} &= e^{-1}(-1 + 2) \\
&= \frac{1}{e}
\end{aligned}$$

which is positive. Therefore, $y = xe^x$ has a minimum at $x = -1$. The coordinates of this minimum point are $(-1, -1/e)$, where $e = 2.7183$ to four decimal places.

SECOND DERIVATIVE TEST (see Theorem 10.2)

Step 1: Find $f'(x)$.

Step 2: Set $f'(x)$ equal to zero and solve for x.

Step 3: Find $f''(x)$.

Step 4: Determine the sign of the second derivative at each of these points.

Step 5: If $f''(x)$ is positive at one of these x values, then the function has a minimum there. If $f''(x)$ is negative, then the function has a maximum. If $f''(x) = 0$ at one of these x values, use the first derivative test.

Step 6: As before, substitute into $y = f(x)$ to get the y coordinate.

PROBLEMS

1. Use the second derivative to show that $y = x^2 + 4$ is concave upward for all values of x and has a minimum at $(0, 4)$.

2. Draw the graph of the function $y = x^2 + 4$ given in Prob. 1.

3. Use the second derivative test to find the maxima and minima of the following functions:

   (a) $y = x^3 + 2x^2 - 36x + 4$ (b) $y = e^{4x} - 4x$

4. Use the second derivative test to find the maximum and minimum points of $y = \frac{1}{3}x^3 + \frac{1}{2}x^2 - 6x + 8$.

5. Test $y = x \ln x \ (0 < x)$ for maxima, minima. Use the second derivative test.

6. Draw the graph of the function in Prob. 5 from $x = 0.1$ to $x = 2$.

7. Test the function $y = (x - 3)^2(x - 4)$ for maxima, minima. Use the second derivative test.

8. Use the second derivative test to find the maximum and minimum of the function $y = x^3 + 6x^2 + 9x + 7$.

9. Let $y = ax^3 + cx$, where $a \neq 0$ and $c \neq 0$. Show that
   (a) The graph of this function has x intercepts other than zero if and only if $c/a < 0$.
   (b) This function has a maximum and a minimum if and only if $c/a < 0$.

10. Let $y = ax^3 + bx^2$, where $a \neq 0$ and $b \neq 0$. Show that
   (a) The graph of this function has x intercepts at $x = 0$ and $x = -b/a$.
   (b) This function has both a maximum and a minimum.

11. Use the results of Prob. 9 or Prob. 10 to test the following functions for the existence of a maximum and a minimum, and illustrate graphically.
   (a) $y = x^3 + 2x^2$ (d) $y = x^3 - 6x$
   (b) $y = x^3 + 6x$ (e) $y = x^3 + 2x^2$
   (c) $y = x^3 - 2x^2$ (f) $y = -x^3 + 6x$

10-4 SUMMARY OF MAXIMA, MINIMA, AND INFLECTION POINTS

In this section we include a sequence of examples starting with a function that has no maximum or minimum and ending with a function that has a maximum, a minimum, and an inflection point. We will also illustrate the procedure for handling the somewhat troublesome case of both y' and y'' being zero for the same value of x.

Example 1.   Test $y = e^{2x}$ for maxima, minima, and inflection points.

Solution:

$$y = e^{2x}$$
$$y' = 2e^{2x}$$
$$y'' = 4e^{2x}$$

Since both y' and y'' are never zero, this function has no maximum, minimum, or inflection point.

Example 2.   Test $y = x^3$ for maxima, minima, and inflection points.

Solution:

$$y = x^3$$
$$y' = 3x^2$$
$$y'' = 6x$$

Both y' and y'' are zero if and only if $x = 0$. This means that the second derivative test fails. By the first derivative test, we find that $y' = 3x^2$ does not change sign; therefore, $y = x^3$ has neither a maximum nor a minimum at $x = 0$. However, using the test for inflection points, we see that $y'' = 6x$ changes sign at $x = 0$; therefore, the point $(0, 0)$ is an inflection point. Some of these facts are illustrated graphically as follows.

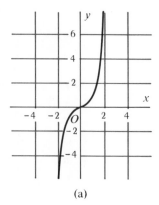

x	-2	-1	0	1	2
$y = x^3$	-8	-1	0	1	8

(a)

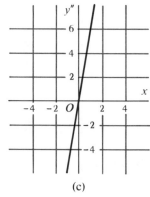

x	-2	-1	0	1	2
$y' = 3x^2$	12	3	0	3	12

(b)

x	-2	-1	0	1	2
$y'' = 6x$	-12	-6	0	6	12

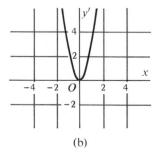

(c)

FIGURE 10-8

Example 3.

Test $y = x^4$ for maxima, minima, and inflection points.

Solution:

$$y = x^4$$
$$y' = 4x^3$$
$$y'' = 12x^2$$

Again y' and y'' are both zero at $x = 0$. The first derivative switches from negative to positive at $x = 0$. Therefore, by the first derivative test, $y = x^4$ has a minimum at $(0, 0)$.

These sign relationships are also illustrated graphically as follows:

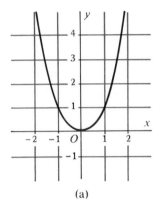

(a)

x	-2	-1	0	1	2
$y = x^4$	16	1	0	1	16

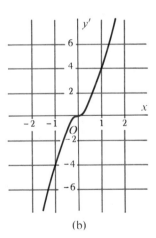

(b)

x	-2	-1	0	1	2
$y' = 4x^3$	-32	-4	0	4	32

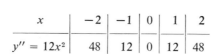

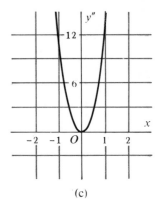

(c)

FIGURE 10-9

Example 4.

Sketch the graphs of y, y', and y'' if $y = x^3 + 2x^2$. Test this function for maxima, minima, and inflection points.

Solution:

$$y = x^3 + 2x^2$$
$$y' = 3x^2 + 4x$$
$$y'' = 6x + 4$$

Let $y' = 0$. This gives the equation $3x^2 + 4x = 0$. Solving for x, we have $x(3x + 4) = 0$ or $x = 0$ and $x = -\frac{4}{3}$ as solutions. Use the second derivative test. Recall that $y'' = 6x + 4$; therefore, we find that

$$y''|_{x=0} = 4 \quad \text{and} \quad y''|_{x=-4/3} = 6(-\tfrac{4}{3}) + 4 = -4$$

This means that $y = x^3 + 2x^2$ has a minimum at $(0, 0)$ and a maximum at $(-\frac{4}{3}, \frac{32}{27})$.

To test for inflection points, we set $y'' = 0$. This gives the equation $6x + 4 = 0$. This equation has the unique solution $x = -\frac{2}{3}$. Since $y'' = 6x + 4$ changes sign at $x = -\frac{2}{3}$, the point $(-\frac{2}{3}, \frac{16}{27})$ is an inflection point. Table 10-6 gives some of the values for $y = x^3 + 2x^2$.

TABLE 10-6

x	y	y'	y''
-2	0	4	-8
$-\frac{4}{3}$	$\frac{32}{27}$	0	-4
-1	1	-1	-2
$-\frac{2}{3}$	$\frac{16}{27}$	$-\frac{4}{3}$	0
0	0	0	4
1	3	7	10
2	16	20	16

266

The graphs of y, y', and y'' are shown in **Fig. 10-10**.

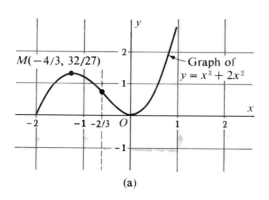

(a)

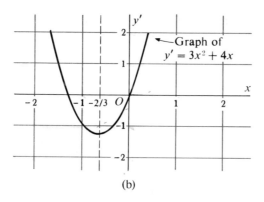

(b)

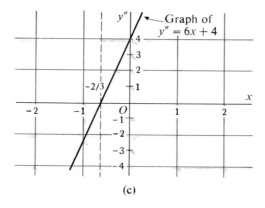

(c)

F I G U R E 10-10

PROBLEMS

> Test the following functions for relative maxima and minima and for inflection points. Illustrate your results with tables and graphs.
>
> **1.** $y = -x^4$ (one maximum)
>
> **2.** $y = (1 - x)^4 + 2$ (one minimum)
>
> **3.** $y = x^3 - 6x^2 + 2x - 6$ (one inflection point, one maximum, and one minimum)
>
> **4.** $y = xe^{-x}$ (one maximum and one inflection point)
>
> **5.** $y = \dfrac{x^3}{3} + \dfrac{x^2}{2} - 6x + 7$ (one maximum, one minimum, and one inflection point)
>
> **6.** $y = x^3 + 3x^2$

10-5 APPLIED MAX-MIN PROBLEMS

Example 1.   Assume that a firm's total revenue is given by the function $R = -2q^2 + 7q$, where R is in thousands of dollars and q, which is the number of units sold, is in hundreds. This function applies only in the range $0 \leq q \leq 3$.

Also assume that the total cost function for this firm is $C = q + 3$, where C is in thousands of dollars and, again, q is in hundreds.

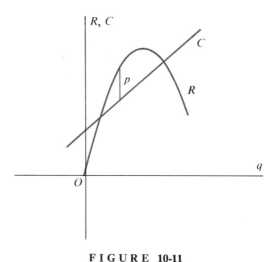

FIGURE 10-11

We can see from Fig. 10-11 that if we produce at the q value (in hundreds), where the vertical distance between the two curves is a maximum, we will be maximizing profits.

If we express the vertical distance between the two functions for any q, we get the following:

Profit $= R - C$
$$P = -2q^2 + 7q - (q + 3)$$
$$P = -2q^2 + 7q - q - 3$$
$$P = -2q^2 + 6q - 3$$

The first and second derivatives are

$$P' = -4q + 6$$
$$P'' = -4$$

Set P' equal to zero. This gives

$$-4q + 6 = 0$$
$$q = \tfrac{3}{2}$$

Substitution into $P = -2q^2 + 6q - 3$ gives $P_{max} = 1.5$ at $q = 1.5$. That is, the sale of 150 units will result in a profit of \$1500.

The following argument justifies the marginalist approach to profit maximization, i.e., *profit is maximized (or loss is minimized) when marginal revenue equals marginal cost.*

Let $R = f(q)$ and $C = g(q)$, where f and g are differentiable functions of quantity, q.

Profit $=$ total revenue $-$ total cost
$$P = f(q) - g(q)$$

$$\frac{dP}{dq} = f'(q) - g'(q) = 0$$

if and only if $f'(q) = g'(q)$.

Recall that $f'(q)$ is called marginal revenue, and $g'(q)$ is called marginal cost. We see that maximum profit or minimum loss occurs when marginal revenue equals marginal cost.

Example 2.   Redo Example 1 using the marginalist approach.
Solution:

$$f(q) = -2q^2 + 7q, \quad g(q) = q + 3$$
$$f'(q) = -4q + 7, \quad g'(q) = 1$$
$$f'(q) = g'(q)$$
$$-4q + 7 = 1$$
$$4q = 6$$
$$q = \tfrac{3}{2}, \text{ as before}$$

Another application of max-min theory can be observed by looking at the classical inventory model. We will use this model to determine the economic order quantity, i.e., the order quantity such that inventory costs are at a minimum. We denote economic order quantity by EOQ.

Inventory costs are made up of two basic factors. The first is holding cost or the cost of holding an item in inventory. If the total number of items in inventory for any period is $x/2$, or one-half the amount that is ordered, then the cost of holding would be equal to

$x/2$ (i.e., the amount of items in inventory during a period) times h, the cost of holding one item. The reader should note that holding cost increases as x, the number of units ordered, is increased. A simple illustration is shown in Fig. 10-12.

We see in this figure that the usage is constant and the receipt of the order occurs exactly when the inventory level falls to zero.

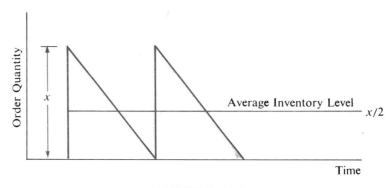

F I G U R E 10-12

The other factor affecting inventory cost is the ordering cost. This cost will decrease as the number of units ordered increases. The total number of orders in a given year is equal to the annual demand, q, divided by the size of the order, x. The ordering cost would be equal to the number of orders times the cost of placing an order.

This gives the following equation:

$$C = \frac{x}{2}(h) + \frac{q}{x}(r)$$

where h = holding cost per item
                  x = order size
                  r = cost of placing an order

We see that holding cost varies directly with x, and reorder cost varies inversely with x. We are faced with a trade-off of costs such that total cost, C, will be at a minimum.

Graphically, these costs appear as shown in **Fig. 10-13**.

We see that the economic order quantity occurs at a point where C is a minimum.

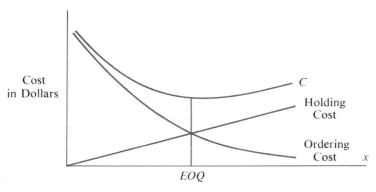

FIGURE 10-13

Example 3. Suppose that the cost of holding one item in inventory is $0.50 and that the cost of placing an order is $10. Also assume that the annual demand for the item is 490 units. Find the value of x at which the cost is minimum.

Solution:

$$C = \frac{x}{2}(0.50) + \frac{490}{x}(10)$$

To find where C is a minimum we find the first derivative of C with respect to x and set it equal to zero.

$$C' = 0.25 - \frac{4900}{x^2} = 0$$

$$\frac{4900}{x^2} = 0.25$$

$$x^2 = \frac{4900}{0.25}$$

$$x = \frac{70}{0.5} = 140$$

$$C'' = -(-2)\frac{4900}{x^3}$$

C'' is positive at $x = 140$, so we have a minimum.

Costs will be minimized if we order 140 units at a time.

We point out that when the two basic factors that make up C are of the form

$$y_1 = ax$$

$$y_2 = \frac{b}{x}$$

then

$$C = ax + \frac{b}{x}$$

and

$$C' = a - \frac{b}{x^2}$$

Setting C' equal to zero gives

$$\frac{b}{x^2} = a$$

$$x^2 = \frac{b}{a}$$

$$x = \sqrt{\frac{b}{a}}$$

It is interesting to note that this result can also be obtained by setting y_1 equal to y_2 and solving for x.

$$ax = \frac{b}{x}$$

$$x^2 = \frac{b}{a}$$

$$x = \sqrt{\frac{b}{a}}$$

Therefore, *in this case*, total cost is a minimum when the holding cost is equal to the ordering cost.

TABLE 10-7

Units Ordered	Ordering Costs	Cost of Carrying	Total Cost
130	37.6923	32.5000	70.1923
131	37.4045	32.7500	70.1545
132	37.1212	33.0000	70.1212
133	36.8421	33.2500	70.0921
134	36.5671	33.5000	70.0671
135	36.2963	33.7500	70.0463
136	36.0294	34.0000	70.0294
137	35.7664	34.2500	70.0164
138	35.5072	34.5000	70.0072
139	35.2518	34.7500	70.0018
140	35.0000	35.0000	70.0000
141	34.7517	35.2500	70.0017
142	34.5070	35.5000	70.0070
143	34.2657	35.7500	70.0157
144	34.0277	36.0000	70.0277
145	33.7931	36.2500	70.0431
146	33.5616	36.5000	70.0616
147	33.3333	36.7500	70.0833
148	33.1081	37.0000	70.1081
149	32.8859	37.2500	70.1359
150	32.6666	37.5000	70.1666

A numerical approach to this same problem, using a computer, is included in Table 10-7. If we let the units ordered vary from 130 to 150, we see that total cost is indeed a minimum at $x = 140$, and that holding cost is equal to ordering cost at this quantity.

PROBLEMS

1. Given the cost function $C = q^2 - 10q + 125$ and the revenue function $R = 100q - 15q^2$, where q, C, and R are in hundreds, find the value of q where marginal revenue equals marginal cost.

2. Determine if the value of q in Prob. 1 gives maximum profit or minimum loss.

3. Given the cost function $C = 2500 + 60x - \dfrac{1000}{x} \left[1 < x \leq 50 \right]$ and the revenue function $R = 160x$, find the maximum profit and loss.

4. The cost of holding one item in inventory is $1.00 and the cost of placing an order is $5.00. Assume a yearly demand for the item of 1000 units. Find the cost function.

5. Find the value for x in Prob. 4 that minimizes cost. Find the minimum cost.

6. The cost of holding one item in inventory is $0.25 and the cost of placing an order is $0.50. Assume a yearly demand for the item of 100 units. Find the value of x for which costs are minimized.

7. An open storage bin is to be constructed with a square base and vertical sides so as to contain 500 cu ft. Show that the cost of lining the bin with aluminum will be minimum if the depth is made half of the width.

8. Repeat Prob. 7. Replace the volume, 500 cu ft, with any fixed volume, V.

9. A rectangular box is to be built with a square base and a square top. The volume is V cubic feet. The cost per square foot for the top and bottom is $0.20 and the cost per square foot for the sides is $0.30. Determine the dimensions that result in the minimum material cost of the box.

10. Repeat Prob. 9. Use a cost of $0.50/sq ft for the top and bottom and $0.40/sq ft for the sides.

10-6 AN ADDITIONAL APPLICATION

In this section we will give cost data at four production levels for a hypothetical company. These data are used to find the third degree polynomial function that passes through the given points. Finally, this function is used in conjunction with the revenue function $R = -2q^2 + 7q$ from Example 1 of the previous section to find the level of production that gives the greatest profit.

Example 1. | Given the following company data, find the third degree polynomial that passes through these four points.

Hundreds of Units	Hundreds of Dollars
0	1
1	2
2	3
3	10

Solution: To find the third degree polynomial function that passes through these four points, we assume

$$C = aq^3 + bq^2 + cq + d$$

When q is equal to zero, $C = 1$. Therefore, $1 = a0^3 + b0^2 + c0 + d$ and $d = 1$.

To find a, b, c, we must solve three equations in three unknowns for a, b, and c.

$$2 = a1^3 + b1^2 + c1 + 1$$
$$3 = a2^3 + b2^2 + c2 + 1$$
$$10 = a3^3 + b3^2 + c3 + 1$$

or

$$a + b + c = 1$$
$$8a + 4b + 2c = 2$$
$$27a + 9b + 3c = 9$$

Written in matrix form, this system of equations becomes

$$\begin{pmatrix} 1 & 1 & 1 \\ 8 & 4 & 2 \\ 27 & 9 & 3 \end{pmatrix} \begin{pmatrix} a \\ b \\ c \end{pmatrix} = \begin{pmatrix} 1 \\ 2 \\ 9 \end{pmatrix}$$

The matrix of coefficients is

$$A = \begin{pmatrix} 1 & 1 & 1 \\ 8 & 4 & 2 \\ 27 & 9 & 3 \end{pmatrix}$$

Evaluating the determinant of A by cofactors, we have

$$|A| = 1(12 - 18) - 1(24 - 54) + 1(72 - 108)$$
$$|A| = \quad -6 \qquad\qquad +30 \qquad\qquad -36$$
$$|A| = -12$$

The inverse can be found by dividing each element of the matrix of cofactors by $|A|$ and transposing the resulting matrix. This gives

$$A^{-1} = \begin{pmatrix} -6/-12 & 30/-12 & -36/-12 \\ 6/-12 & -24/-12 & 18/-12 \\ -2/-12 & 6/-12 & -4/-12 \end{pmatrix}^t$$

$$= \begin{pmatrix} 1/2 & -5/2 & 3 \\ -1/2 & 2 & -3/2 \\ 1/6 & -1/2 & 1/3 \end{pmatrix}^t$$

Multiplying the constant vector by the inverse to find the values of a, b, and c, we have

$$\begin{pmatrix} a \\ b \\ c \end{pmatrix} = \begin{pmatrix} \frac{1}{2} & -\frac{1}{2} & \frac{1}{6} \\ -\frac{5}{2} & 2 & -\frac{1}{2} \\ 3 & -\frac{3}{2} & \frac{1}{3} \end{pmatrix} \begin{pmatrix} 1 \\ 2 \\ 9 \end{pmatrix} = \begin{pmatrix} 1 \\ -3 \\ 3 \end{pmatrix}$$

This gives $a = 1$, $b = -3$, $c = 3$, and $C = q^3 - 3q^2 + 3q + 1$ is the desired function.

Example 2. | Find the level of production that gives the maximum profit, assuming the cost function $C = q^3 - 3q^2 + 3q + 1$ from Example 1 and the revenue function $R = -2q^2 + 7q$ from Example 1 of the previous section.

Solution:

$$P = R - C$$
$$P = -2q^2 + 7q - (q^3 - 3q^2 + 3q + 1)$$
$$P = -2q^2 + 7q - q^3 + 3q^2 - 3q - 1$$
$$P = -q^3 + q^2 + 4q - 1$$

Setting the first derivative equal to zero gives

$$\frac{dP}{dq} = -3q^2 + 2q + 4$$

$$0 = -3q^2 + 2q + 4$$

Using the quadratic formula[1] to solve for q we have

$$q = \frac{-2 \pm \sqrt{4 + 48}}{-6}$$

$$= \frac{-2 \pm \sqrt{52}}{-6}$$

$$= \frac{-2 \pm 7.2}{-6}$$

$$q = \frac{-9.2}{-6} \quad \text{or} \quad q = \frac{5.2}{-6}$$

Clearly, $q < 0$ is not operationally meaningful in this example. Using the positive value for q gives $q = 1.53$ and the maximum profit occurs when 153 units are produced.

---

1. Equations of the type $ax^2 + bx + c = 0$ have solutions $x = \dfrac{-b \pm \sqrt{b^2 - 4ac}}{2a}$.

This expression is called the quadratic formula.

PROBLEMS

Table 10-8 is from *The Price System and Resource Allocation* by Richard H. Leftwich.[2]

TABLE 10-8

Quantity of X	Total Fixed Cost	Total Variable Cost	Total Cost
1	$100	$40	$140
2	100	70	170
3	100	85	185
4	100	96	196
5	100	104	204
6	100	110	210
7	100	115	215
8	100	120	220
9	100	126	226
10	100	134	234
11	100	145	245
12	100	160	260
13	100	180	280
14	100	206	306
15	100	239	339
16	100	280	380
17	100	330	430
18	100	390	490
19	100	461	561
20	100	544	644

1. (a) Use price = $25 and the data in Table 10-8 to complete Table 10-9.

TABLE 10-9

x	C	MC	MR	R	P
0	100				
1	140	70	25	25	−115
.					
.					
.					
20	644				

(b) What level of production gives the largest profit?

2. Richard H. Leftwich, *The Price System and Resource Allocation.* New York: Holt, Rinehart and Winston, Inc., 1966, p. 131.

2. The least-squares procedure was used to fit a cubic cost function to the cost data of Prob. 1(a). The resulting cost function is $C = 0.173x^3 - 3.74x^2 + 31.944x + 116$. Use this fitted cost function and the revenue function $R = 25x$ to find the production level that gives the maximum profit. How does your result compare with the result of Prob. 1(b)?

ELEVEN

Integral calculus

11-1 DEFINITION OF THE DEFINITE INTEGRAL

The subject of calculus can be divided into two main branches, differential calculus and integral calculus. The basic concept of differential calculus is the *derivative*, which has been discussed in the last few chapters. In this chapter, we will give a brief treatment of integral calculus. The basic concept of integral calculus is the *definite integral*. Both of these concepts have a natural geometric interpretation. We have seen that the derivative gives the slope of the tangent line to a curve at a given point. It will be shown in this chapter that the definite integral can be interpreted geometrically as the *area under a curve*.

The definition of the integral involves, among other things, subdivisions of certain intervals on the x axis. We will illustrate this idea before giving a definition of the integral.

Consider the interval $[a, b]$ consisting of the points x, such that $a \leq x \leq b$. Divide the interval $[a, b]$ into n subintervals of length $\frac{b - a}{n}$. This gives $n + 1$ points on the x axis, each of which is the endpoint of at least one subinterval. It is customary to label these points as follows: $x_0, x_1, x_2, \ldots, x_{n-1}, x_n$, where $x_0 = a$ and $x_n = b$.

This labelling is illustrated further in **Fig. 11-1**. This figure illustrates the special case where $n = 9$.

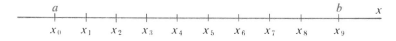

FIGURE 11-1

DEFINITION 11.1. *Let* $y = f(x)$ *be a function defined for all* x *between* $x = a$ *and* $x = b$. *Then* $\int_a^b f(x)\,dx$, *called the definite integral of* $f(x)$ *between* a *and* b, *is defined to be the following limit:*

$$\int_a^b f(x)\,dx = \lim_{n \to \infty} [f(t_1)\,\Delta x + f(t_2)\,\Delta x + \cdots + f(t_n)\,\Delta x]$$

where $\Delta x = (b - a)/n$
           $t_i =$ any point belonging to the ith subinterval, i.e., $x_{i-1} \le t_i \le x_i$ for $i = 1, 2, 3, \ldots, n$

By arithmetic interpretation, a definite integral is the limit of a sum of products. This concept also has an important geometric interpretation. This interpretation will be discussed later. The next few examples illustrate the various parts of Definition 11.1. A sum of products of the form $f(t_1)\,\Delta x + f(t_2)\,\Delta x + \cdots + f(t_n)\,\Delta x$ will be denoted by the symbol S_n.

Example 1. Describe S_5 as fully as possible for $\int_2^3 f(x)\,dx$ if $t_1, t_2, \ldots, t_n$ are taken as the left-hand endpoints of each of the subintervals.

Solution: $a = 2$ and $b = 3$; therefore,

$$\Delta x = \frac{3 - 2}{5} = \frac{1}{5} = 0.2$$

The subintervals are normally labelled as follows with $a = x_0$ and $b = x_n$.

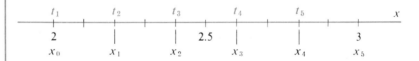

FIGURE 11-2

$$S_5 = f(t_1)\,\Delta x + f(t_2)\,\Delta x + f(t_3)\,\Delta x + f(t_4)\,\Delta x + f(t_5)\,\Delta x$$
$$S_5 = f(2)0.2 + f(2.2)0.2 + f(2.4)0.2 + f(2.6)0.2 + f(2.8)0.2$$

Example 2. Describe S_5 as fully as possible for $\int_2^3 f(x)\,dx$ if $t_1, t_2, \ldots, t_n$ are taken at the midpoint of each of the subintervals.

Solution: As in Example 1, $\Delta x = 0.2$. In this case, $t_1 = 2.1$, $t_2 = 2.3$, $t_3 = 2.5$, $t_4 = 2.7$, and $t_5 = 2.9$.

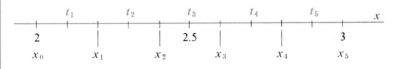

FIGURE 11-3

$$S_5 = f(t_1)\,\Delta x + f(t_2)\,\Delta x + \cdots + f(t_5)\,\Delta x$$
$$S_5 = f(2.1)0.2 + f(2.3)0.2 + f(2.5)0.2 + f(2.7)0.2 + f(2.9)0.2$$

Example 3.   Calculate S_5 for Examples 1 and 2 if $f(x) = x^2$.

Solution: From Example 1,

$$S_5 = f(2)0.2 + f(2.2)0.2 + f(2.4)0.2 + f(2.6)0.2 + f(2.8)0.2$$
$$= 2^2(0.2) + (2.2)^2(0.2) + (2.4)^2(0.2) + (2.6)^2(0.2) + (2.8)^2(0.2)$$
$$= 0.2[4 + 4.84 + 5.76 + 6.76 + 7.84]$$
$$= 0.2[29.2]$$
$$S_5 = 5.84$$

From Example 2, $S_5 = f(2.1)0.2 + \cdots + f(2.9)0.2$.

$$S_5 = (2.1)^2 0.2 + (2.3)^2 0.2 + (2.5)^2 0.2 + (2.7)^2 0.2 + (2.9)^2 0.2$$
$$= 0.2[4.41 + 5.29 + 6.25 + 7.29 + 8.41]$$
$$= 0.2(26.65)$$
$$S_5 = 6.33$$

We see from Example 3 that the value of S_n for fixed n depends on the choice of $t_1, t_2, \ldots, t_n$. It is shown, however, in more advanced treatments of calculus that if $f(x)$ is continuous on $a \le x \le b$, then $\lim_{n \to \infty} S_n$ exists, and this limit is not dependent on the choice of $t_1, t_2, \ldots, t_n$. A proof of this fact is well beyond the scope of this text.

The value of S_n for some particular choice of $t_1, t_2, \ldots, t_n$ gives an approximate value of $\int_a^b f(x)\,dx$. The larger the value of n, the better this approximation becomes. Both of these statements follow from the fact that the definite integral is defined to be the limit as n approaches infinity of S_n.

Example 4.   Find an approximation for $\int_0^2 x^3\,dx$ using $n = 4$ and taking t_i at the right-hand side of the ith subinterval.

Solution:

$$a = 0, \quad b = 2, \quad \Delta x = \frac{2-0}{4} = \frac{1}{2} = 0.5$$

$$t_1 = 0.5, \quad t_2 = 1, \quad t_3 = 1.5, \quad \text{and} \quad t_4 = 2$$

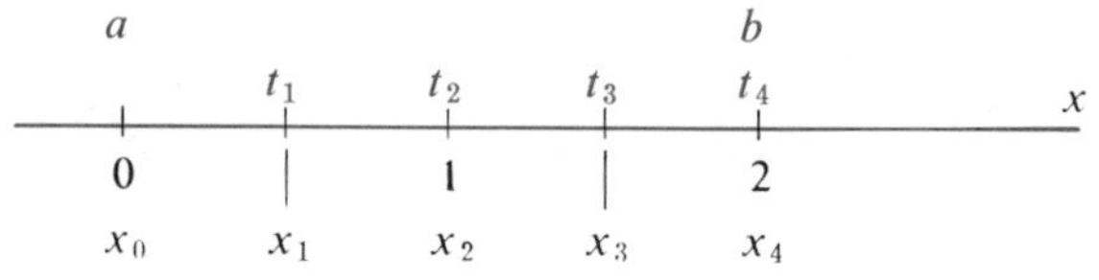

FIGURE 11-4

$$S_4 = \left(\frac{1}{2}\right)^3 \frac{1}{2} + (1)^3 \frac{1}{2} + \left(\frac{3}{2}\right)^3 \frac{1}{2} + (2)^3 \frac{1}{2}$$

$$= \frac{1}{2}\left(\frac{1}{8} + 1 + \frac{27}{8} + 8\right) = \frac{1}{2}\left(\frac{25}{2}\right)$$

Therefore, $S_4 = 6\frac{1}{4}$ is a rough (since n is only 4) approximation for $\int_0^2 x^3\,dx$.

PROBLEMS

1. Consider the *definite integral* $\int_1^2 x^2\,dx$.
   (a) Calculate S_5 by taking function values at the left endpoint of each subinterval.
   (b) Calculate S_5 by taking function values at the right endpoint of each subinterval.
   (c) Calculate S_5 by taking function values at the midpoint of each subinterval.

2. Consider the *definite integral* $\int_2^4 (2x + 3)\,dx$.
   (a) Calculate S_4 by taking function values at the left endpoint of each subinterval.
   (b) Calculate S_4 by taking function values at the right endpoint of each subinterval.

3. Consider the *definite integral* $\int_0^1 e^x\,dx$. Compute S_5 by taking function values at the midpoint of each subinterval.

4. Consider the *definite integral* $\int_1^2 \dfrac{1}{x}\,dx$. Compute S_4 by taking function values at the midpoint of each subinterval.

5. State the definition of $\int_a^b f(x)\,dx$.

6. State the definition of S_n.

7. What is the relationship of $\int_a^b f(x)\,dx$ to S_n?

11-2   A GEOMETRIC INTERPRETATION OF THE DEFINITE INTEGRAL

Let C be the graph of $y = f(x)$ between $x = a$ and $x = b$, where $f(x)$ is continuous and positive on the interval $a \le x \le b$. The area, A, of the part of the xy plane bounded by the vertical lines $x = a$ and $x = b$, the x axis, and the curve C is called the *area under the curve C*.

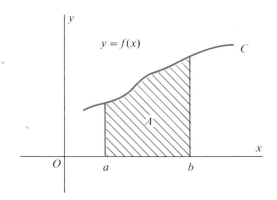

FIGURE 11-5

The area, A, is equal to $\int_a^b f(x)\,dx$.

As a first step in the explanation of the above statement, we consider the geometric interpretation of a typical S_4.

Taking the function values at the midpoints, we have

$$S_4 = f(t_1)\,\Delta x + f(t_2)\,\Delta x + f(t_3)\,\Delta x + f(t_4)\,\Delta x$$

The first term of S_4 is $f(t_1)\,\Delta x$, where t_1 is at the midpoint of the first subinterval. Now, $f(t_1)$ gives the vertical distance between the x axis and the graph of $y = f(x)$ at $x = t_1$. Therefore, $f(t_1)$ times Δx gives the area, A_1, of the first rectangle shown in Fig. 11-6.

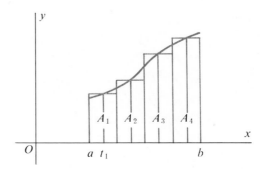

F I G U R E 11-6

Similarly, $f(t_2)\,\Delta x$ gives the area, A_2, of the second rectangle, and so forth. Figure 11-6 suggests that $S_4 = A_1 + A_2 + A_3 + A_4$ gives an approximation for the area under the graph of $y = f(x)$ between $x = a$ and $x = b$.

In general, we have $S_n = A_1 + A_2 + \cdots + A_n \approx A$. Furthermore, this approximation of A by S_n gets better as n increases. In fact, the area under the graph of $y = f(x)$ between $x = a$ and $x = b$ is defined to be $A = \lim_{n \to \infty} (A_1 + A_2 + \cdots + A_n)$. This can be restated as

$$A = \lim_{n \to \infty} [f(t_1)\,\Delta x + f(t_2)\,\Delta x + \cdots + f(t_n)\,\Delta x]$$

$$A = \int_a^b f(x)\,dx \qquad \text{by Definition 11.1}$$

Example 1.   Consider the definite integral $\int_0^1 (x - x^2)\,dx$. Compute S_4 taking function values at the left endpoints of each subinterval and interpret each term in S_4 as the area of a rectangle.

Solution:

$$f(x) = x - x^2,\ \Delta x = 0.25$$
$$x_0 = 0,\ x_1 = \tfrac{1}{4},\ x_2 = \tfrac{1}{2},\ x_3 = \tfrac{3}{4},\ x_4 = 1$$
$$t_1 = 0,\ t_2 = \tfrac{1}{4},\ t_3 = \tfrac{1}{2},\ t_4 = \tfrac{3}{4}$$

$$S_4 = (0)0.25 + (\tfrac{1}{4} - \tfrac{1}{16})0.25 + (\tfrac{1}{2} - \tfrac{1}{4})0.25 + (\tfrac{3}{4} - \tfrac{9}{16})0.25$$
$$S_4 = (0 \cdot \tfrac{1}{4}) + (\tfrac{3}{16} \cdot \tfrac{1}{4}) + (\tfrac{1}{4} \cdot \tfrac{1}{4}) + (\tfrac{3}{16} \cdot \tfrac{1}{4})$$
$$S_4 = 0 + \tfrac{3}{64} + \tfrac{1}{16} + \tfrac{3}{64}$$
$$S_4 = A_1 + A_2 + A_3 + A_4$$

where

$$A_1 = 0, \ A_2 = \tfrac{3}{64}, \ A_3 = \tfrac{1}{16}, \text{ and } A_4 = \tfrac{3}{64}$$

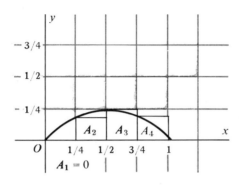

F I G U R E 11-7

$$S_4 = \frac{0 + 3 + 4 + 3}{64} = \frac{10}{64} = \frac{5}{32} \approx A$$

Example 2. Draw the rectangles that correspond to the two terms of S_2 for $\int_0^1 x^2 \, dx$, where $t_1 = \tfrac{1}{4}$ and $t_2 = \tfrac{3}{4}$.

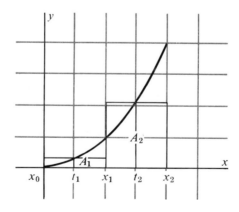

F I G U R E 11-8

Solution:

$$A_1 = \tfrac{1}{16} \cdot \tfrac{1}{2} = \tfrac{1}{32}$$
$$A_2 = \tfrac{9}{16} \cdot \tfrac{1}{2} = \tfrac{9}{32}$$
$$A_1 + A_2 = \tfrac{10}{32} = \tfrac{5}{16}$$

283

The reader should observe that the rectangles in Example 2 *overestimate* the area under the curve between x_0 and t_1 and between x_1 and t_2. On the other hand, they *underestimate* the area between t_1 and x_1 and between t_2 and x_2. This *averaging* effect, which results from choosing the t_i's at the *midpoints* of the subintervals, is used in the next section to *approximate* some definite integrals.

PROBLEMS

1. Draw the rectangles that correspond to the terms of S_5 for the definite integral $\int_0^1 (x^2 + 2x)\, dx$. Take the function values at the left endpoints.

2. Repeat Prob. 1 taking the function values at the right endpoints.

3. Compute S_5 in Probs. 1 and 2.

4. Draw the graph of $y = x + e^{-x}$ from $x = 1$ to $x = 3$ and shade the area under the curve between $x = 1$ and $x = 3$.

5. Find an approximation for the area in Prob. 4 using four rectangles.

6. Shade the area that is given by $\int_2^5 \dfrac{2}{x}\, dx$.

7. Draw the *two* rectangles that correspond to the terms of S_2 for the integral $\int_0^1 x^2\, dx$, where $t_1 = \frac{1}{2}$ and $t_2 = 1$.

8. Calculate S_2 for Prob. 7.

11-3 INTEGRALS BY APPROXIMATION

Consider the problem of approximating $\int_a^b f(x)\, dx$. First, we choose some positive integer n and divide the interval $a \le x \le b$ into n subintervals of length $\Delta x = \dfrac{b - a}{n}$. Next, we must make a choice for t_1, $t_2, \ldots, t_n$, the points at which the function $f(x)$ is to be evaluated. In this section, we will choose $t_1, t_2, \ldots, t_n$ at the midpoint of their respective subintervals to take advantage of the averaging effect discussed in the previous section. This is a permissable choice for $t_1, t_2, \ldots, t_n$ according to **Definition 11.1**. Using the notation of the previous section, we have

$$S_n = [f(t_1)\, \Delta x] + [f(t_2)\, \Delta x] + \cdots + [f(t_n)\, \Delta x]$$

where

$$\Delta x = \frac{b - a}{n} \qquad \text{and} \qquad t_k = x_{k-1} + \frac{1}{2}\Delta x \qquad (k = 1, 2, 3, \ldots, n)$$

By Definition 11.1,

$$\int_a^b f(x)\, dx = \lim_{n \to \infty} S_n$$

The method of approximating a definite integral by S_n, where S_n is formed as above, is called the *midvalue rule*.

Example 1.   Use the midvalue rule with $n = 5$ to approximate $\int_0^1 x^2 \, dx$.

Solution:

$a = 0, b = 1$

$b - a = 1 - 0 = 1$

$\Delta x = \frac{1}{5} = 0.2$

$t_1 = 0.1, \ t_2 = 0.3, \ t_3 = 0.5, \ t_4 = 0.7, \ t_5 = 0.9$

$S_5 = [(0.1)^2 \cdot 0.2] + [(0.3)^2 \cdot 0.2] + [(0.5)^2 \cdot 0.2]$
$\qquad\quad + [(0.7)^2 \cdot 0.2] + [(0.9)^2 \cdot 0.2]$

$\quad = (0.01 + 0.09 + 0.25 + 0.49 + 0.81)0.2$

$\quad = (1.65)(0.2)$

$S_5 = 0.33$

$\int_0^1 x^2 \, dx \approx 0.33$ *based on S_5*

Example 2.   Use the midvalue rule with $n = 5$ to approximate $\int_0^1 e^{x^2} \, dx$.

Solution:

$S_5 = [e^{(0.1)^2}0.2] + [e^{(0.3)^2}0.2] + [e^{(0.5)^2}0.2]$
$\qquad\quad + [e^{(0.7)^2}0.2] + [e^{(0.9)^2}0.2]$

$S_5 = 0.2(e^{0.01} + e^{0.09} + e^{0.25} + e^{0.49} + e^{0.81})$

$S_5 = 0.2(1.0101 + 1.0942 + 1.2840 + 1.6323 + 2.2479)$

$S_5 = 0.2(7.2685)$

$S_5 = 1.4537$

$\int_0^1 e^{x^2} \, dx \approx 1.454$ *based on $n = 5$*

The values of S_5, S_{10}, and S_{50} for the definite integral $\int_1^2 3x^2 \, dx$ were found on a computer using the midvalue rule. Table 11-1 indicates these values.

TABLE 11-1

n	S_n	Δx
5	6.9899	0.20
10	6.9974	0.10
50	6.9998	0.02

These data suggest that $\int_1^2 3x^2 \, dx = 7$. This will be found to be the case in the next section.

In the next section we will present the fundamental theorem of integral calculus. This theorem provides a means of finding the exact value of certain definite integrals.

PROBLEMS

1. Given the definite integral $\int_4^{10} f(x)\, dx$, find $t_1, t_2, \ldots, t_{12}$ and $x_0, x_1, \ldots, x_{12}$ for S_{12} using the midvalue rule.

2. Using the data in Prob. 1, describe S_{12} as fully as possible.

3. Use the midvalue rule to approximate $\int_1^2 3x^2\, dx$ using $n = 5$, i.e., S_5. (Compare your result with the computer result given in Table 11-1.)

4. Repeat Prob. 3 using $n = 10$ and compare your result with the computer result.

5. Use the midvalue rule with $n = 3$ to approximate $\int_0^6 2^x\, dx$.

6. What definite integral is approximated by the following?

$$S_5 = \{[(1.1)^2 + e^{1.1}] + [(1.3)^2 + e^{1.3}] + [(1.5)^2 + e^{1.5}]$$
$$+ [(1.7)^2 + e^{1.7}] + [(1.9)^2 + e^{1.9}]\}\, 0.2$$

11-4 THE FUNDAMENTAL THEOREM OF INTEGRAL CALCULUS

A large class of definite integrals can be evaluated exactly and with very little work by making use of the fundamental theorem of integral calculus. This is one reason that this theorem is so important. The fundamental theorem of integral calculus is also important for theoretical reasons in that it involves a relationship between definite integrals and derivatives, the basic concepts of integral calculus and differential calculus, respectively.

THEOREM 11.1. *The following is a statement of the fundamental theorem of integral calculus. If $f(x)$ is continuous on the interval $a \leq x \leq b$ and $F(x)$ is a function whose derivative is $f(x)$, i.e., $F'(x) = f(x)$, then $\int_a^b f(x)\, dx = F(b) - F(a)$.*

We have not included a proof of this theorem.
Theorem 11.1 is applied in two steps:

Step 1: We must find a function $F(x)$ whose derivative is $f(x)$. $F(x)$ is called an *antiderivative* of $f(x)$.

Step 2: Next, evaluate $F(x)$ at $x = a$ and at $x = b$ and compute the difference $F(b) - F(a)$.

Example 1. Use the fundamental theorem of integral calculus to evaluate $\int_0^1 x^2\, dx$.

Solution:

Step 1:

$$f(x) = x^2, \qquad a = 0 \qquad \text{and} \qquad b = 1$$

Recall that $\dfrac{d}{dx}(x^n) = nx^{n-1}$. We see that $F(x)$ must have the form $F(x) = kx^3$, where k is still undetermined. Since $F'(x)$ must equal $f(x) = x^2$, we have $3kx^2 = x^2$.

$$3k = 1$$
$$k = \tfrac{1}{3}$$

Therefore, the function $F(x) = \tfrac{1}{3}x^3$ has the desired property.

Step 2:

$$\int_0^1 x^2 \, dx = F(1) - F(0)$$
$$= \tfrac{1}{3}(1)^3 - \tfrac{1}{3}(0)^3$$
$$= \tfrac{1}{3} - 0$$
$$\int_0^1 x^2 \, dx = \tfrac{1}{3} = 0.333 \ldots$$

The reader should recall the calculation in the previous section where it was found that $\int_0^1 x^2 \, dx \approx 0.33$ (based on the midvalue rule with $n = 5$).

The following table of antiderivatives can be verified by differentiation.

TABLE 11-2

$f(x)$	$F(x)$
1. $cx^n (n \neq -1)$	$\dfrac{cx^{n+1}}{n+1}$
2. $cx^{-1} = \dfrac{c}{x}$	$c \ln x$
3. ce^{ax}	$\dfrac{c}{a} e^{ax}$
4. ca^x	$\dfrac{ca^x}{\ln a}$

Example 2. Use the fundamental theorem to evaluate $\int_1^2 3x^2 \, dx$ and compare with the computer result given in Table 11-1.

Solution:

$$\int_1^2 3x^2 \, dx, \qquad f(x) = 3x^2, \qquad F(x) = x^3$$
$$F(2) - F(1) = 8 - 1 = 7$$
$$\int_1^2 3x^2 \, dx = 7$$

The computer results are as follows:

$$S_5 = 6.9899$$
$$S_{10} = 6.9974$$
$$S_{50} = 6.9998$$

Example 3. Use the fundamental theorem of integral calculus to evaluate

$$\int_1^3 (x^2 + 3x + 4)\, dx$$

Solution:

$$f(x) = x^2 + 3x + 4 = x^2 + 3x + 4x^0$$

$F(x) = \dfrac{x^3}{3} + \dfrac{3x^2}{2} + 4x$ is obtained by repeated application of item (1) of Table 11-2. Note that the derivative of a sum of functions is the sum of the derivatives of these functions.

Let $a = 1$, $b = 3$.

$$F(b) - F(a) = \frac{(3)^3}{3} + \frac{3(3)^2}{2} + 4(3) - \left(\frac{1}{3} + \frac{3}{2} + 4\right)$$

$$= \left(9 + \frac{27}{2} + 12\right) - \left(\frac{1}{3} + \frac{3}{2} + 4\right)$$

$$= \frac{54 + 81 + 72 - 2 - 9 - 24}{6}$$

$$= \frac{172}{6}$$

$$= 28\tfrac{2}{3}$$

Example 4. Evaluate $\int_1^2 \dfrac{1}{x}\, dx$.

Solution:

$$f(x) = \frac{1}{x}, \qquad F(x) = \ln x$$

$$\int_1^2 \frac{1}{x}\, dx = \ln (2) - \ln (1) = \ln (2) - 0 = \ln 2$$

Example 5. Evaluate $\int_2^4 \dfrac{1}{x^2}\, dx$.

Solution:

$$f(x) = \frac{1}{x^2} = x^{-2}$$

$$F(x) = \frac{x^{-1}}{-1}, \qquad a = 2, \qquad b = 4$$

$$F(b) - F(a) = -4^{-1} - (-2^{-1})$$

$$= \frac{-1}{4} + \frac{1}{2}$$

$$= \frac{1}{4}$$

Example 6. Evaluate $\int_1^4 \sqrt{x}\, dx$.

Solution:

$$f(x) = \sqrt{x}$$
$$f(x) = x^{1/2}$$

$$F(x) = \frac{x^{(1/2)+1}}{(1/2) + 1} = \frac{x^{3/2}}{3/2}$$

$$F(x) = \frac{2}{3} x^{3/2}$$

$$\int_1^4 \sqrt{x} \, dx = \frac{2}{3}(4)^{3/2} - \frac{2}{3}(1)^{3/2}$$

$$= \frac{2}{3}[8 - 1] = \frac{14}{3}$$

Example 7. Use the fundamental theorem to evaluate $\int_{-1}^2 4e^{0.3x} \, dx$.

Solution:

$$f(x) = 4e^{0.3x}, \qquad a = -1, \qquad b = 2$$

$$F(x) = \frac{4}{0.3} e^{0.3x}$$

$$\int_{-1}^2 4e^{0.3x} \, dx = F(2) - F(-1)$$

$$= \frac{4}{0.3} e^{0.3(2)} - \frac{4}{3} e^{0.3(-1)}$$

$$= \frac{4}{0.3} [e^{0.6} - e^{-0.3}]$$

$$= \frac{40}{3} [1.8221 - 0.7408]$$

$$= \frac{40}{3} (1.0713)$$

$$\int_{-1}^2 4e^{0.3x} \, dx = 14.284$$

PROBLEMS

1. Find an antiderivative for each of the following functions:
   (a) $f(x) = x^2$
   (b) $f(x) = 6/x$
   (c) $g(x) = e^{4x}$
   (d) $g(x) = 5^x$

2. Find an antiderivative for each of the following functions:
   (a) $f(x) = 3x^3 + 4x^2$
   (b) $f(x) = \sqrt{x^3}$
   (c) $f(x) = x^2 + 2/x$
   (d) $f(x) = e^x + x^3$

3. Evaluate the following definite integrals by the fundamental theorem:
   (a) $\int_1^3 (x^2 + 2x + 3) \, dx$
   (b) $\int_0^4 (4x - x^3) \, dx$
   (c) $\int_1^2 \frac{1}{x} \, dx$
   (d) $\int_1^2 x^4 \, dx$
   (e) $\int_{-1}^2 (x^2 + 4) \, dx$
   (f) $\int_1^e (2/x) \, dx$

289

4. Evaluate the following definite integrals:

(a) $\int_0^1 e^{2x}\, dx$ (c) $\int_{1/3}^1 e^{3x}\, dx$

(b) $\int_0^1 2^x\, dx$ (d) $\int_0^2 3^x\, dx$

5. Verify by differentiation the antiderivatives given in Table 11-2.

6. Evaluate the following definite integrals:

(a) $\int_0^2 (3x^2 + 2x + 3)\, dx$ (c) $\int_0^1 (e^{2x} + 3^x)\, dx$

(b) $\int_1^2 (e^x + 2x)\, dx$ (d) $\int_1^{e^2} 3x^{-1}\, dx$

7. Evaluate

(a) $\int_{-2}^2 x^3\, dx$ (b) $\int_{-2}^1 x^5\, dx$

8. State the fundamental theorem using $g(x)$ and $G(x)$.

11-5 APPLICATIONS OF THE DEFINITE INTEGRAL

The reader will recall from Sec. 11-2 that the areas under curves can be found using definite integrals. This fact will be illustrated further in this section.

Example 1. Use the midvalue rule to approximate $\int_0^4 x\, dx$ with $n = 4$.

Solution:

$$b = 4, \qquad a = 0, \qquad \Delta x = \frac{4}{4} = 1$$

$$S_4 = \frac{1}{2}(1) + \frac{3}{2}(1) + \frac{5}{2}(1) + \frac{7}{2}(1)$$

$$= \frac{1 + 3 + 5 + 7}{2}$$

$$= \frac{16}{2} = 8$$

This is the exact value because $f(x) = x$ is a linear function.

Example 2. Use the fundamental theorem to evaluate $\int_0^4 x\, dx$.

Solution:

$$f(x) = x, \qquad F(x) = \frac{x^2}{2}$$

$$\int_0^4 x\, dx = \frac{(4)^2}{2} - 0 = \frac{16}{2} = 8$$

Example 3. Use the fact that a definite integral gives the area under the curve and the formula for the area of a triangle to find $\int_0^4 x\, dx$.

Solution:

$$\int_0^4 x\,dx = \text{area under the graph of } y = x \text{ between } x = 0 \text{ and } x = 4$$

$$= \tfrac{1}{2}bh, \text{ i.e., } \tfrac{1}{2} \text{ base times height}$$

$$= \tfrac{1}{2}(4)(4)$$

Therefore,

$$\int_0^4 x\,dx = 8 \qquad \textit{as found in Examples 1 and 2}$$

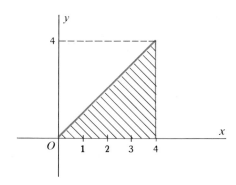

F I G U R E 11-9

Example 4.   Find the area under $y = x^2$ between $x = 1$ and $x = 3$.

$$A = \int_1^3 x^2\,dx$$

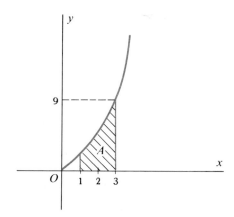

F I G U R E 11-10

$$f(x) = x^2, \qquad F(x) = \frac{x^3}{3}$$

$$\int_1^3 x^2 \, dx = \frac{27}{3} - \frac{1}{3} = \frac{26}{3} = 8\frac{2}{3}$$

Example 5.   Find the area under $y = 4 - x^2$ between $x = -1$ and $x = 2$.

Solution:

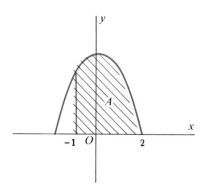

F I G U R E 11-11

$$A = \int_{-1}^{2} (4 - x^2) \, dx$$

$$f(x) = 4 - x^2$$

$$F(x) = 4x - \frac{x^3}{3}$$

$$A = \left[4(2) - \frac{(2)^3}{3} \right] - \left[4(-1) - \frac{(-1)^3}{3} \right]$$

$$A = 8 - \frac{8}{3} + 4 - \frac{1}{3}$$
$$A = 12 - \frac{9}{3}$$
$$A = 9$$

Example 6.   A certain firm sells its product for \$2.00 per unit. This gives the revenue function $R = 2x$. Find the area bounded by $R = 2x$, the vertical lines $x = 100$ and $x = 300$, and the x axis.

Solution: $A = \int_{100}^{300} 2x \, dx$. An antiderivative for this function is $F(x) = x^2$. Applying the fundamental theorem, we have $A = F(300) - F(100)$, which simplifies to $A = 80,000$.

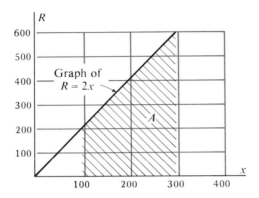

F I G U R E 11-12

Example 7.

Let the total cost and total revenue functions be given as $C = x + 4$ and $R = -2x^2 + 7x$. Find the area between the cost and revenue functions between $x = 1$ and $x = 2$, i.e., the x coordinates of the break-even points.

Solution: The area in question can be found by subtracting the area under the cost function from the area under the revenue function between these two points. Let A_2 denote the area under the revenue function, and let A_1 denote the area under the cost function.

Then

$$A_1 = \int_1^2 (x + 4)\, dx \qquad \text{and} \qquad A_2 = \int_1^2 (-2x^2 + 7x)\, dx$$

Therefore,

$$A_1 = 5\tfrac{1}{2} \qquad \text{and} \qquad A_2 = 5\tfrac{5}{6}$$

and the desired area is $\tfrac{1}{3}$.

PROBLEMS

1. Approximate $\int_0^2 x^2\, dx$ by the midvalue rule using $n = 5$.

2. Evaluate the integral in Prob. 1 by the fundamental theorem and compare the results.

3. Shade the area given by the integral in Prob. 1.

4. Approximate $\int_2^4 (2x + 3)\, dx$ using the midvalue rule with $n = 5$.

5. Evaluate the integral in Prob. 4 in two ways, i.e., by the fundamental theorem and by plane geometry.

6. Explain why the answer in Prob. 4 gives the exact value of the integral.

7. Use the midvalue rule with $n = 2$, 4, and 8 to approximate $\int_0^4 e^x\, dx$. Evaluate this integral by the fundamental theorem. Interpret these numerical results in light of the theory given in this chapter.

8. Approximate $\int_{-1}^{0} x^3 \, dx$ by the midvalue rule with $n = 5$.
9. Evaluate the integral in Prob. 8 by the fundamental theorem.
10. Evaluate A_1 and A_2 and draw the graph for Example 7 of this section.

11-6 AREAS UNDER A NORMAL CURVE

The function $y = \dfrac{1}{\sqrt{2\pi}} \, e^{-x^2/2}$ is encountered frequently in the study of statistics. In particular, the area under the graph of this function between $x = 0$ and $x = z$ is of interest. The graph of the function under discussion is shown below.

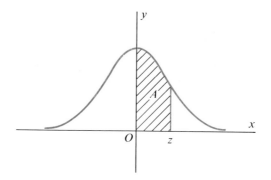

FIGURE 11-13

The area under the graph of $y = \dfrac{1}{\sqrt{2\pi}} \, e^{-x^2/2}$ between $x = 0$ and $x = z$ is equal to the definite integral, $\int_{0}^{z} \dfrac{1}{\sqrt{2\pi}} \, e^{-x^2/2} \, dx$. Now, $f(x) = \dfrac{1}{\sqrt{2\pi}} \, e^{-x^2/2}$ is continuous between $x = 0$ and $x = z$ for any z. If we could find an antiderivative $F(x)$, then the desired area would be given by $A = F(z) - F(0)$. However, it has been shown by mathematicians that the function $f(x) = \dfrac{1}{\sqrt{2\pi}} \, e^{-x^2/2}$ does not have an antiderivative in closed form, i.e., expressed as a formula with a finite number of terms. This means that some technique must be used to approximate $\int_{0}^{z} \dfrac{1}{\sqrt{2\pi}} \, e^{-x^2/2} \, dx$ to a prescribed degree of accuracy.

The midvalue rule is used in the next example to obtain an approximation for $z = 1$.

Example 1. Approximate $\int_0^1 \frac{1}{\sqrt{2\pi}} e^{-x^2/2} \, dx$ using the midvalue rule with $n = 5$.

Solution:

TABLE 11-3

x	$\dfrac{x^2}{2}$	$e^{-x^2/2}$
0.1	0.005	0.995
0.3	0.045	0.956
0.5	0.125	0.882
0.7	0.245	0.783
0.9	0.405	0.667

$\Delta x = \frac{1}{5} = 0.2$

$\dfrac{1}{\sqrt{2\pi}} = 0.3989$

$$S_5 = \frac{1}{\sqrt{2\pi}} \, 0.2[0.995 + 0.956 + 0.882 + 0.783 + 0.667]$$

$$S_5 = (0.3989)(0.2)(4.283)$$
$$S_5 = 0.3417$$

Therefore,

$$\int_0^1 \frac{1}{\sqrt{2\pi}} e^{-x^2/2} \, dx \approx 0.3417 = S_5$$

The following table gives the value to 4 decimal places for the area under the graph of the normal curve $y = \frac{1}{\sqrt{2\pi}} e^{-x^2/2}$ between $x = 0$ and $x = z$.

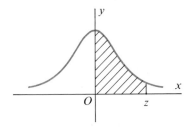

F I G U R E 11-14

Example 2. Use Table 11-4 to find the value to 4 decimal places of $\int_0^1 \frac{1}{\sqrt{2\pi}} e^{-x^2/2} \, dx$ and compare the result with Example 1. (See Fig. 11-14.)

Solution: Since z is given as 1, from the table we obtain 0.3413 for the area under the curve between $x = 0$ and $x = 1$. Since the area under a curve is

TABLE 11-4[1]

z	.00	.01	.02	.03	.04	.05	.06	.07	.08	.09
0.0	.0000	.0040	.0080	.0120	.0160	.0199	.0239	.0279	.0319	.0359
0.1	.0398	.0438	.0478	.0517	.0557	.0596	.0636	.0675	.0714	.0753
0.2	.0793	.0832	.0871	.0910	.0948	.0987	.1026	.1064	.1103	.1141
0.3	.1179	.1217	.1255	.1293	.1331	.1368	.1406	.1443	.1480	.1517
0.4	.1554	.1591	.1628	.1664	.1700	.1736	.1772	.1808	.1844	.1879
0.5	.1915	.1950	.1985	.2019	.2054	.2088	.2123	.2157	.2190	.2224
0.6	.2257	.2291	.2324	.2357	.2389	.2422	.2454	.2486	.2518	.2549
0.7	.2580	.2612	.2642	.2673	.2704	.2734	.2764	.2794	.2823	.2852
0.8	.2881	.2910	.2939	.2967	.2995	.3023	.3051	.3078	.3106	.3133
0.9	.3159	.3186	.3212	.3238	.3264	.3289	.3315	.3340	.3365	.3389
1.0	.3413	.3438	.3461	.3485	.3508	.3531	.3554	.3577	.3599	.3621
1.1	.3643	.3665	.3686	.3708	.3729	.3749	.3770	.3790	.3810	.3830
1.2	.3849	.3869	.3888	.3907	.3925	.3944	.3962	.3980	.3997	.4015
1.3	.4032	.4049	.4066	.4082	.4099	.4115	.4131	.4147	.4162	.4177
1.4	.4192	.4207	.4222	.4236	.4251	.4265	.4279	.4292	.4306	.4319
1.5	.4332	.4345	.4357	.4370	.4382	.4394	.4406	.4418	.4429	.4441
1.6	.4452	.4463	.4474	.4484	.4495	.4505	.4515	.4525	.4535	.4545
1.7	.4554	.4564	.4573	.4582	.4591	.4599	.4608	.4616	.4625	.4633
1.8	.4641	.4649	.4656	.4664	.4671	.4678	.4686	.4693	.4699	.4706
1.9	.4713	.4719	.4726	.4732	.4738	.4744	.4750	.4756	.4761	.4767
2.0	.4772	.4778	.4783	.4788	.4793	.4798	.4803	.4808	.4812	.4817
2.1	.4821	.4826	.4830	.4834	.4838	.4842	.4846	.4850	.4854	.4857
2.2	.4861	.4864	.4868	.4871	.4875	.4878	.4881	.4884	.4887	.4890
2.3	.4893	.4896	.4898	.4901	.4904	.4906	.4909	.4911	.4913	.4916
2.4	.4918	.4920	.4922	.4925	.4927	.4929	.4931	.4932	.4934	.4936
2.5	.4938	.4940	.4941	.4943	.4945	.4946	.4948	.4949	.4951	.4952
2.6	.4953	.4955	.4956	.4957	.4959	.4960	.4961	.4962	.4963	.4964
2.7	.4965	.4966	.4967	.4968	.4969	.4970	.4971	.4972	.4973	.4974
2.8	.4974	.4975	.4976	.4977	.4977	.4978	.4979	.4979	.4980	.4981
2.9	.4981	.4982	.4982	.4983	.4984	.4984	.4985	.4985	.4986	.4986
3.0	.49865	.4987	.4987	.4988	.4988	.4989	.4989	.4989	.4990	.4990
4.0	.4999683									

given by the definite integral, we have $\int_0^1 \frac{1}{\sqrt{2\pi}} e^{-x^2/2} \, dx = 0.3413$ to 4 decimal places.

In Example 1, we obtained 0.3417 as an approximate value using the midvalue rule with $n = 5$.

Example 3. | Use Table 11-4 to find $\int_1^2 \frac{1}{\sqrt{2\pi}} e^{-x^2/2} \, dx$.

---

1. Adapted from Table A-1 in John Neter, William Wasserman, and G. A. Whitmore, *Fundamental Statistics for Business and Economics*, fourth ed. Boston: Allyn and Bacon, Inc., 1973.

Solution: Since areas are additive, we have

$$\int_1^2 \frac{1}{\sqrt{2\pi}} e^{-x^2/2}\, dx = \int_0^2 \frac{1}{\sqrt{2\pi}} e^{-x^2/2}\, dx - \int_0^1 \frac{1}{\sqrt{2\pi}} e^{-x^2/2}\, dx$$

$$= 0.4772 - 0.3413$$

$$\int_1^2 \frac{1}{\sqrt{2\pi}} e^{-x^2/2}\, dx = 0.1359 \text{ to 4 decimal places}$$

PROBLEMS

1. Calculate the y coordinate for $x = 0$, $x = \pm 1$, $x = \pm 2$ for the function $y = e^{-x^2/2}$.
2. Use the results of Prob. 1 to sketch the graph of $y = e^{-x^2/2}$.
3. Calculate the y coordinate for $x = 0$, $x = \pm 1$, $x = \pm 2$ for the function

    $$y = \frac{1}{\sqrt{2\pi}} e^{-x^2/2}, \text{ where } \frac{1}{\sqrt{2\pi}} = 0.3989.$$

4. Use the results of Prob. 3 to sketch the graph of $y = \dfrac{1}{\sqrt{2\pi}} e^{-x^2/2}$.

5. Use logs to calculate $\dfrac{1}{\sqrt{2\pi}}$; $\pi = 3.142$.

6. Use the midvalue rule with $n = 5$ to approximate $\displaystyle\int_0^z \frac{1}{\sqrt{2\pi}} e^{-x^2/2}\, dx$;

    $z = \frac{1}{2}$.

7. Use Table 11-4 to find $\displaystyle\int_0^z \frac{1}{\sqrt{2\pi}} e^{-x^2/2}\, dx$, where $z = \frac{1}{2}$. How does this result compare with the answer obtained in Prob. 6?
8. Use Table 11-4 to find the following:

    (a) $\displaystyle\int_0^2 \frac{1}{\sqrt{2\pi}} e^{-x^2/2}\, dx$ (c) $\displaystyle\int_0^3 \frac{1}{\sqrt{2\pi}} e^{-x^2/2}\, dx$

    (b) $\displaystyle\int_2^3 \frac{1}{\sqrt{2\pi}} e^{-x^2/2}\, dx$ (d) $\displaystyle\int_0^{0.25} \frac{1}{\sqrt{2\pi}} e^{-x^2/2}\, dx$

9. Use Table 11-4 to find $\int_0^{0.8} e^{-x^2/2}\, dx$.

11-7   THE INDEFINITE INTEGRAL AND APPLICATIONS

In Sec. 11-4 we introduced the notion of an antiderivative in connection with the fundamental theorem of integral calculus. In this section we will discuss this concept further and introduce additional notation. Also, we will show some additional applications of antiderivatives.

We will begin by showing that a whole family of antiderivatives can be constructed for a given function once a single antiderivative has been found. To illustrate this, let $F_1(x)$ be an antiderivative of $f(x)$ and consider the function $F_2(x) = F_1(x) + C$, where C is an arbitrary constant. Since the derivative of a constant is zero and the derivative of a sum of functions is the sum of their derivatives, we have

$$\frac{d}{dx} F_2(x) = \frac{d}{dx} F_1(x) + C$$

$$= f(x) + 0 \qquad \text{recall the definition of antiderivative}$$
$$= f(x)$$

Therefore, $F_2(x)$ is also an antiderivative of $f(x)$.

This motivates the following definition.

DEFINITION 11.2. $\int f(x)\, dx = F(x) + C$, *where $F(x)$ is an antiderivative of $f(x)$ and C is an arbitrary constant, is called the indefinite integral of $f(x)$.*

This arbitrary constant in this definition is called a *constant of integration.*

Two important properties of indefinite integrals are:

1. $\int cf(x)\, dx = c \int f(x)\, dx$
2. $\int [f(x) + g(x)]\, dx = \int f(x)\, dx + \int g(x)\, dx$

A very brief list of indefinite integrals is included below. Extensive tables of indefinite integrals can be found in mathematical handbooks.

I-1 $\displaystyle\int x^n\, dx = \frac{x^{n+1}}{n+1} + C \qquad (n \neq -1)$

I-2 $\displaystyle\int \frac{1}{x}\, dx = \ln |x| + C$

I-3 $\displaystyle\int e^{bx}\, dx = \frac{1}{b} e^{bx} + C$

I-4 $\displaystyle\int a^{bx}\, dx = \frac{1}{b \ln a} a^{bx} + C$

I-5 $\displaystyle\int \frac{1}{x+b}\, dx = \ln |x + b| + C$

I-6 $\displaystyle\int \frac{x}{(x+b)^2}\, dx = \ln |x + b| + \frac{b}{x+b} + C$

Example 1.   Find the indefinite integral of $f(x) = 3x^2 + 2x$ and select the antiderivative of $f(x)$ that passes through point $A = (1, 4)$.

Solution:

$$\int (3x^2 + 2x)\, dx = x^3 + x^2 + C$$

To select the antiderivative that passes through point A, we let $y = x^3 + x^2 + C$.

$$4 = (1)^3 + (1)^2 + C$$
$$4 = 2 + C$$
$$C = 2$$

Therefore, $y = x^3 + x^2 + 2$ is the desired antiderivative.

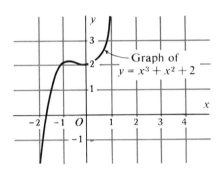

Graph of
$y = x^3 + x^2 + 2$

F I G U R E   11-15

Example 2.

Find the area bounded by $y = 2^{3x}$, the vertical lines $x = 1$ and $x = 2$, and the x axis.

Solution: Let A denote the desired area. Then $A = \int_1^2 2^{3x}\, dx$. Let $f(x) = 2^{3x}$. Then, by I-4, the indefinite integral of $f(x)$ is $\dfrac{2^{3x}}{3 \ln 2} + C$. By the fundamental theorem of integral calculus, we have

$$\int_1^2 2^{3x}\, dx = \left[\frac{2^{3(2)}}{3 \ln 2} + C\right] - \left[\frac{2^{3(1)}}{3 \ln 2} + C\right]$$

$$\int_1^2 2^{3x}\, dx = \frac{1}{3 \ln 2} (2^6 - 2^3)$$

Therefore, $A = 56/2.07944 = 26.93032$.

The reader will note that the arbitrary constant is retained in the solution of Example 2. This constant is cancelled when the fundamental theorem is applied. For this reason, it is customary to omit the constant of integration when the indefininte integral is used to find an antiderivative for use in the fundamental theorem.

Example 3.

Given the marginal revenue function $MR = \dfrac{a}{x + b} - \dfrac{ax}{(x + b)^2} + k$, find the revenue function.

Solution: Since marginal revenue is the derivative of the revenue function, we have

$$R = \int \frac{a}{x+b}\,(dx) + \int \frac{-ax\,dx}{(x+b)^2} + \int k\,dx$$

$$R = a \ln|x+b| - a\left[\ln|x+b| + \frac{b}{x+b}\right] + kx + C$$

$$R = \frac{-ab}{x+b} + kx + C$$

Assume $R = 0$ at $x = 0$. We have $0 = -a + C$, or $C = a$. This gives

$$R = a + kx - \frac{ab}{x+b}$$

This can be simplified, algebraically, to give

$$R = \frac{ax}{x+b} + kx$$

PROBLEMS

1. Find the following indefinite integrals:

   (a) $\displaystyle \int (x^3 + 2x + 4)\,dx$ (c) $\displaystyle \int \frac{1}{x+4}\,dx$

   (b) $\displaystyle \int e^{4x}\,dx$ (d) $\displaystyle \int \frac{x}{(x-3)^2}\,dx$

2. Verify the following integration formulas by differentiation:

   (a) $\displaystyle \int xe^{bx}\,dx = \frac{x}{b}e^{bx} - \frac{1}{b^2}e^{bx} + C$

   (b) $\displaystyle \int \ln(bx)\,dx = x \ln(bx) - x + C$

3. Evaluate the following definite integrals:

   (a) $\displaystyle \int_0^2 (x^3 - 2x)\,dx$ (c) $\displaystyle \int_0^1 e^{(1/2)x}\,dx$

   (b) $\displaystyle \int_2^4 \frac{1}{x-1}\,dx$ (d) $\displaystyle \int_3^6 \frac{1}{x}\,dx$

4. In Example 3 of this section we showed that if

   $$MR = \frac{a}{x+b} - \frac{ax}{(x+b)^2} + k$$

   then $R = \dfrac{ax}{x+b} + kx$. Use this result to show that the demand law, which corresponds to this marginal revenue function, is $p = \dfrac{a}{x+b} + k$.

   [*Hint:* $p = R/x$.]

5. Given $MR = 2 - 6x$, where MR denotes marginal revenue, find the demand law. Assume revenue equals zero when x equals zero.

6. Repeat Prob. 5 using $MR = ax + b$, where a and b are constants.

7. Find and shade the *area under the curve* $y = \ln 3x$ between $x = 1/3$ and $x = 1$. Use the formula given in Prob. 2(b).

8. Exponential growth. Assume that the rate of growth, $\dfrac{dy}{dx}$, of y is proportional to the value of y for all values of x.

   (a) Express the above statement in the form $\dfrac{dy}{dx} = ky$, where k is a constant.

   (b) Rewrite $\dfrac{dy}{dx} = ky$ in the form $\dfrac{dy}{y} = kdx$, and integrate both sides of this equation. *Answer:* $\ln y = kx + C_1$.

   (c) Let $C_1 = \ln C_2$ in (b) and show that $y = C_2 e^{kx}$.

9. Use the result of Prob. 8 to determine y as a function of x if $\dfrac{dy}{dx} = 0.06y$ for all $x \geq 0$ and $y = 100$ at $x = 0$.

10. It was shown in Sec. 8-8 that if a principal is compounded continuously for n years at interest rate i, then the compound amount V_n is given by the formula $V_n = Pe^{ni}$. Use the result of Prob. 8 to derive this result.

11. Complete Table 11-5.

TABLE 11-5

$f(x)$	x^2	e^{3x}	xe^{x^2}
$f'(x)$			
$f'(2)$			
$\int f(x)\,dx$			
$\int_1^3 f(x)\,dx$			
$\ln f(x)$			
$\dfrac{d}{dx}[\ln f(x)]$			

REFERENCES

Allen, R.G.D. *Mathematical Analysis for Economists*. New York: St. Martin's Press, Inc., 1967.

Andree, Richard V. *Introduction to Calculus with Analytic Geometry*. New York: McGraw-Hill Book Co., Inc., 1962.

Brabb, George J. *Introduction to Quantitative Management*. New York: Holt, Rinehart and Winston, Inc., 1968.

Daus, Paul H., and Whyburn, William M. *Introduction to Mathematical Analysis with Applications to Problems in Economics*. Reading, Mass.: Addison-Wesley Publishing Co., Inc., 1962.

Draper, Jean E., and Klingman, Jane S. *Mathematical Analysis Business and Economic Applications*. New York: Harper & Row, Publishers, 1972.

Johnson, R. E., Kiokemeister, F. L., and Wolk, E. S. *Calculus with Analytic Geometry*, fifth ed. Boston: Allyn and Bacon, Inc., 1974.

Leftwich, Richard H. *The Price System and Resource Allocation*. New York: Holt, Rinehart and Winston, 1966.

McBrien, V. O. *Introductory Analysis*. New York: Appleton-Century-Crofts, Inc., 1961.

McConnell, Campbell R. *Economics*. New York: McGraw-Hill Book Co., Inc., 1966.

Stockton, R. Stansburg. *Basic Inventory Systems: Concepts and Analysis*. Boston: Allyn and Bacon, Inc., 1965.

Tierney, John A. *Calculus and Analytic Geometry*, third ed. Boston: Allyn and Bacon, Inc., 1975.

Wasson, Chester R. *Understanding Quantitative Analysis*. New York: Appleton-Century-Crofts, 1969.

Youse, Bevon K., and Stalnaker, Ashford. *Calculus for Students of Business and Management*. Scranton, Pa.: International Textbook Co., Inc., 1967.

TWELVE

Introduction to probability

12-1 SETS AND SUBSETS

In the first two sections of this chapter we will discuss elementary topics from set theory. In the remaining sections some basic probability concepts will be introduced in terms of set ideas and notation. Our first discussion of sets can be found in Sec. 1-1 of this text. Several examples of sets are given below using the standard brace notation.

$\{1, 3, 5, 7\}$

$\{x_1, x_2, x_3, x_4, x_5\}$

$\{\text{product 1, product 2, product 3}\}$

$\{(\text{head, head}), (\text{head, tail}), (\text{tail, head}), (\text{tail, tail})\}$

In Example 2, x_1, x_2, x_3, x_4, and x_5 are said to be *elements* of the given set.

The symbol $\in$ is used to indicate membership in a set. The expression $x \in A$, read "x belongs to A," means that x is an element of the set A. The symbol $x \notin A$ means that "x does not belong to A."

Examples using $A = \{1, 2, 3\}$ and $B = \{x, y, z, w\}$:

$2 \in A$ and $x \in B$

$4 \notin A$ but $w \in B$

303

The set of all elements in a given discussion or situation is called the *universal* set.

DEFINITION 12.1. *Two sets A and B are said to be equal if every element of A is an element of B and every element of B is an element of A.*

The following examples illustrate this definition.

$\{1, 2, 4\} = \{1, 2, 4\}$

$\{1, 3, 7\} \neq \{1, 4, 7\}$

$\{2, 5, 8\} = \{8, 5, 2\}$ *order is not important*

$\{1, 4, 10\} \ .. \ \{1, 4, 10, 13\}$ *13 is in the set on the right but not in the set on the left*

DEFINITION 12.2. *A set A is said to be a subset of a set B if every element of A is also an element of B. A is a subset of B is denoted by $A \subset B$.*

$\{2, 3, 5\} \subset \{1, 2, 3, 5, 8\}$

$A = \{1, 2, 5\}$ is not a subset of $\{1, 4, 5\} = B$ *2 is in A but not in B*

$\{a, b, c\} \subset \{c, d, a, b\}$

$\{x, y, z\} \subset \{x, y, z\}$, i.e., if $A = B$, then $A \subset B$ and $B \subset A$.

It is useful to consider the set with no elements. This set is called the *null* set, or the *empty* set, and is frequently denoted by the symbol $\emptyset$.

DEFINITION 12.3. *Let Ω be the universal set and A be a subset of Ω. Then the set of all x such that $x \in \Omega$ and $x \notin A$ is called the complement of A.*

The complement of A is denoted by A'.
Definition 12.3 is illustrated by the following examples.

If $\Omega = \{1, 2, 3, 4, 5, 6, 7, 8, 9, 10\}$ and $A = \{2, 4, 6, 8, 10\}$, then $A' = \{1, 3, 5, 7, 9\}$.

If the universal set consists of the letters of the alphabet and C is the set of consonants, then the complement of C is the set of vowels, i.e., $C' = \{a, e, i, o, u\}$.

Much insight can be gained into set relationships by representing sets by shaded regions in a plane. To illustrate this, diagrams, called *Venn diagrams*, are used. Some examples of Venn diagrams are given in Figure 12-1.

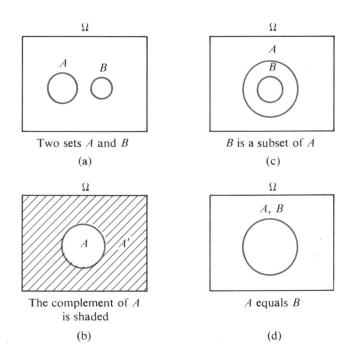

Two sets A and B

(a)

B is a subset of A

(c)

The complement of A
is shaded

(b)

A equals B

(d)

FIGURE 12-1

PROBLEMS

1. Give some examples of sets.

2. Which of the following sets are equal?

(a) $\{2, 6, 9\}$? $\{6, 2, 9\}$ (c) $\{2, 5, 4\}$? $\{2, 5, 4, 3\}$
(b) $\{5, 7, 3\}$? $\{5, 7, 2, 3\}$ (d) $\{4, 9, 6\}$? $\{9, 6, 8\}$

3. In the following, is A a subset of B?

(a) $A = \{5, 2, 9\}$, $B = \{8, 6, 2, 4, 5, 9\}$
(b) $A = \{1, 2, 3\}$, $B = \{1, 2, 3, 4\}$
(c) $A = \{5, 7, 9\}$, $B = \{5, 9, 11\}$
(d) $A = \{4, 3, 2\}$, $B = \{4, 2, 3\}$
(e) $A = \{2, 4, 6\}$, $B = \{2, 4, 6\}$
(f) $A = \{5, 6, 7, 8\}$, $B = \{8, 6, 7\}$

4. Repeat Prob. 3, and answer the question: Is B a subset of A?

5. Given $A = \{1, 3, 5, 9\}$, $B = \{2, 4, 6, 8\}$, $C = \{1, 4, 5, 8\}$, and $D = \emptyset$, which of the following statements are true?

(a) D is the empty set   (e) $A \subset C$
(b) $3 \in A$ (f) $C \subset B$
(c) $4 \in A$ (g) $6 \in B$
(d) $1 \in A$ and $1 \in C$ (h) $2 \notin A$

6. Represent the set B by a Venn diagram and shade its complement.

7. Use Venn diagrams to illustrate the following:

(a) $A \subset B$ (c) *A* is not a subset of *B*

(b) $B \subset A$ (d) *B* is not a subset of *A*

12-2 INTERSECTIONS AND UNIONS

DEFINITION 12.4. *Let A and B be sets. The set $A \cap B$, which is read A intersect B, consists of all the elements that belong to both A and B.*

Example 1. | $\{2, 3, 4, 6\} \cap \{1, 4, 5, 6\} = \{4, 6\}$

Example 2. | $\{a, b, c\} \cap \{d, e\} = \varnothing$, the empty set

Example 3. | {plant 1, plant 2, plant 3} ∩ {plant 2, plant 3, plant 4} = {plant 2, plant 3}

Definition 12.4 is illustrated further by the Venn diagrams in Fig. 12-2.

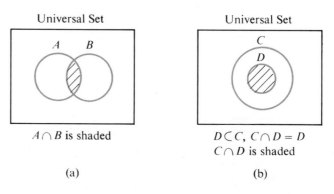

Universal Set	Universal Set
$A \cap B$ is shaded	$D \subset C, C \cap D = D$
	$C \cap D$ is shaded
(a)	(b)

FIGURE 12-2

DEFINITION 12.5. *Let A and B be sets. The set $A \cup B$, which is read A union B, consists of the elements that belong to A or B or both.*

Example 4. | $\{1, 4, 7\} \cup \{3, 5, 7, 8\} = \{1, 3, 4, 5, 7, 8\}$. Note that 7 is a member of both sets, but is only listed once in the union.

Example 5. | $\{a, b, c\} \cup \varnothing = \{a, b, c\}$

Example 6. | {product 1, product 2} ∪ {plant 1, plant 2} = {product 1, product 2, plant 1, plant 2}

Definition 12.5 is illustrated further by the Venn diagrams in Fig. 12-3.

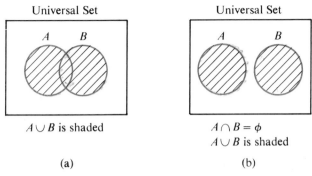

$A \cup B$ is shaded

(a)

$A \cap B = \phi$

$A \cup B$ is shaded

(b)

F I G U R E 12-3

The following notation is in current use: $A = \{x: x \text{ has property } p\}$. This would be read "$A$ is the set of x *such that* x has property p." Note that the colon is read *such that*.

Example 7. | $A \cap B = \{x: x \in A \text{ and } x \in B\}$

Example 8. | $A \cup B = \{x: x \in A \text{ or } x \in B \text{ or both}\}$

PROBLEMS

1. Given $A = \{1, 2, 3, 4\}$ and $B = \{2, 4, 7, 9\}$, find
   (a) $A \cap B$ (b) $A \cup B$

2. Given $A = \{\text{product 1, product 2, product 3}\}$ and $B = \{\text{plant 1, plant 2, plant 3, plant 4}\}$, find
   (a) $A \cap B$ (b) $A \cup B$

3. Use Venn diagrams to illustrate Prob. 1.

4. Use Venn diagrams to illustrate Prob. 2.

5. Given $A \subset B$, find
   (a) $A \cap B$ (b) $A \cup B$

6. Use Venn diagrams to illustrate Prob. 5.

7. Let $\Omega = \{1, 2, 3, \ldots, 10\}$
   $A = \{1, 2, 5\}$
   $B = \{3, 5, 9\}$

   Find
   (a) A' (c) $A' \cap B$
   (b) B' (d) $A \cup B'$

8. Use Venn diagrams to illustrate Prob. 7.

12-3 SAMPLE SPACES

The term *experiment* as used in probability refers to the performance of an act. The process of flipping a coin is an example of an experiment. Other examples of experiments are drawing a card from a deck, choosing an account from a file, and setting up a machine.

The set of all possible outcomes of a given experiment is called the *sample space* for the experiment.

Example 1. Consider the experiment of tossing a coin. What is the sample space for this experiment?

Solution: Considering the outcome of landing on its edge as impossible, we have the set $\{H, T\}$, where H stands for head and T stands for tail, as the sample space.

Example 2. A sample space for the experiment, which consists of setting up a given machine, is $\{C, I\}$, where C denotes a correct set-up and I denotes an incorrect set-up.

Consider an experiment with a finite number of outcomes with a sample space $\{x_1, x_2, x_3, \ldots, x_n\}$. The individual outcomes x_1, x_2, $\ldots$ are called *sample points*.

Example 3. Consider the experiment of choosing an account from an accounts receivable file where the maximum balance is $1000. List the sample points for this experiment.

Solution:

$$x_1 = 0, \ x_2 = \$0.01, \ldots, x_{101} = \$1.00, \ldots, x_{100,000} = \$1000$$

Not all experiments have a finite number of outcomes. In this case, we cannot list all of the sample points. We can list typical sample points and possibly describe all of them.

Example 4. The thickness of a tablet is known to be between 0.4 and 0.6 centimeters. Discuss the sample space consisting of the possible thicknesses of this tablet.

Solution: Let x denote a possible thickness. Then the resulting sample space is $S = \{x: 0.4 \text{ cm.} \leq x \leq 0.6 \text{ cm.}\}$.

In Examples 1 and 2, the sample points are described *qualitatively*. In Examples 3 and 4, the sample points are described *quantitatively*. Sample spaces that are described quantitatively can be further classified as *discrete* or *continuous*. The sample space in Example 3 is discrete; the sample space in Example 4 is continuous. These classifications are extremely important in statistics.

PROBLEMS

1. List the elements of the sample space for the experiment of tossing two coins.

2. List the elements of the sample space for the experiment of tossing three coins. [*Hint:* List the triples (*H*, *T*, *H*), etc.]

3. A class of students received letter grades *A*, *B*, *C*, *D*, and *F* on a certain exam. List the elements of the sample space for the experiment of picking a student's name at random from the professor's roll book and recording the student's grade.

4. A certain battery manufacturer produces batteries advertised to last at least 10 hours under continuous use. Consider the experiment of testing and recording the lifetime of every 100th battery from the production line.
   (a) List three possible outcomes, in your judgment, of this experiment.
   (b) Is the sample space of this experiment continuous or discrete?

5. Give an example of a discrete sample space.

6. Give an example of a continuous sample space.

7. Give an example of a qualitative sample space.

12-4 ASSIGNMENT OF PROBABILITIES

It was pointed out in the previous section that a sample point is a possible outcome of an experiment. A probability value is the likelihood of a sample point occurring. To be useful in decision making, we require a measure of likelihood that will enable us to compare the likelihood of any given sample point with the likelihoods of all other sample points. In this section we discuss the methods of assigning a number, i.e., a probability value between 0 and 1 inclusive, to each sample point in the given sample space. These numbers are called probabilities and are denoted by $p(x_i)$, where x_i is the ith sample point. There are three ways to assign a probability value to a sample point. These are relative frequency, subjective judgment, and the use of known probability distributions. This last method is generally taken up in a statistics course. In this section we will concentrate on the method of relative frequency.

To illustrate the process of assigning probabilities, we consider the simple experiment of tossing a coin. The sample space for this experiment has two points, $x_1 = H$ and $x_2 = T$. Intuitively, we would assign a probability of $\frac{1}{2}$ to x_1 and a probability of $\frac{1}{2}$ to x_2. Similarly, if the experiment consists of covering a pea with one of three cups, we would assign a probability of $\frac{1}{3}$ to each sample point.

The assignment of the probabilities in the previous experiments is based on the assumption that the coin is fair and the person covering the pea is honest. The assignment is also based on the *subjective* judgment that all of the outcomes are equally likely. Note that the probabilities were found by dividing 1 by the number of sample points.

Example 1. | Consider an experiment with sample space $x_1, x_2, \ldots, x_{12}$. Assign a probability to each sample point assuming equal likelihood.

Solution:

$$p(x_1) = \tfrac{1}{12}, p(x_2) = \tfrac{1}{12}, \ldots, p(x_{12}) = \tfrac{1}{12}$$

In general, for experiments with n sample points, the assumption of equal likelihood leads to $p(x_i) = 1/n$ for each i between 1 and n.

In the discussion so far we were forced to make some assumptions or judgments about the outcomes. In other words, the probabilities were assigned on a subjective basis. Next we discuss an objective method of assigning probabilities.

For the experiment of tossing a coin, an objective method of assigning probabilities consists of flipping the coin 10 times and recording the number of times each possible outcome occurs. The following is a possible outcome of flipping a coin 10 times: *H, T, H, H, T, H, T, H, T, H*. Recording these results in tabular form, we have

TABLE 12-1

Outcome	Number of Times
H	6
T	4

Sample Point	Frequency
x_1	6
x_2	4

Let $f(x_i)$ denote the number of times x_i occurs. We have

Sample Point	$f(x_i)$
x_1	6
x_2	4
	10

Calculating probabilities, we have

$$p(x_1) = \frac{f(x_1)}{f(x_1) + f(x_2)} \quad \text{and} \quad p(x_2) = \frac{f(x_2)}{f(x_1) + f(x_2)}$$

$$p(x_1) = \frac{6}{6+4} \qquad \text{and} \qquad p(x_2) = \frac{4}{6+4}$$

$$p(x_1) = 0.6 \qquad\qquad\qquad p(x_2) = 0.4$$

TABLE 12-2

x_i	$f(x_i)$	$p(x_i)$
x_1	6	0.6
x_2	4	0.4

In general,

$$p(x_i) = \frac{f(x_i)}{f(x_1) + f(x_2) + \cdots + f(x_n)}$$

When applying this formula to experiments with a large number of sample points, it is convenient to use the summation notation, $\sum_{i=1}^{n} f(x_i)$, where $\sum_{i=1}^{n} f(x_i) = f(x_1) + f(x_2) + \cdots + f(x_n)$.

The symbol $\sum_{i=1}^{n} f(x_i)$ would be read summation of $f(x_i)$ from $i = 1$ to $i = n$.

Example 2. Express the sum $f(x_1) + f(x_2) + \cdots + f(x_7)$. Use summation notation.

Solution:

$$f(x_1) + f(x_2) + \cdots + f(x_7) = \sum_{i=1}^{7} f(x_i)$$

The hypothetical outcome *H, T, H, H, T, H, T, H, T, H* used in the above discussion, which leads to $p(H) = 0.6$ and $p(T) = 0.4$, may seem inconsistent with the subjective probabilities, $p(H) = 0.5$ and $p(T) = 0.5$. This apparent discrepancy does not mean that the coin is not fair, but results from the small number of times that the coin was tossed. If the reader cared to flip a coin 1000 times and record the results, he would expect his resulting objective probabilities to be much closer to $p(H) = 0.5$ and $p(T) = 0.5$.

Let S be a sample space for a given experiment. Consider the situation where the experiment is repeated a large number of times, N. If x_i is a typical sample point in S, then $P(x_i) = \lim_{N \to \infty} f(x_i)/N$, where $f(x_i)$ denotes the number of times that x_i occurs for a given number of trials. In this way, probability is defined as relative frequency in the long run.

PROBLEMS

1. Consider an experiment with sample space $\{x_1, x_2, \ldots, x_6\}$. Assign a probability to each sample point. Assume equal likelihood.

2. Flip a coin 20 times and record your results.

3. Use the data obtained in Prob. 2 to calculate the probability of a head or a tail.

4. **Group Problem.** Gather the probability of a head and the probability of a tail as calculated by each student in Prob. 2. Add them and divide by the number of students. If you have a class of 20 students, the result obtained is equivalent to flipping a coin 400 times.

5. Write the following in expanded form:

   (a) $\sum_{i=1}^{5} f(x_i)$ (c) $(\sum_{i=1}^{4} x_i)^2$

   (b) $\sum_{i=1}^{4} x_i^2$ (d) $\sum_{i=1}^{5} x_i f(x_i)$

6. Use summation notation to express the following:

   (a) $x_1^2 f(x_1) + x_2^2 f(x_2) + x_3^2 f(x_3)$

   (b) $[x_1 f(x_1) + x_2 f(x_2) + x_3 f(x_3)]^2$

12-5 EVENTS

The reader will recall that the set of all possible outcomes of an experiment is called the sample space for the experiment.

DEFINITION 12.6.   *Consider an experiment E with sample space S. Then any subset of S is called an event.*

Example 1.   Let $S = \{x_1, x_2, x_3, x_4, x_5\}$. List three events.

Solution:

$A = \{x_2\}$

$B = \{x_1, x_3\}$

$C = \{x_2, x_4, x_5\}$

We should point out that the sample space itself is always an event and the empty set is also an event.

Next we will define the terms *exhaustive* and *mutually exclusive*.

DEFINITION 12.7.   *Two events A and B are said to be exhaustive if $A \cup B = S$, where S is the sample space.*

DEFINITION 12.8.   *Two events A and B are said to be mutually exclusive if $A \cap B = \varnothing$, where $\varnothing$ denotes the empty set.*

Example 2.   Describe the events *A*, *B*, and *C* of Example 1 using the terms exhaustive and mutually exclusive.

Solution:

$A = \{x_2\},$ $B = \{x_1, x_3\},$ and $C = \{x_2, x_4, x_5\}$

Events *B* and *C* are exhaustive since

$B \cup C = \{x_1, x_3\} \cup \{x_2, x_4, x_5\}$

$\qquad = \{x_1, x_2, x_3, x_4, x_5\}$

$B \cup C = S$

Events A and B are mutually exclusive since

$$A \cap B = \{x_2\} \cap \{x_1, x_3\}$$
$$A \cap B = \varnothing$$

In Sec. 12-4 it was pointed out that the probability of a sample point is a number between zero and one.

DEFINITION 12.9.   *Let A be an event. Then the probability of A denoted by p(A) is defined to be the sum of the probabilities of all of the sample points in A.*

Example 3.   Consider the experiment of drawing a single card from a standard deck of playing cards. Let K be the event of drawing a king. Find $p(K)$.

Solution: $K = \{K_h, K_s, K_c, K_d\}$. The probability of each sample point in K is $\frac{1}{52}$.
Therefore,

$$p(K) = p(K_h) + p(K_s) + p(K_c) + p(K_d)$$
$$= \frac{1}{52} + \frac{1}{52} + \frac{1}{52} + \frac{1}{52}$$
$$p(K) = \frac{4}{52} = \frac{1}{13}$$

Let $A = \{a_1, a_2, \ldots, a_n\}$ be an event. Then $p(A) = p(a_1) + p(a_2) + \cdots + p(a_n)$ by Definition 12.9. Next, we ask the question: Can probabilities be added if the events are not just sample points? This question is answered below.

Let A and B be two *mutually exclusive* events. Then $p(A \cup B) = p(A) + p(B)$. This result is a consequence of the definition of $A \cup B$ and Definitions 12.8 and 12.9.

Example 4.   Let Q be the event of drawing a queen and K be the event of drawing a king from a standard deck of playing cards. Find $p(K \cup Q)$.

Solution:

$$K \cap Q = \varnothing$$

Therefore, K and Q are mutually exclusive.

$$p(K \cup Q) = p(K) + p(Q)$$
$$p(K \cup Q) = \frac{4}{52} + \frac{4}{52}$$
$$p(K \cup Q) = \frac{2}{13}$$

The probability of drawing a king or a queen is $\frac{2}{13}$.

If A and B are not mutually exclusive, then $p(A \cup B) = p(A) + p(B) - p(A \cap B)$. The additional term $p(A \cap B)$ is needed to compensate for double counting which occurs in this case. This formula is illustrated below with a Venn diagram.

Sample Space

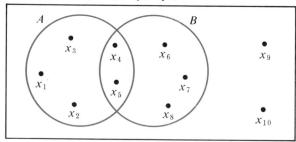

FIGURE 12-4

$$p(A) = p(x_1) + p(x_2) + p(x_3) + p(x_4) + p(x_5)$$
$$p(B) = p(x_4) + p(x_5) + p(x_6) + p(x_7) + p(x_8)$$
$$p(A \cap B) = p(x_4) + p(x_5)$$
$$p(A \cup B) = p(A) + p(B) - p(A \cap B)$$
$$p(A \cup B) = [p(x_1) + p(x_2) + p(x_3) + p(x_4) + p(x_5)]$$
$$+ [p(x_6) + p(x_7) + p(x_8)]$$

Example 5.

Consider the experiment of drawing numbers between 1 and 6 from a hat. Let $A = \{3, 4, 6\}$ and $B = \{1, 4, 5, 6\}$. Compute $p(A \cup B)$.

Solution: The sample space has 6 elements. If we assume equal likelihood, we have $p(1) = \frac{1}{6}$, $p(3) = \frac{1}{6}$, etc.

$$p(A) = \tfrac{3}{6}, \qquad p(B) = \tfrac{4}{6}, \qquad p(A \cap B) = p\{4, 6\} = \tfrac{2}{6}$$

Note that $p(A) + p(B) = \frac{7}{6}$, which clearly could not be $p(A \cup B)$, since the probability of an event never exceeds one. If we apply the correct formula, we have

$$p(A \cup B) = p(A) + p(B) - p(A \cap B)$$
$$p(A \cup B) = \tfrac{3}{6} + \tfrac{4}{6} - \tfrac{2}{6}$$
$$p(A \cup B) = \tfrac{5}{6}$$

PROBLEMS

1. Consider an experiment with sample space $S = \{x_1, x_2, \ldots, x_5\}$. Which of the following pairs of events are mutually exclusive?
   - **(a)** $A = \{x_1, x_3, x_5\}$
   - **(b)** $B = \{x_2, x_4\}$
   - **(c)** $D = \{x_2, x_4, x_5\}$
   - **(d)** $E = \{x_2, x_5\}$

2. Which pairs of events in Prob. 1 are exhaustive?

3. An experiment consists of drawing a card from a standard deck of playing cards. Determine the following probabilities:
   - **(a)** p(drawing a 10)
   - **(b)** p(drawing a king)
   - **(c)** p(drawing a face card)

4. Let K be the event of drawing a king and A be the event of drawing an ace. Refer to Prob. 3. Compute the following:
    (a) $p(A \cap K)$
    (b) $p(A \cup K)$

5. Are the events in Prob. 4 mutually exclusive? Exhaustive?

6. A number between 1 and 10, inclusive, is drawn from a hat. Events A, B, C, and D are defined as follows: $A = \{1, 3, 5, 7, 9\}$, $B = \{2, 4, 6, 8, 10\}$, $C = \emptyset$, and $D = \{3, 4, 5\}$. Assume equal likelihood. Compute the probability of the events listed below.

    (a) $p(A)$ (e) $p(A \cap D)$
    (b) $p(A \cap B)$ (f) $p(A \cup D)$
    (c) $p(C)$ (g) $p(C \cup A)$
    (d) $p(A \cup B)$ (h) $p(C \cup D)$

12-6 AN APPLICATION

A final exam was given to a class of 33 students and the grades were as follows. Listed alphabetically the grades are

86	70	67	73	69	80	78	79	73	67	94
73	73	70	78	70	79	77	78	82	77	95
93	65	63	69	77	65	73	70	69	77	67

Arranging the grades in ascending order, we form the following table.

TABLE 12-3

x_i	$f(x_i)$	$p(x_i)$
63	1	$1/33$
65	2	$2/33$
67	3	$3/33$
69	3	$3/33$
70	4	$4/33$
73	5	$5/33$
77	4	$4/33$
78	3	$3/33$
79	2	$2/33$
80	1	$1/33$
82	1	$1/33$
86	1	$1/33$
93	1	$1/33$
94	1	$1/33$
95	1	$1/33$
	33	1

To assign grades A, B, C, and D, we group the data into 4 mutually exclusive events. This results in the following table.

TABLE 12-4

Grade	Event	Mark	$f(E_i)$	$p(E_i)$
A	E_1	90–100	3	$\frac{3}{33}$
B	E_2	80–89	3	$\frac{3}{33}$
C	E_3	70–79	18	$\frac{18}{33}$
D	E_4	60–69	9	$\frac{9}{33}$
			$\overline{33}$	1

A sample calculation for $p(E_4)$ based on Definition 12.9:

$$E_4 = \{63, 65, 67, 69\}$$
$$p(E_4) = p(63) + p(65) + p(67) + p(69)$$

$$p(E_4) = \frac{1}{33} + \frac{2}{33} + \frac{3}{33} + \frac{3}{33}$$

$$p(E_4) = \frac{9}{33} \qquad \text{as shown in the table above}$$

We point out that it is not by coincidence that this number can also be obtained by dividing $f(E_4)$ by 33. In fact, the following formula is valid:

$$p(E_i) = \frac{f(E_i)}{f(E_1) + f(E_2) + \cdots + f(E_n)}$$

Or, using summation notation,

$$p(E_i) = \frac{f(E_i)}{\sum_{i=1}^{n} f(E_i)}$$

Sample calculation for $p(E_3)$ using the above formula is

$$p(E_3) = \frac{f(E_3)}{f(E_1) + f(E_2) + f(E_3) + f(E_4)}$$

$$p(E_3) = \frac{18}{3 + 3 + 18 + 9}$$

$$p(E_3) = \frac{18}{33}$$

PROBLEMS

1. A sample of 20 accounts was taken from an accounts receivable file. The balances of these 20 accounts are as follows:

$191	$ 61	$ 22	$ 35	$186
$ 90	$ 16	$115	$ 74	$ 83
$146	$159	$ 67	$125	$135
$ 48	$104	$163	$176	$ 79

Arrange the balances in ascending order.

2. Classify the sample points in Prob. 1 into four events and record the frequency of each event (i.e., 0–49, 50–99, 100–149, 150–199).

3. Calculate the probability of the events in Prob. 2.

4. The height of 15 students in a class rounded to the nearest inch is as follows:

75	68	71	67	62
69	64	61	73	67
65	73	67	74	71

Arrange the heights in ascending order and present them in a table that includes the $f(x_i)$.

5. Calculate the probability of each of the sample points in Prob. 4.

6. Classify the sample points of Prob. 4 into 3 events and record the frequency of each event (i.e., 61–65, 66–70, 71–75).

7. Calculate the probability of each event in Prob. 6 two different ways.

12-7 SOME COUNTING FORMULAS

Before stating the formulas that will be discussed in this section, we will describe a simple seating arrangement problem that involves counting.

Suppose three students, Jim, Jack, and Mary, are instructed to be seated in three chairs. The chairs are in a row. We are asked to determine the total number of possible seating arrangements. Since there are only three people involved, we can simply list the possible ways as follows:

Jim, Jack, Mary
Jim, Mary, Jack
Jack, Jim, Mary
Jack, Mary, Jim
Mary, Jim, Jack
Mary, Jack, Jim

We see that there are six possible seating arrangements in this case. It will be shown later in this section that if there are five people instead of three, then the total number of possible ways of seating them is 120.

Example 1. | Refer to the seating arrangement problem of Jim, Jack, and Mary and randomly select one of the possible seating arrangements. Determine the probability of Jim getting to sit next to Mary.

Solution: Of the 6 possible seating arrangements, Jim gets to sit next to Mary in 4 of them. Therefore, the desired probability is $\frac{2}{3}$.

The three counting formulas derived in this section are based on the following counting principle. *Suppose an act or procedure can be performed in N_1 different ways and a second act or procedure can be performed in N_2 different ways. Then the total number of ways that the* *two procedures can be performed consecutively is given by the product* $N_1 N_2$.

Imagine a set of n objects (real or mathematical) arranged in some definite order. The given arrangement or any possible rearrangement of the n objects is called a *permutation* of the objects involved. It follows from the counting principle, stated above, that the total number of possible permutations or rearrangements of n objects is given by $n!$, where $n! = n(n-1) \cdots (2)1$. The symbol $n!$ is read n factorial. To see this we note that the first position can be filled in n ways, the second position can be filled in $n-1$ ways, and so on. The next to the last position can be filled in 2 ways and the last position can be filled with the one remaining object. Therefore, it follows from a repeated application of the counting principle that the total number of ways that these n procedures can be performed sequentially is given by $n!$

Example 2. | How many ways can five people be seated in five chairs? The chairs are in a row.

Solution: Five objects of any kind can be rearranged in five positions in $5! = 120$ ways.

When dealing with permutations, we have n objects to be rearranged in the same number of positions. Suppose now that there may be fewer available positions than there are objects, say n objects and k positions with $k \leq n$. It follows from the counting principle that the number of possible rearrangements of n objects in k positions, where order is regarded, is given by $n(n-1) \cdots (n-k+1)$. This formula can be written in factorial form as $n!/(n-k)!$ If we introduce the notation $p(n, k)$ to indicate the number of possible rearrangements of n objects taken k at a time, we have

$$p(n, k) = \frac{n!}{(n-k)!} \tag{1}$$

We know from above that

$$p(n, n) = n! \tag{2}$$

Furthermore, if we adopt the usual definition $0! = 1$, we see that Eq. (2) is a special case of Eq. (1). Frequently, it is of little interest to determine all possible rearrangements of n objects taken k at a time. The matter of interest is the number of ways (disregarding order) that k objects can be chosen from a set of n objects ($k \leq n$). Each possible choice is called a *combination*. We use the notation $c(n, k)$ to denote the number of combinations, or k element subsets, that can be formed from n objects. The formula for $c(n, k)$, the number of combinations of n objects taken k at a time, is as follows:

$$c(n, k) = \frac{n!}{k!(n-k)!} \tag{3}$$

Proof of (3):   It follows from the counting principle and the definitions of $p(n, k)$, $c(n, k)$, and $p(k, k)$ that

$$p(n, k) = c(n, k)p(k, k)$$

Therefore, $n!/(n - k)! = c(n, k)k!$ and the result follows.

The notation $c(n, k) = \binom{n}{k}$ is also common.

SUMMARY

$p(n, k) = n!/(n - k)!$	order is regarded	(1)
$p(n, n) = n!$	order is regarded	(2)
$c(n, k) = \dfrac{n!}{k!(n - k)!}$	order is not regarded	(3)

Example 3.

Consider an urn that contains 8 red balls, 7 green balls, and 5 blue balls. Assume equal likelihood. Compute the probability, $p(R)$, of drawing 4 red balls on a given 4-ball draw. Assume the balls are drawn without replacement.

Solution: The sample space contains $c(20, 4)$ points. The event R will occur at $c(8, 4)$ of these sample points. Therefore,

$$p(R) = \frac{c(8, 4)}{c(20, 4)} = \frac{\dfrac{8!}{4!4!}}{\dfrac{20!}{16!4!}}$$

$$= \frac{\dfrac{8 \cdot 7 \cdot 6 \cdot 5}{4 \cdot 3 \cdot 2 \cdot 1}}{\dfrac{20 \cdot 19 \cdot 18 \cdot 17}{4 \cdot 3 \cdot 2 \cdot 1}} = \frac{14}{19(51)}$$

$$= 0.014$$

Example 4.

Consider the experiment of tossing 4 coins. Let the events A, B, C, D, and E be defined as follows:

A—0 heads, B—1 head, C—2 heads, D—3 heads,   and E—4 heads

Compute $p(A)$, $p(B)$, $p(C)$, $p(D)$, and $p(E)$.

Solution: A is the sample point (T, T, T, T); E is the sample point (H, H, H, H). B contains 4 sample points (H, T, T, T), (T, H, T, T), and so on. D contains 4 sample points (T, H, H, H) and so on. To find the number of sample points in C, we compute

$$\binom{4}{2} = \frac{4!}{2!2!} = 6$$

The total number of sample points is given by

$$1 + 4 + 6 + 4 + 1 = 16$$
$$p(A) = \tfrac{1}{16}, \quad p(B) = \tfrac{4}{16}, \quad p(C) = \tfrac{6}{16}, \quad p(D) = \tfrac{4}{16}, \quad p(E) = \tfrac{1}{16}$$

PROBLEMS

1. Compute the following:

   (a) 6!

   (b) $\dfrac{5!}{3!\ 2!}$

   (c) 7!

   (d) $\dfrac{7!}{2!\ 5!}$

2. Use logs to compute 5!

3. Compute the following:

   (a) $\dbinom{5}{2} = c(5, 2)$

   (b) $\dbinom{6}{0} = c(6, 0)$

   (c) $\dbinom{4}{1}$

   (d) $\dbinom{4}{0} + \dbinom{4}{1} + \dbinom{4}{2} + \dbinom{4}{3} + \dbinom{4}{4}$

4. How many 3-element subsets can be formed from a set containing 8 elements?

5. If a part has to be worked on in five different departments and can be worked on in any order, how many different ways are there for the part to be produced?

6. How many committees of four can be formed from a class of 25 students?

7. A committee of four is to be selected in a completely random fashion from the class of 20 students. The professor has the students listed in his roll book in alphabetical order. What is the probability that the first four students listed in the roll book will be chosen for the committee?

8. How many slates of officers (p, v, s, t) can be formed from a class of 15 students? Assume that no student may hold more than one office.

9. A 12-member club elects its officers (p, v, s, t) by a completely random process and no club member can hold more than one office at a time. Determine the probability that a given slate of officers will be elected.

10. How many different samples of size 5 can be chosen from a lot of 104?

11. Given that we have a file of accounts receivable containing 5 accounts, we want to choose a sample of 3 accounts to estimate the average balance of the file. (Note that, in practice, when working with a small population one would not take a sample.) The balances in the five accounts are as follows:

Account	Balance
001	$100.00
002	160.00
003	120.00
004	150.00
005	130.00

    (a) How many samples of size 3 can be drawn from the file? [Note: order is not important.]

    (b) List the possible samples that can be chosen.

(c) Compute the arithmetic average for each sample in part *b*.

Problems 12 and 13 are based on the following definition from statistics.

Mean of sampling distribution is denoted by $\mu_{\bar{x}}$. Therefore,

$$\mu_{\bar{x}} = \frac{\sum_{i=1}^{c(n,k)} (\text{sample mean})_i}{c(n,k)}$$

where n = the population size
k = the sample size

12. Calculate $\mu_{\bar{x}}$ for Prob. 11.

13. Find the upper index of the summation symbol in $\mu_{\bar{x}}$ for a population size of 12 and a sample size of 4.

14. A question of interest to many managers is—How many subordinates can a supervisor handle effectively in a given situation? One of the variables to be considered is the number of interpersonal relationships inherent in a given situation. Graicunas's law states that there are three kinds of relationships:

A. Direct single relationships, $= n$
i.e., supervisor with subordinate
B. Cross relationships, $= n(n - 1)$
i.e., subordinate with subordinate
C. Direct group relationships, $= n\left(\dfrac{2^n}{2} - 1\right)$
i.e., supervisor with subordinate,
modified by presence of another subordinate

where n = number of persons being supervised. The total number of relationships is

$$f = A + B + C \qquad \text{or} \qquad f = n\left(\frac{2^n}{2} + n - 1\right)$$

Calculate f for $n = 1, 2, 3, 4, 5, 6, 7, 8, 9, 10$.

15. Show that

$$n + n(n - 1) + n\left(\frac{2^n}{2} - 1\right) = n\left(\frac{2^n}{2} + n - 1\right)$$

Refer to Prob. 14.

16. The Braille alphabet using the six-dot cell was developed by Louis Braille in about 1829. The six dots of the Braille cell are arranged and numbered thus:

321

The arrangement can be a single dot in any position, two dots in any position, etc. To represent k, the dots numbered 1 and 3 appear.

Note that the absence of all dots is not a valid character. In how many possible combinations can we arrange these dots? In other words, how many characters are there in this touch-alphabet?

THIRTEEN

Additional topics in probability

13-1 UNIVARIATE vs. BIVARIATE DATA

In each example of the previous chapter there was only one characteristic of interest. A case in point is the grade problem taken up in the
previous chapter, where the grade is the characteristic or variable of
interest.

If we repeat the table from Sec. 12-6, we have

TABLE 13-1

Grade	Event	$f(E_i)$	$p(E_i)$
A	E_1	3	$\frac{3}{33}$
B	E_2	3	$\frac{3}{33}$
C	E_3	18	$\frac{18}{33}$
D	E_4	9	$\frac{9}{33}$

We can read directly from this table $p(A) = \frac{3}{33}$, $p(B) = \frac{3}{33}$, etc.
These probabilities are called *marginal probabilities*.

These students could also be classified according to I.Q. This
classification is given in Table 13-2.

TABLE 13-2

Event	I.Q.	$f(F_i)$	$p(F_i)$
F_1	low = L	11	$\frac{1}{3}$
F_2	medium = M	11	$\frac{1}{3}$
F_3	high = H	11	$\frac{1}{3}$

This means $p(L) = 1/3$, $p(M) = 1/3$, and $p(H) = 1/3$.

Although information classified according to one variable is useful, it is more significant to classify the data according to two or more variables. A set of data is said to be univariate when classified according to one variable and bivariate when classified according to two variables. In the next section the above students are classified according to two variables, grades and I.Q. Once this has been done, we can determine, for example, the probability of a student having a medium I.Q. and a grade of *B*.

A typical format for displaying bivariate data is shown in Table 13-3.

TABLE 13-3

Grade \ I.Q.	F_1	F_2	F_3	Total
E_1				3
E_2				3
E_3				18
E_4				9
Total	11	11	11	33

To fill in the remaining 12 entries in this table we must go through the list of students and take note of both characteristics of interest at the same time. This can be done by forming a separate tally sheet and then transferring the totals from the tally sheet to the table. The tally sheet must have the same number of lines as there are blank entries in the table.

TABLE 13-4 TALLY SHEET

I.Q.	Grade	Tally Marks	Total
L	*A*	/	1
L	*B*	/	1
L	*C*	𝍸 /	6
L	*D*	///	3
M	*A*	/	1
M	*B*	/	1
M	*C*	𝍸 /	6
M	*D*	///	3
H	*A*	/	1
H	*B*	/	1
H	*C*	𝍸 /	6
H	*D*	///	3

Using the information from the tally sheet, we have the following bivariate frequency table.

TABLE 13-5

Grade \ I.Q.	L	M	H	Total
A	1	1	1	3
B	1	1	1	3
C	6	6	6	18
D	3	3	3	9
Total	11	11	11	33

PROBLEMS

1. Given the following table of employees at the XYZ Company:

TABLE 13-6

Employees	Earnings	$f(E_i)$
E_1	1.50–2.49	15
E_2	2.50–3.49	20
E_3	3.50–4.49	30
E_4	4.50–5.49	20
E_5	5.50–6.49	15
		100

   (a) Calculate all marginal probabilities.
   (b) What is the probability that an employee chosen at random earns between $2.50 and $3.49?
   (c) Calculate $p(E_1 \cup E_2)$.
   (d) Explain in words the probability calculated in (c).

2. If the same group of 100 employees that work for the company in Prob. 1 are classified according to skill level, we have the following table:

TABLE 13-7

Employees	Skill Level	
F_1	unskilled	17
F_2	semi-skilled	50
F_3	skilled	33
		100

(a) Calculate the marginal probabilities.
(b) What is the probability that a given employee chosen at random is a skilled worker?
(c) Calculate $p(F_2 \cup F_3)$.
(d) Explain in words the probability calculated in (c).
(e) Would it be more meaningful if these employees were classified by earnings and skill level simultaneously?

3. Given the following tally sheet for the 100 employees of the XYZ Company, set up the bivariate frequency table. (U = unskilled, SS = semi-skilled, and S = skilled)

TABLE 13-8

Earnings	Type of Worker	Total
1.50–2.49	U	10
1.50–2.49	SS	5
1.50–2.49	S	0
2.50–3.49	U	6
2.50–3.49	SS	11
2.50–3.49	S	3
3.50–4.49	U	1
3.50–4.49	SS	22
3.50–4.49	S	7
4.50–5.49	U	0
4.50–5.49	SS	10
4.50–5.49	S	10
5.50–6.49	U	0
5.50–6.49	SS	2
5.50–6.49	S	13
		100

4. The 10,500 employees of a certain company are classified according to sex and type of work, i.e., sales or production. Given that 6000 employees are male production workers and 3500 workers are in sales. Of the 3500 workers engaged in sales, 1500 are females.

(a)   Set up the bivariate frequency table.
(b)   How many males work at this company?
(c)   How many females are production workers?
(d)   How many females or production workers are employed?

5.   Given the following table:

TABLE 13-9

		A_1 Freshmen	A_2 Sophomores	A_3 Juniors	A_4 Seniors	Total
B_1	Have financial assistance	—	40	60	70	200
B_2	No financial assistance	270	—	—	—	800
	Total	300	250	250	200	1000

(a)   Complete the table.
(b)   How many elements are in A_1?
(c)   How many elements are in B_2?
(d)   How many elements are in the population?
(e)   What is $p(A_1)$?
(f)   What is $p(B_2)$?

13-2   JOINT AND MARGINAL PROBABILITIES

Converting Table 13-5 of the previous section to a table of probabilities by dividing each entry by 33, we have

TABLE 13-10

Grade \ I.Q.	L	M	H	Total
A	$\frac{1}{33}$	$\frac{1}{33}$	$\frac{1}{33}$	$\frac{3}{33}$
B	$\frac{1}{33}$	$\frac{1}{33}$	$\frac{1}{33}$	$\frac{3}{33}$
C	$\frac{6}{33}$	$\frac{6}{33}$	$\frac{6}{33}$	$\frac{18}{33}$
D	$\frac{3}{33}$	$\frac{3}{33}$	$\frac{3}{33}$	$\frac{9}{33}$
Total	$\frac{11}{33}$	$\frac{11}{33}$	$\frac{11}{33}$	1

This is a typical probability table for bivariate data. The probabilities in the total row and total column are called *marginal* probabilities. The other entries are called *joint* probabilities.

327

The marginal probabilities correspond to a univariate classification of the given data and the joint probabilities correspond to a bivariate classification of the data. For example, $p(A) = \frac{3}{33}$, $p(M) = \frac{11}{33}$, etc. Also $p(A \cap M) = \frac{1}{33}$, $p(C \cap H) = \frac{6}{33}$, etc.

Example 1. | Compute $p(A \cup H)$ using Table 13-10.

Solution:

$$p(A \cup H) = p(A) + p(H) - p(A \cap H)$$
$$= \frac{3}{33} + \frac{11}{33} - \frac{1}{33}$$
$$p(A \cup H) = \frac{13}{33}$$

In other words, 13 of the 33 students in this class have either a grade of A or a high I.Q. or both a grade of A and a high I.Q.

Next we include a bivariate classification of a standard deck of playing cards.

TABLE 13-11

		D_1	D_2	D_3	D_4	D_5	
		2–10	J	Q	K	A	Total
E_1	Diamonds	9	1	1	1	1	13
E_2	Spades	9	1	1	1	1	13
E_3	Hearts	9	1	1	1	1	13
E_4	Clubs	9	1	1	1	1	13
	Total	36	4	4	4	4	52

Example 2. | Use the data in Table 13-11 to find $p(E_2)$, $p(D_3)$, $p(E_1 \cap D_4)$, and $p(E_4 \cup D_1)$.

Solution:

$$p(E_2) = \frac{13}{52} = \frac{1}{4}$$
$$p(D_3) = \frac{4}{52} = \frac{1}{13}$$
$$p(E_1 \cap D_4) = \frac{1}{52}$$
$$p(E_4 \cup D_1) = p(E_4) + p(D_1) - p(E_4 \cap D_1) = \frac{13}{52} + \frac{36}{52} - \frac{9}{52}$$
$$p(E_4 \cup D_1) = \frac{40}{52}$$

We point out that the sum of the joint probabilities in a given row or column equals the marginal probability of that row or column. Also, the marginal probabilities in the bottom row and right-hand column both add up to one. These remarks are true because we classify our data into exhaustive and mutually exclusive events.

Example 3. A sample space S is classified into exhaustive and mutually exclusive events A_1 and A_2. It is also classified into exhaustive and exclusive events B_1 and B_2. It is known that $p(A_1) = 0.6$, $p(B_2) = 0.3$, and $p(A_1 \cap B_1) = 0.5$. Set up a complete probability table from this information.

Solution:

Step 1:   Record the given information.

TABLE 13-12(a)

	A_1	A_2	Total
B_1	0.5		
B_2			0.3
Total	0.6		1

Step 2:   After performing the required subtractions, we have the following complete table:

TABLE 13-12(b)

	A_1	A_2	Total
B_1	0.5	0.2	0.7
B_2	0.1	0.2	0.3
Total	0.6	0.4	1

PROBLEMS

1. Convert Table 13-11 to a table of joint and marginal probabilities.
2. What rules should be followed in classifying data?
3. An experiment consists of tossing a coin and a six-sided die.
    (a) Set up a bivariate probability table for this experiment.
    (b) Determine the joint probability of a head on the coin and a 4 on the die.
    (c) Determine the joint probability $p(T \cap 5)$.
    (d) Compute $p(H \cup 3)$.
4. Given the data in Table 13-13.

TABLE 13-13. ANNUAL INCOME IN THOUSANDS

	B_1 $5,000–10,000	B_2 $10,000–15,000	B_3 $15,000–20,000	Total
A_1 owns a camping trailer	80	60	10	150
A_2 does not own a camping trailer	420	340	90	850
Total	500	400	100	1000

Explain the following symbols in words:

(a) $p(A_1)$ (c) $p(A_1 \cap B_2)$

(b) $p(B_2)$ (d) $p(A_2 \cup B_1)$

5. Compute the probabilities in Prob. 4.

6. Which of the probabilities in Prob. 5 are marginal probabilities? Which are joint probabilities?

7. Given the data in Table 13-14.

TABLE 13-14

Car Ownership Grade Average	B_1 A	B_2 B	B_3 C	B_4 D	Total
A_1 owns a car	30	100	350	80	500
A_2 does not own a car	70	100	250	20	500
Total	100	200	600	100	1000

Express the following symbolically:

(a) The probability that a student has an A average.
(b) The probability that a student owns a car.
(c) The probability that a student has a C average or owns a car.
(d) The probability that a student has a B average and owns a car.

8. Calculate the probabilities in Prob. 7 if the student was chosen at random.

9. Which of the probabilities in Prob. 7 are marginal probabilities? Which are joint probabilities?

13-3   CONDITIONAL PROBABILITY

In this section the concept of conditional probability is introduced in connection with the bivariate data given in Table 13-10 of the previous section. This table is repeated below for convenience.

TABLE 13-15

Grade\I.Q.	L	M	H	Total
A	$\frac{1}{33}$	$\frac{1}{33}$	$\frac{1}{33}$	$\frac{1}{11}$
B	$\frac{1}{33}$	$\frac{1}{33}$	$\frac{1}{33}$	$\frac{1}{11}$
C	$\frac{2}{11}$	$\frac{2}{11}$	$\frac{2}{11}$	$\frac{6}{11}$
D	$\frac{1}{11}$	$\frac{1}{11}$	$\frac{1}{11}$	$\frac{3}{11}$
Total	$\frac{1}{3}$	$\frac{1}{3}$	$\frac{1}{3}$	1

The reader will recall that this table was obtained by dividing the entries in the bivariate frequency Table 13-5 by the total population of 33. Table 13-15 is a table of joint and marginal probabilities.

The probability of a student with a low I.Q. getting an A is an example of a *conditional probability*. This would be written symbolically as $p(A/L)$ and is read "the probability of A given L."

The following procedure can be used to obtain a table of conditional probabilities. The first column of the table, which gives $p(A/L)$, $p(B/L)$, $p(C/L)$, and $p(D/L)$, is shown below.

L COLUMN OF TABLE 13-16

	L
A	$\frac{1}{11}$
B	$\frac{1}{11}$
C	$\frac{6}{11}$
D	$\frac{3}{11}$
Total	$\frac{11}{11} = 1$

Note that the frequencies were divided by the reduced population of 11 rather than the total population of 33. That is, we divided by the number of students with low I.Q. to get the entries in the L column. The remaining columns of a complete conditional probability table are obtained by dividing by the number of students with medium I.Q. and the number of students with high I.Q. Both of these numbers happen to also be 11 in this problem. The complete table is shown below.

TABLE 13-16

	L	M	H
A	$\frac{1}{11}$	$\frac{1}{11}$	$\frac{1}{11}$
B	$\frac{1}{11}$	$\frac{1}{11}$	$\frac{1}{11}$
C	$\frac{6}{11}$	$\frac{6}{11}$	$\frac{6}{11}$
D	$\frac{3}{11}$	$\frac{3}{11}$	$\frac{3}{11}$
Total	1	1	1

Example 1.   Determine $p(B/M)$ and $p(D/H)$ from Table 13-16.

Solution:

$$p(B/M) = \frac{1}{11} \quad \text{and} \quad p(D/H) = \frac{3}{11}$$

From Table 13-16 we can read the probability of getting a certain grade subject to the condition that the student has a given I.Q. The next table shows the probabilities that result if the condition is placed on grades rather than I.Q.

TABLE 13-17

	L	M	H		
A	$\frac{1}{3}$	$\frac{1}{3}$	$\frac{1}{3}$	1	(*dividing by* 3)
B	$\frac{1}{3}$	$\frac{1}{3}$	$\frac{1}{3}$	1	(*dividing by* 3)
C	$\frac{6}{18}$	$\frac{6}{18}$	$\frac{6}{18}$	1	(*dividing by* 18)
D	$\frac{3}{9}$	$\frac{3}{9}$	$\frac{3}{9}$	1	(*dividing by* 9)

Example 2.   Determine $p(M/B)$ and $p(H/D)$ from Table 13-17.

Solution:

$$p(M/B) = \frac{1}{3} \quad \text{and} \quad p(H/D) = \frac{3}{9} = \frac{1}{3}$$

To preview the next section, we point out that $p(L) = \frac{1}{3}$ (from Table 13-15) and $p(L/D) = \frac{1}{3}$ (from Table 13-17). In other words, $p(L/D) = p(L)$ in this case. The significance of this will be explained in Sec. 13-4.

Before giving the final example of this section, we develop the following important formula. Let A and B be two events in a sample space S. Then $p(A/B) = [p(A \cap B)]/p(B)$.

To establish this formula for the case of a finite sample space where all sample points are equally likely, we recall that $p(A/B)$ is computed by dividing the number of elements in the event $A \cap B$ by the number of elements in B. If we denote the number of elements in $A \cap B$ by h and the number of elements in B by b, this gives $p(A/B) = h/b$. Dividing numerator and denominator of this fraction by the number of elements n in the sample space gives

$$p(A/B) = \frac{h}{b} = \frac{h/n}{b/n}$$

But,

$$\frac{h}{n} = p(A \cap B) \quad \text{and} \quad \frac{b}{n} = p(B)$$

Therefore,

$$p(A/B) = \frac{p(A \cap B)}{p(B)}$$

In general, $p(A/B)$, the conditional probability of A given B, is defined by the formula

$$p(A/B) = \frac{p(A \cap B)}{p(B)}$$

Example 3. The sample space of a certain experiment is classified two different ways into pairs of exhaustive events A_1, A_2 and B_1, B_2. Given that $p(A_1) = 0.3$, $p(B_1) = 0.4$, and $p(A_1/B_1) = 0.6$, complete the joint and conditional probability tables.

Solution: The following tables reflect the given information.

TABLE 13-18

	B_1	B_2			B_1	B_2
A_1		0.3		A_1	0.6	
A_2				A_2		
	0.4		1		1	1

We know that

$$p(A_1/B_1) = \frac{p(A_1 \cap B_1)}{p(B_1)} = 0.6$$

Then

$$p(A_1 \cap B_1) = p(A_1/B_1)p(B_1)$$
$$0.24 = (0.6)(0.4)$$

With this information we can complete the joint probability table as follows:

TABLE 13-19

	B_1	B_2	
A_1	0.24	0.06	0.3
A_2	0.16	0.54	0.7
	0.4	0.6	1.0

We can now calculate

$$p(A_1/B_2) = \frac{p(A_1 \cap B_2)}{p(B_2)}$$

$$0.10 = \frac{0.06}{0.6}$$

With this information we can complete the conditional probability table as follows:

TABLE 13-20

	B_1	B_2
A_1	0.6	0.1
A_2	0.4	0.9
	1.0	1.0

PROBLEMS

1. Given the experiment of randomly drawing a single card from a standard deck.
   (a) What is the probability of drawing a jack-of-hearts?
   (b) What is the probability of drawing a king or a queen?
   (c) What is the probability of drawing a spade?
   (d) What is the probability of drawing a heart given that the card is a king?
   (e) What is the probability of drawing an ace given that the card is a spade?

2. Express the probabilities in Prob. 1 symbolically.

3. Determine if the probabilities in Prob. 1 are marginal, joint, or conditional.

4. Given the following bivariate table, set up the joint and conditional probability tables.

TABLE 13-21

	A_1	A_2	A_3	
B_1	10	5	15	30
B_2	10	5	5	20
B_3	5	5	40	50
	25	15	60	100

5. Given the following information: $p(A_1) = 0.7$, $p(B_1) = 0.5$, and $p(B_1/A_1) = 0.4$, complete the joint and marginal probability table. Assume the pairs A_1, A_2 and B_1, B_2 are exhaustive.

6. Given the following partial tables:

TABLE 13-22(a)

	A_1	A_2	A_3	
B_1				0.4
B_2				
		0.3	0.2	1

TABLE 13-22(b)

	A_1	A_2	A_3	
B_1				1
B_2		0.3		1

TABLE 13-22(c)

	A_1	A_2	A_3
B_1			0.2
B_2			
	1	1	1

Complete the tables. Assume A_1, A_2, A_3 and B_1, B_2 are both collectively exhaustive.

7. Given Table 13-23.

TABLE 13-23

		A_1 Freshmen	A_2 Sophomores	A_3 Juniors	A_4 Seniors	Total
B_1	Have financial assistance	30	40	60	70	200
B_2	No financial assistance	270	210	190	130	800
	Total	300	250	250	200	1000

Calculate the following:

(a) $p(B_2)$
(b) $p(A_3)$
(c) $p(A_4 \cap B_2)$
(d) $p(A_2/B_1)$
(e) $p(B_2/A_1)$
(f) $p(A_4 \cup B_2)$

8. Explain the probabilities calculated in Prob. 7 in words.

9. Which of the probabilities in Prob. 7 are joint probabilities? Which are conditional probabilities?

10. Given that $p(A) = 0.3$, $p(B') = 0.2$, and $p(A \cap B') = 0.1$. Calculate
   (a) $p(A')$ (d) $p(A \cup B')$
   (b) $p(B)$ (e) $p(B'/A)$
   (c) $p(A/B')$

11. Given that $p(A) = 0.4$, $p(B'/A) = 0.3$, and $p(A \cup B') = 0.6$. Calculate
   (a) $p(A \cap B')$ (d) $p(A')$
   (b) $p(B')$ (e) $p(A/B')$
   (c) $p(B)$

13-4 INDEPENDENCE

In the previous section it was pointed out that $p(L/D) = p(L)$ for a certain class of students, where L stands for low I.Q. and D is a grade. Whenever two events are related in this way, they are said to be independent.

DEFINITION 13.1.   *Two events, A and B, are said to be independent if* $p(A/B) = p(A)$.

In words, two events are independent if the conditional probability, $p(A/B)$, is equal to the corresponding marginal probability, $p(A)$.

Next we illustrate this definition using the I.Q. example. From Table 13-15, we have $p(A) = \frac{1}{11}$, $p(B) = \frac{1}{11}$, $p(C) = \frac{6}{11}$, and $p(D) = \frac{3}{11}$. This information and probability Table 13-16 are given below.

TABLE 13-24

	F_1 L	F_2 M	F_3 H	$p(E_i)$
$E_1 = A$	$\frac{1}{11}$	$\frac{1}{11}$	$\frac{1}{11}$	$\frac{1}{11}$
$E_2 = B$	$\frac{1}{11}$	$\frac{1}{11}$	$\frac{1}{11}$	$\frac{1}{11}$
$E_3 = C$	$\frac{6}{11}$	$\frac{6}{11}$	$\frac{6}{11}$	$\frac{6}{11}$
$E_4 = D$	$\frac{3}{11}$	$\frac{3}{11}$	$\frac{3}{11}$	$\frac{3}{11}$
	1	1	1	

It is clear from Table 13-24 that the conditional probabilities $p(A/L)$, $P(A/M)$, and $p(A/H)$ are all equal to the marginal probability $p(A)$. Therefore, by Definition 13.1, the three pairs of events A, L; A, M; and A, H are all independent. Similar statements are true for the remaining three rows of Table 13-24.

Since $p(E_i/F_j) = P(E_i)$ for $i = 1, 2, 3$, and $j = 1, 2, 3$, it follows that grades are independent of I.Q. for this particular example.

Example 1. | Given the following data, determine whether or not the variables x and y are independent.

TABLE 13-25

	x_1	x_2	x_3	Total
y_1	0.3	0.1	0.2	0.6
y_2	0.3	0.1	0	0.4
Total	0.6	0.2	0.2	1.0

Solution:

$$p(y_1/x_1) = \frac{0.3}{0.6} = 0.5$$

$$p(y_1) = 0.6 \neq 0.5$$

Therefore, x and y are not independent.

Example 2. Form the conditional probability table with x as the given variable from the joint probability table given in Example 1.

Solution:

TABLE 13-26

	x_1	x_2	x_3
y_1	0.5	0.5	1
y_2	0.5	0.5	0
	1	1	1

dividing the x_1 column by 0.6, and so forth

We point out that the nonequal entries 0.5, 0.5, and 1 in the y_1 row are an indication that the variables x and y are **not** independent. Since $p(y_1/x_1) \neq p(y_1/x_3)$, it follows that at least one of them and possibly both are not equal to $p(y_1)$. Conversely, if a table of conditional probabilities is formed and the entries within each row are equal, then the two variables are independent.

By Definition 13.1, if A and B are independent, then $p(A/B) = p(A)$. Next we show that this relationship is equivalent to $p(A \cap B) = p(A)p(B)$. To see this we recall that $p(A/B) = \dfrac{p(A \cap B)}{p(B)}$. Multiplying both sides by $p(B)$ gives $p(A \cap B) = p(A/B)p(B)$. But if A and B are independent, then $p(A/B) = p(A)$. By substitution, we have $p(A \cap B) = p(A)p(B)$, whenever A and B are independent. Conversely, if $p(A \cap B) = p(A)p(B)$, then $p(A/B) = p(A)$ and the events A and B are independent in the sense of Definition 13.1.

From now on, we can test pairs of events for independence either by Definition 13.1 or by comparing the joint probability $p(A \cap B)$ with the product $p(A)p(B)$. The two events are independent if and only if $p(A \cap B) = p(A)p(B)$.

Example 3. Test the two events x_2 and y_2 given in Example 1 for independence by the method described above.

Solution: $p(x_2 \cap y_2) = 0.1$, $p(x_2) = 0.2$, $p(y_2) = 0.4$, and $p(x_2)p(y_2) = 0.08 \neq p(x_2 \cap y_2)$. Therefore, x_2 and y_2 are not independent.

PROBLEMS

1. Let the following table of joint probabilities be given.

TABLE **13-27**

y \ x	x_1	x_2	x_3	Total
y_1	0.2	0.15	0.15	0.5
y_2	0.2	0.05	0.25	0.5
Total	0.4	0.2	0.4	1.0

Which of the following pairs of events are independent? Use the method of comparing the product of the marginals with the joint probability.

(a) y_1, x_1 (d) y_2, x_1
(b) y_1, x_2 (e) y_2, x_2
(c) y_1, x_3 (f) y_2, x_3

2. Construct a conditional probability table from **Table 13-27**.

3. Check the pairs of events listed in Prob. 1 for independence. Use Definition 13.1 and the conditional probability table calculated in Prob. 2.

4. Are the variables x and y of Prob. 1 independent? Explain briefly.

5. Under what conditions are two variables independent in the probability sense?

6. Given that the two variables A and B are independent, complete Table 13-28.

TABLE **13-28**

B \ A	A_1	A_2	
B_1		0.4	
B_2			
	0.3		1.0

7. Given that the two variables A and B are independent, complete Table 13-29.

TABLE 13-29(a)

	A_1	A_2	
B_1	0.12		
B_2			
			1.0

TABLE 13-29(b)

	A_1	A_2	
B_1	0.3		
B_2			
	1.0	1.0	

8. Given Table 13-30.

TABLE 13-30

B \ A	A_1 Freshmen	A_2 Sophomores	A_3 Juniors	A_4 Seniors	Total
B_1 Have financial assistance	30	40	60	70	200
B_2 No financial assistance	270	210	190	130	800
Total	300	250	250	200	1000

Are the variables A and B independent?

9. A student must take an exam with five questions. He believes that his success on any one problem does not depend on his success or failure on the other problems. He assigns a probability of 0.7 to answering a particular question correctly. Determine the probability of getting
   (a) all five correct
   (b) none correct
   (c) exactly two correct
   (d) exactly three correct
   (e) at least two correct
   (f) at least three correct

10. A fair coin is tossed 6 times. Determine the probability of
    (a) six heads
    (b) exactly three heads
    (c) six tails
    (d) at least three heads

11. An experiment consists of n independent trials. Each trial can result in a success with probability p or a failure with probability $g = 1 - p$. Let X denote the number of successes in n trials. Show that

$$p(X = x) = \binom{n}{x} p^x (1 - p)^{n-x}, \qquad \text{where } \binom{n}{x} = \frac{n!}{x!(n-x)!}$$

and that the formula applies for $x = 0, 1, 2, \ldots, n$.

12. Verify the formula in Prob. 11 by applying it to Probs. 9 and 10.

13. The manager of a department store in a suburban mall in Connecticut is interested in learning more about the shopping habits of Massachusetts residents. He is particularly interested in how much they spent, how long they stayed in the store, and their plans for future visits to the store. In

order to increase the percentage of questionnaires returned, he offers to send each respondent a gift certificate. This same questionnaire was used the previous year with a sample of 50. A tabulation of these questionnaires is given in the following table:

	B_1 (gift certificate offered)	B_2 (no gift certificate offered)	Total
A_1 (returned)	35	25	60
A_2 (not returned)	15	25	40
Total	50	50	100

(a)   Complete the following table by inserting the theoretical or expected frequencies assuming no relationship (i.e., variables are independent).

	B_1	B_2	Total
A_1			60
A_2			40
Total	50	50	100

(b)   Are the variables independent?

13-5   TREE DIAGRAMS

Consider the experiment of tossing a coin and drawing a card from a deck that contains one jack, one queen, and one king. The sample space for this experiment is

$$S = \{(J, H), (J, T), (Q, H), (Q, T), (K, H), (K, T)\}$$

The subjective probabilities, assuming equal likelihood, are displayed in Table 13-31.

TABLE 13-31

	H	T	Total
J	$\frac{1}{6}$	$\frac{1}{6}$	$\frac{1}{3}$
Q	$\frac{1}{6}$	$\frac{1}{6}$	$\frac{1}{3}$
K	$\frac{1}{6}$	$\frac{1}{6}$	$\frac{1}{3}$
Total	$\frac{1}{2}$	$\frac{1}{2}$	1

It is sometimes meaningful to display the sample points in a so-called *tree diagram*. This method is illustrated below.

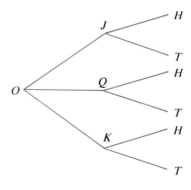

F I G U R E 13-1

The "total path" $0 \to J \to H$ corresponds to the pair (J, H), etc. The number of sample points can still be counted by counting the number of "total paths." In this case, there are six such paths or, equivalently, six sample points. The probability of each "total path" is ⅙.

Example 1. | Construct a tree diagram for the experiment which consists of tossing 3 coins and determine the number of sample points.

Solution:

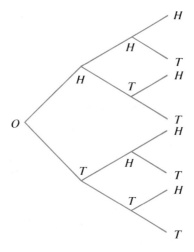

F I G U R E 13-2

There are 8 "total paths" and 8 sample points.

Next we relate the concepts of joint, marginal, and conditional probabilities to tree diagrams. Let the following probability table be given.

TABLE 13-32

	A_1	A_2	A_3	Total
B_1	0.2	0.3	0.1	0.6
B_2	0.1	0.1	0.2	0.4
Total	0.3	0.4	0.3	1

Translating this data into a tree diagram format, we have

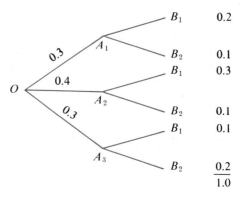

FIGURE 13-3

Example 2. | Compute $p(B_2)$ from the tree diagram.

Solution:

$$p(B_2) = p(A_1 \cap B_2) + p(A_2 \cap B_2) + p(A_3 \cap B_2)$$
$$p(B_2) = 0.1 + 0.1 + 0.2$$

Therefore, $p(B_2) = 0.4$, which agrees with the information given in Table 13-32.

Example 3. | Compute $p(A_1 \cup B_2)$ from the tree diagram and the result of Example 2.

Solution:

$$p(A_1 \cup B_2) = p(A_1) + p(B_2) - p(A_1 \cap B_2)$$
$$= 0.3 + 0.4 - 0.1$$
$$p(A_1 \cup B_2) = 0.6$$

The following figure illustrates the probability interpretation of the various branches and *total paths* of a typical tree diagram.

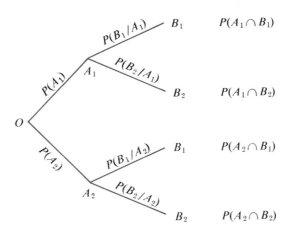

F I G U R E 13-4

Finally, we solve an applied problem using a tree diagram approach.

Example 4. | The probability that a machine is correctly set up is assumed to be 0.8. Furthermore, experience has shown that if the machine is correctly set up, then the probability of obtaining a good part is 0.90. However, if the machine is not correctly set up, the probability of a good part is only 0.2. Given the fact that the first part produced was tested and found to be satisfactory, determine the probability that the machine is set up correctly.

Solution: We must determine the conditional probability, p(correct set-up/ first part is satisfactory) $= p(C/S)$. Figure 13-5 illustrates a partial tree diagram that includes the obvious information.

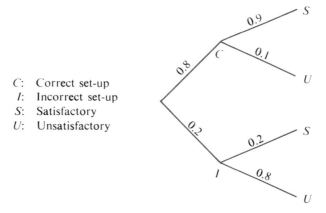

C: Correct set-up
I: Incorrect set-up
S: Satisfactory
U: Unsatisfactory

F I G U R E 13-5

Compute the appropriate products to obtain the 4 joint probabilities.

343

$$p(S \cap C) = p(S/C)p(C)$$
$$= (0.9)(0.8)$$
$$p(S \cap C) = 0.72, \text{ etc.}$$

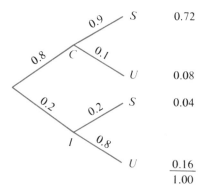

F I G U R E 13-6

$$p(C/S) = \frac{p(C \cap S)}{p(S)}$$

$$p(S) = p(C \cap S) + p(I \cap S)$$
$$= 0.72 + 0.04$$
$$p(S) = 0.76$$

Therefore,

$$p(C/S) = \frac{0.72}{0.76} = \frac{18}{19}$$

$$p(C/S) = 0.95$$

PROBLEMS

1. Compute the conditional probabilities, which correspond to the branches $A_1 - B_1$, $A_1 - B_2$, etc. in the tree diagram that result from Table 13-32.
2. Translate the following probability tables into a tree diagram.

TABLE 13-33(a)

B \ A	A_1	A_2	Total
B_1	0.11	0.05	0.16
B_2	0.44	0.4	0.84
Total	0.55	0.45	1.0

TABLE 13-33(b)

	A_1	A_2
B_1	$\frac{1}{5}$	$\frac{1}{9}$
B_2	$\frac{4}{5}$	$\frac{8}{9}$
	1	1

3. Translate the following tree diagram into a joint and a conditional probability table.

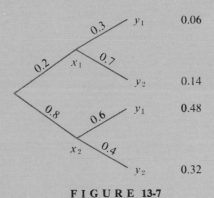

                          F I G U R E 13-7

4. Determine the remaining probabilities in the following tree diagram.

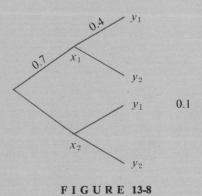

                          F I G U R E 13-8

5. Set up a tree diagram showing all probabilities for the experiment of tossing a coin and rolling a 6-faced die.

6. Use the tree diagram found in Prob. 5 to determine the following probabilities:

    (a) $p(H)$ (c) $p(T \cap 4)$
    (b) $p(3)$ (d) $p(H \cup 5)$

7. Given the data in Example 4 of this section, calculate $p(C/U)$.

8. Do Prob. 9 of Sec. 13-4 using tree diagrams.

9. Do Prob. 10 of Sec. 13-4 using tree diagrams.

13-6 PROBABILITY VECTORS, MARKOV ANALYSIS

In this section we will illustrate the combined use of probabilities expressed as vectors and introduce the concept of a *Markov process*.

A vector $\mathbf{p} = (p_1, p_2, \ldots, p_n)$, $\mathbf{p}\begin{pmatrix} p_1 \\ p_2 \\ \vdots \\ p_n \end{pmatrix}$ is called a *probability vector* if the components are nonnegative and their sum is 1.

Example 1.

Which of the following vectors are probability vectors?

$\mathbf{a} = (\frac{1}{3}, \frac{1}{3}, \frac{1}{3})$ $\mathbf{b} = (0.4, -0.2, 0.8)$

$\mathbf{c} = (0.4, 0.2, 0.3, 0.2)$ $\mathbf{d} = \begin{pmatrix} 0.5 \\ 0.3 \\ 0.2 \end{pmatrix}$

Solution: **a** is a probability vector. **b** is not a probability vector because the second component is negative. **c** is not a probability vector because the sum of the components is greater than 1. **d** is a probability vector.

A square matrix with nonnegative elements such that the sum of the elements in each row is 1 is called a *transition matrix*.

Example 2.

Which of the following are transition matrices?

$$A = \begin{pmatrix} 0.8 & 0.2 \\ 0.6 & 0.4 \end{pmatrix}, \qquad B = \begin{pmatrix} 0.3 & 0.6 & 0.1 \\ 0.2 & 0.7 & 0.1 \end{pmatrix}, \qquad C = \begin{pmatrix} 0.3 & 0.2 & 0.5 \\ 0.2 & 0.4 & 0.3 \\ 0.5 & 0.4 & 0.1 \end{pmatrix}$$

Solution: A is a transition matrix. B is not a transition matrix because it is not a square matrix. C is not a transition matrix because the sum of the elements of row two is not equal to 1.

One of the primary concerns of the business manager is his market share. The *Markov process* is a method of analyzing present market share and the future of that share. A very important factor in the determination of future share is customer loyalty. In the remainder of the section we will use a transition matrix to depict purchase probabilities. Once this is done we will predict the market share of future periods and finally determine the market equilibrium.

Example 3.

Three possible texts can be used for a given course. The three texts are *EP*, *XY*, and *WZ*. If the *EP* text is presently being used, the probability of it being used again is 0.8 and the probability that users of *EP* switch to *XY* or *WZ* is 0.1 and 0.1. If the *XY* text is in use, the probability of it being continued is 0.5 and the probability that users will switch to *EP* or *WZ* is 0.4 and 0.1, respectively. If the *WZ* text is in use the probability of it being continued is 0.3 and the probability that users will switch to *EP* or *XY* is 0.4 and 0.3, respectively. Use a transition matrix to display these probabilities.

Solution:

NEXT PURCHASE

		EP	XY	WZ
	EP	0.8	0.1	0.1
Presently in Use	XY	0.4	0.5	0.1
(Previous Purchase)	WZ	0.4	0.3	0.3

The reader should note that a transition matrix is equivalent to a table of conditional probabilities where the condition imposed is the previous purchase. At present, 200 schools are using the *EP* text, 400 are using the *XY* text, and 400 are using the *WZ* text, i.e., the current market share is 20 percent, 40 percent, and 40 percent, respectively. Assume no new customers and no old customers leaving the market. What will be the market share in the next period if the transition matrix of Example 3 applies? Of the 200 *EP* users, 0.8(200) or 160 will purchase *EP*, and so forth.

TABLE 13-34

		Purchase of		
		EP	XY	WZ
	EP	160	20	20
Purchase by	XY	160	200	40
	WZ	160	120	120
		480	340	180

The market share expressed as probabilities will be 0.48, 0.34, and 0.18, respectively.

We could have used the tree diagram in Fig. 13-9 to obtain the same result.

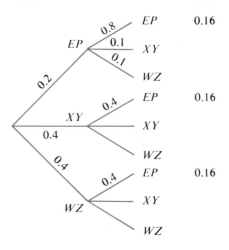

FIGURE 13-9

The market share of $EP = 0.16 + 0.16 + 0.16$, or 0.48. The reader should complete the tree diagram and verify the results.

Example 4.   Use matrix multiplication to find the market share of period 2, as calculated above.

Solution: Define $\mathbf{s} = (s_1, s_2, s_3)$, where s_1 is the market share expressed as a probability of *EP*, and so forth. Then

$$\mathbf{s} = (0.2, 0.4, 0.4) = \text{market share in period 1 expressed as a probability vector}$$

$$T = \begin{pmatrix} 0.8 & 0.1 & 0.1 \\ 0.4 & 0.5 & 0.1 \\ 0.4 & 0.3 & 0.3 \end{pmatrix} = \text{transition matrix}$$

$\mathbf{s}' = \mathbf{s}T = \text{market share in the next period}$
$\mathbf{s}' = (0.48, 0.34, 0.18)$

A sample calculation follows.

$s_1' = t_{11}s_1 + t_{21}s_2 + t_{31}s_3$
$s_1' = (0.8)(0.2) + (0.4)(0.4) + (0.4)(0.4)$
$s_1' = 0.48$

The increase in the market share for the *EP* text was considerable. However, at some point in time the gains will be exactly offset by losses and the market will achieve an equilibrium. When this happens the following will be the case:
Share next period $\doteq$ Share this period

EP	s_1'	$=$	s_1
XY	s_2'	$=$	s_2
WZ	s_3'	$=$	s_3

Expanding,

$$t_{11}s_1 + t_{21}s_2 + t_{31}s_3 = s_1$$
$$t_{12}s_1 + t_{22}s_2 + t_{32}s_3 = s_2$$
$$t_{13}s_1 + t_{23}s_2 + t_{33}s_3 = s_3$$

Also, because **s** is a probability vector, we know that $s_1 + s_2 + s_3 = 1$. Using the values in the transition matrix we have

$$0.8s_1 + 0.4s_2 + 0.4s_3 = s_1 \tag{1}$$
$$0.1s_1 + 0.5s_2 + 0.3s_3 = s_2 \tag{2}$$
$$0.1s_1 + 0.1s_2 + 0.3s_3 = s_3 \tag{3}$$

and

$$s_1 + s_2 + s_3 = 1 \tag{4}$$

Using equations (1), (2), and (4) to solve for s_1, s_2 and s_3, we have

$$-0.2s_1 + 0.4s_2 + 0.4s_3 = 0$$
$$0.1s_1 - 0.5s_2 + 0.3s_3 = 0$$
$$s_1 + s_2 + s_3 = 1$$

If we write the above as a matrix equation, we have

$$\begin{pmatrix} -0.2 & 0.4 & 0.4 \\ 0.1 & -0.5 & 0.3 \\ 1.0 & 1.0 & 1.0 \end{pmatrix} \begin{pmatrix} s_1 \\ s_2 \\ s_3 \end{pmatrix} = \begin{pmatrix} 0 \\ 0 \\ 1 \end{pmatrix}$$

Multiplying each side by T^{-1} will give a solution.

$$\begin{pmatrix} s_1 \\ s_2 \\ s_3 \end{pmatrix} = \begin{pmatrix} \dfrac{-0.80}{0.48} & 0 & \dfrac{0.32}{0.48} \\ \dfrac{0.20}{0.48} & \dfrac{-0.20}{0.48} & \dfrac{0.10}{0.48} \\ \dfrac{0.50}{0.48} & \dfrac{-0.20}{0.48} & \dfrac{0.06}{0.48} \end{pmatrix} \begin{pmatrix} 0 \\ 0 \\ 1 \end{pmatrix} = \begin{pmatrix} 0.67 \\ 0.21 \\ 0.12 \end{pmatrix}$$

If we verify this result, we see that the market share in the next period is the same as the market share in this period.[1]

$$\mathbf{s}' = (0.67, 0.21, 0.12) \begin{pmatrix} 0.8 & 0.1 & 0.1 \\ 0.4 & 0.5 & 0.1 \\ 0.4 & 0.3 & 0.3 \end{pmatrix} = (0.668, 0.208, 0.124)$$

Therefore, we have an equilibrium.

---

1. There is a slight discrepancy due to rounding.

PROBLEMS

1. Which of the following are probability vectors?

   (a) $\mathbf{p} = \begin{pmatrix} 0.3 \\ 0.4 \\ 0.3 \end{pmatrix}$ (c) $\mathbf{p} = (0.2, 0.3, 0.1, 0.3)$

   (b) $\mathbf{p} = (-0.1, 0.8, 0.3)$ (d) $\mathbf{p} = (\frac{2}{3}, \frac{1}{6}, \frac{1}{6})$

2. Write out in words the meaning of the following transition matrix:

$$
\begin{array}{c}
 & \begin{array}{ccc} A & B & C \end{array} \\
\begin{array}{c} A \\ B \\ C \end{array} & \begin{pmatrix} 0.5 & 0.3 & 0.2 \\ 0.1 & 0.6 & 0.3 \\ 0.2 & 0.2 & 0.6 \end{pmatrix}
\end{array}
$$

3. Which of the following are transition matrices?

   (a) $\begin{array}{c} & \begin{array}{ccc} A & B & C \end{array} \\ \begin{array}{c} A \\ B \\ C \end{array} & \begin{pmatrix} 0.5 & 0.2 & 0.3 \\ \frac{1}{3} & \frac{1}{3} & \frac{1}{3} \\ 0.2 & 0.2 & 0.6 \end{pmatrix} \end{array}$ (b) $\begin{array}{c} & \begin{array}{ccc} A & B & C \end{array} \\ \begin{array}{c} A \\ B \\ C \end{array} & \begin{pmatrix} 0.4 & 0.4 & 0.2 \\ 0.3 & 0.5 & 0.2 \\ 0.3 & 0.1 & 0.5 \end{pmatrix} \end{array}$

4. Do the calculations necessary to obtain Table 13-34.

5. Use the transition matrix and the result of Example 4 to find the market share of EP, XY, and WZ in period 3.

6. Show that the long run market share is $\frac{1}{3}$ for all brands given the following transition matrix:

$$
\begin{array}{c}
 & \text{Switched to} \\
 & \begin{array}{ccc} X & Y & Z \end{array} \\
\begin{array}{c} X \\ Y \\ Z \end{array} & \begin{pmatrix} 0.8 & 0.1 & 0.1 \\ 0.1 & 0.8 & 0.1 \\ 0.1 & 0.1 & 0.8 \end{pmatrix}
\end{array}
$$

7. Using the transition matrix given in Prob. 6 and given that the present market share is 0.4, 0.2, and 0.4 for X, Y, and Z, respectively, what will the market share be in the next period for X, Y, and Z?

8. Given the following transition matrix.

$$
\begin{array}{c}
 & \text{Switched to} \\
 & \begin{array}{ccc} A & B & C \end{array} \\
\begin{array}{c} A \\ B \\ C \end{array} & \begin{pmatrix} 0.6 & 0.2 & 0.2 \\ 0.2 & 0.6 & 0.2 \\ 0.2 & 0.2 & 0.6 \end{pmatrix}
\end{array}
$$

   (a) What is the long run market share for brands A, B, and C?
   (b) Does the answer to (a) depend on the starting market share?
   (c) Does the number of periods required to reach the equilibrium depend on the starting market share?

13-7 AN APPLICATION OF PRESENT VALUE, MATRIX TECHNIQUES, AND PROBABILITY TO A CAPITAL BUDGETING PROBLEM

First we will present a capital budgeting problem with a determinate view (i.e., one cash flow for each investment alternative) and provide a simple illustration of the present value technique. Then a risk situation is presented (i.e., more than one cash flow for each investment alternative) and probabilities are introduced. All of the above is done in a matrix setting. Relaxing the assumption of a determinate world, a more complicated cash flow is then introduced where depreciation and taxes are taken into account. Because these calculations can become lengthy, the computer can be introduced. Finally, the sensitivity of the decision is examined in regard to the probabilities. To begin, let us assume that we can invest in either Machine A or Machine B, both of which require an outlay of $5000. The schedule below shows a payoff matrix by year before discounting.

$$\begin{array}{c}\qquad\qquad\quad Year\ 1 \quad Year\ 2 \\ Machine\ A \\ Machine\ B \end{array} \begin{pmatrix} 0 & 10{,}000 \\ 10{,}000 & 10{,}000 \end{pmatrix}$$

Example 1.

Discount the payoffs using a cost of capital (i.e., discount rate) of 10%.

Solution: Using Tables A-5 and A-7 we have

$$\begin{array}{c}\qquad\qquad Year\ 0 \\ Machine\ A \\ Machine\ B \end{array} \begin{pmatrix} 8{,}264 \\ 17{,}355 \end{pmatrix}$$

The present value of future cash inflows less investment outlay gives the following:

	Inflows *Year 0*	*Investment outlay* *Year 0*	*Net excess Present value*
Machine A	$\begin{pmatrix} 8{,}264 \\ 17{,}355 \end{pmatrix}$	$-\begin{pmatrix} 5{,}000 \\ 5{,}000 \end{pmatrix}$	$=\begin{pmatrix} 3{,}264 \\ 12{,}355 \end{pmatrix}$
Machine B			

Thus far we have assumed a definite cash inflow for each investment alternative. If this assumption is valid, we would clearly invest in Machine B. Suppose, on the other hand, that the cash inflows were based on the assumption that demand is high and that, if demand just happened to be low, the following payoff matrix, before discounting, would result.

$$\begin{array}{c}\qquad\qquad\quad Year\ 1 \quad Year\ 2 \\ Machine\ A \\ Machine\ B \end{array} \begin{pmatrix} 0 & 5000 \\ 1000 & 1000 \end{pmatrix}$$

Example 2.

Discount the payoffs using a cost of capital rate of 10%.
Solution: Using Tables A-5 and A-7 as in Example 1 we have

$$\begin{array}{c}\qquad\qquad Year\ 0 \\ Machine\ A \\ Machine\ B \end{array} \begin{pmatrix} 4132 \\ 1736 \end{pmatrix}$$

The present value of future cash inflows less investment outlay gives the following:

$$
\begin{array}{cccc}
 & \begin{array}{c}\textit{Inflows}\\\textit{Year 0}\end{array} & \begin{array}{c}\textit{Investment}\\\textit{outlay}\\\textit{Year 0}\end{array} & \begin{array}{c}\textit{Net excess}\\\textit{Present}\\\textit{value}\end{array}\\
\textit{Machine A} & \begin{pmatrix}4132\\1736\end{pmatrix} & -\begin{pmatrix}5000\\5000\end{pmatrix} & =\begin{pmatrix}(868)\\(3264)\end{pmatrix}\\
\textit{Machine B}
\end{array}
$$

Now that we have made life a little more complicated, we are not yet in a position to make a decision. That is, the basis for selecting an act (i.e., what machine to purchase) is a more complex issue than in the case of decision-making under certainty where each act has a simple known payoff.

Decision-making under uncertainty involves not knowing the probability that one or another of the outcome states will prevail. Three of the most popular criteria that are used for decision-making under uncertainty are the maximin, the maximax, and the minimax-regret criteria. However, decision-makers frequently do have information about the probability that each outcome state will occur, even though they are uncertain as to the actual outcome state. The sources of information with regard to probability are:

1. Relative frequency.
2. Theoretical probability distributions.
3. Subjective judgment.

Decision-making, when there are a number of possible outcome states for which the probability distribution is known, is called *decision-making under risk*.

Returning to our problem, let us assume that the market research department estimates the probability of high demand to be 0.4 and low demand to be 0.6. Note that demand must be either high or low, hence 0.4 plus 0.6 equals 1.

When making a decision under risk the *criterion* used is to *maximize expected payoff*. To calculate expected payoff it is necessary to multiply each outcome (column) by its respective probability and then add the entries in each row. The probabilities can be expressed as a column vector which is then multiplied by the payoff matrix.

Example 3.   Calculate the expected values of Machines A and B.

Solution:

$$
\begin{array}{ccccc}
 & \multicolumn{2}{c}{\textit{Demand}} & \begin{array}{c}\textit{Probabilities}\\\textit{of outcomes}\end{array} & \begin{array}{c}\textit{Expected}\\\textit{value}\end{array}\\
 & \textit{high} & \textit{low} & & \\
\textit{Machine A} & \begin{pmatrix}3,300 & -900\\12,400 & -3,300\end{pmatrix} & & \begin{pmatrix}0.4\\0.6\end{pmatrix} & =\begin{pmatrix}780\\2,980\end{pmatrix}\\
\textit{Machine B}
\end{array}
$$

Note that the entries in the payoff matrix were rounded to the nearest hundredth and minus signs were used to indicate a loss rather than ( ). Using the criterion of maximizing expected payoff, we would invest in Machine B.

Clearly the expected value will not agree with the actual results on any one trial; however, this does not diminish the usefulness of this criterion to select amongst alternatives.

In general, then,

$$
\begin{array}{c}
\begin{array}{cccc} O_1 & O_2 & \cdots & O_n \end{array} \\
\begin{array}{c} A_1 \\ A_2 \\ \\ \\ \\ A_m \end{array}
\begin{pmatrix}
P_{11} & P_{12} & \cdots & P_{1n} \\
P_{21} & P_{22} & \cdots & P_{2n} \\
. & . & . & . \\
. & . & . & . \\
. & . & . & . \\
P_{m1} & P_{m2} & \cdots & P_{mn}
\end{pmatrix}
\begin{pmatrix}
P(O_1) \\ P(O_2) \\ . \\ . \\ . \\ P(O_n)
\end{pmatrix}
=
\begin{pmatrix}
EV_1 \\ EV_2 \\ . \\ . \\ . \\ EV_m
\end{pmatrix}
\end{array}
$$

where A_i, O_j, and P_{ij} indicate acts, outcomes, and payoffs, respectively, and where $P(O_j)$ and EV_i indicate the probability of Outcome j and the expected value of Act i, respectively.

Going a step further, let us consider the following example.

Example 4. Given the following cash inflows which are to be discounted at a rate of 10%.

	Demand high		Demand low	
	Years 1–3	Years 4–5	Years 1–3	Years 4–5
Machine A	10,000	5,000	4,000	2,500
Machine B	7,500	7,000	5,000	3,000

Also assume that Machines A and B each require a cash outlay in Year 0 of $10,000, that the useful life of both machines is five years, and that they are depreciated using the straight-line method. A federal tax of 50% is also assumed. Formulate the payoff matrix.

Solution: Summarizing the information obtained by using a library program (computer) we have:

	Demand high	Demand low
Machine A	9484	394
Machine B	7680	1963

The library program calculates an investment's annual depreciation and its after-tax effect on a stream of gross cash flows. The resulting net cash flow stream is then discounted at the user's specified rate.

Assuming the probability of demand being high as 0.4 and the probability of demand being low as 0.6, the expected value of Act 1, the purchase of Machine A, is $4030. The expected value of Act 2, the purchase of Machine B, is $4249. Since the expected values of both acts are almost equal, one would probably make a decision on a basis other than quantitative factors. Using the criterion of maximizing expected value, one would choose Machine B.

An interesting question is—Just how sensitive is our answer to these probabilities? That is, would the same decision be arrived at if the probabilities were 0.5 and 0.5 respectively?

Example 5.   Using the above information, for what probabilities would we be indifferent (i.e., $EV_1 = EV_2$)?

Solution:

$$9484P(O_1) + 394P(O_2) = 7680P(O_1) + 1963P(O_2)$$

$$1804P(O_1) - 1569P(O_2) = 0 \tag{1}$$

We also know that

$$P(O_1) + P(O_2) = 1 \tag{2}$$

Writing (1) and (2) as a matrix equation we have

$$\begin{pmatrix} 1804 & -1569 \\ 1 & 1 \end{pmatrix} \begin{pmatrix} P(O_1) \\ P(O_2) \end{pmatrix} = \begin{pmatrix} 0 \\ 1 \end{pmatrix}$$

Multiplying each side by the inverse of the matrix of coefficients gives $P(O_1) = 0.47$ and $P(O_2) = 0.53$. That is, for any $P(O_1) \geq 0.47$ we would invest in Machine A.

In conclusion, we can say that the typical capital budgeting problem is certain to be more complex than the above examples. However, most of the complications have to do with organizing the information (cash flows in particular) into a meaningful analysis prior to the application of discounting, matrix, and decision-making techniques.

PROBLEMS

1. What would the payoff matrix in Example 4 be if one simply discounted the cash inflows using a discount rate of 10%?
2. Find the inverse of the matrix of coefficients presented in Example 5.
3. Use a tree diagram to summarize the information given in the solution of Example 3.
4. Use the general result of this section to show that

$$EV_i = \sum_{j=1}^{n} P_{ij}P(O_j)$$

5. Given the following information:

	Outcome 1	Outcome 2
Act 1	$10,000	$20,000
Act 2	15,000	5,000

where the entries in the table are payoffs for various acts when coupled with an outcome state. Also assume that Outcome 1 has occurred 60% of the time in the past, whereas Outcome 2 has occurred 40% of the time in the past. Calculate the expected value of both acts.

6. A company president is faced with two options, both of which require an immediate cash outlay of $50,000. If he chooses the first option and demand is low, he will have a cash flow of $10,000 for ten years. If demand is high, there will be a cash flow of $20,000 for ten years. If he chooses the second option and demand is low, there will be cash flow of $20,000 for

five years. If demand is high, there will be a flow of $25,000 for five years.
(a) Use a discount rate of 10% to find the present value of these cash flows.
(b) If each outcome state is equally likely, what is the expected net present value of both options?

REFERENCES

Bierman, Harold, Bonini, C. P.,and Hausman, W. H. *Quantitative Analysis for Business Decisions*. Homewood, Ill.: Richard D. Irwin, Inc., 1969.

Kemeny, John G., Schleifer, A. Snell, J. L.,and Thompson, G. L. *Finite Mathematics with Business Applications*. Englewood Cliffs, N.J.: Prentice-Hall, Inc., 1964.

Levin, Richard I., and Kirkpatrick, C. A. *Quantitative Approaches to Management*. New York: McGraw-Hill Book Co., Inc., 1968.

Lipschutz, Seymour. *Theory and Problems of Probability*. New York: Schaum's Outline Series, McGraw-Hill Book Co., Inc., 1968.

Neter, John, Wasserman, William, and Whitmore, G. A. *Fundamental Statistics for Business and Economics*, fourth ed. Boston: Allyn and Bacon, Inc., 1973.

Scheerer, Anne E. *Probability on Discrete Sample Spaces with Applications*. Scranton, Pennsylvania: International Textbook Company, 1969.

Schellenberger, Robert E. *Managerial Analysis*. Homewood, Ill.: Richard D. Irwin, Inc., 1969.

Schlaifer, Robert. *Probability and Statistics for Business Decisions*. New York: McGraw-Hill Book Co., Inc., 1959.

Simone, Albert J. *Probability: An Introduction with Applications*. Boston: Allyn and Bacon, Inc., 1967.

Theodore, Chris A. *Applied Mathematics: An Introduction; Mathematical Analysis for Management*. Homewood, Illinois: Richard D. Irwin, Inc., 1965.

APPENDIX A

Tables

Table A-1 Table of Common Logarithms

N	L 0	1	2	3	4	5	6	7	8	9
0	$-\infty$	00 000	30 103	47 712	60 206	69 897	77 815	84 510	90 309	95 424
1	00 000	04 139	07 918	11 394	14 613	17 609	20 412	23 045	25 527	27 875
2	30 103	32 222	34 242	36 173	38 021	39 794	41 497	43 136	44 716	46 240
3	47 712	49 136	50 515	51 851	53 148	54 407	55 630	56 820	57 978	59 106
4	60 206	61 278	62 325	63 347	64 345	65 321	66 276	67 210	68 124	69 020
5	69 897	70 757	71 600	72 428	73 239	74 036	74 819	75 587	76 343	77 085
6	77 815	78 533	79 239	79 934	80 618	81 291	81 954	82 607	83 251	83 885
7	84 510	85 126	85 733	86 332	86 923	87 506	88 081	88 649	89 209	89 763
8	90 309	90 849	91 381	91 908	92 428	92 942	93 450	93 952	94 448	94 939
9	95 424	95 904	96 379	96 848	97 313	97 772	98 227	98 677	99 123	99 564
10	00 000	00 432	00 860	01 284	01 703	02 119	02 531	02 938	03 342	03 743
11	04 139	04 532	04 922	05 308	05 690	06 070	06 446	06 819	07 188	07 555
12	07 918	08 279	08 636	08 991	09 342	09 691	10 037	10 380	10 721	11 059
13	11 394	11 727	12 057	12 385	12 710	13 033	13 354	13 672	13 988	14 301
14	14 613	14 922	15 229	15 534	15 836	16 137	16 435	16 732	17 026	17 319
15	17 609	17 898	18 184	18 469	18 752	19 033	19 312	19 590	19 866	20 140
16	20 412	20 683	20 952	21 219	21 484	21 748	22 011	22 272	22 531	22 789
17	23 045	23 300	23 553	23 805	24 055	24 304	24 551	24 797	25 042	25 285
18	25 527	25 768	26 007	26 245	26 482	26 717	26 951	27 184	27 416	27 646
19	27 875	28 103	28 330	28 556	28 780	29 003	29 226	29 447	29 667	29 885
20	30 103	30 320	30 535	30 750	30 963	31 175	31 387	31 597	31 806	32 015
21	32 222	32 428	32 634	32 838	33 041	33 244	33 445	33 646	33 846	34 044
22	34 242	34 439	34 635	34 830	35 025	35 218	35 411	35 603	35 793	35 984
23	36 173	36 361	36 549	36 736	36 922	37 107	37 291	37 475	37 658	37 840
24	38 021	38 202	38 382	38 561	38 739	38 917	39 094	39 270	39 445	39 620
25	39 794	39 907	40 140	40 312	40 483	40 654	40 824	40 993	41 162	41 330
26	41 497	41 664	41 830	41 996	42 160	42 325	42 488	42 651	42 813	42 975
27	43 136	43 297	43 457	43 616	43 775	43 933	44 091	44 248	44 404	44 560
28	44 716	44 871	45 025	45 179	45 332	45 484	45 637	45 788	45 939	46 090
29	46 240	46 389	46 538	46 687	46 835	46 982	47 129	47 276	47 422	47 567
30	47 712	47.857	48 001	48 144	48 287	48 430	48 572	48 714	48 855	48 996
31	49 136	49 276	49 415	49 554	49 693	49 831	49 969	50 106	50 243	50 379
32	50 515	50 651	50 786	50 920	51 055	51 188	51 322	51 455	51 587	51 720
33	51 851	51 983	52 114	52 244	52 375	52 504	52 634	52 763	52 892	53 020
34	53 148	53 275	53 403	53 529	53 656	53 782	53 908	54 033	54 158	54 283
35	54 407	54 531	54 654	54 777	54 900	55 023	55 145	55 267	55 388	55 509
36	55 630	55 751	55 871	55 991	56 110	56 229	56 348	56 467	56 585	56 703
37	56 820	56 937	57 054	57 171	57 287	57 403	57 519	57 634	57 749	57 864
38	57 978	58 092	58 206	58 320	58 433	58 546	58 659	58 771	58 883	58 995
39	59 106	59 218	59 329	59 439	59 550	59 660	59 770	59 879	59 988	60 097
40	60 206	60 314	60 423	60 531	60 638	60 746	60 853	60 959	61 066	61 172
41	61 278	61 384	61 490	61 595	61 700	61 805	61 909	62 014	62 118	62 221
42	62 325	62 428	62 531	62 634	62 737	62 839	62 941	63 043	63 144	63 246
43	63 347	63 448	63 548	63 649	63 749	63 849	63 949	64 048	64 147	64 246
44	64 345	64 444	64 542	64 640	64 738	64 836	64 933	65 031	65 128	65 225
45	65 321	65 418	65 514	65 610	65 706	65 801	65 896	65 992	66 087	66 181
46	66 276	66 370	66 464	66 558	66 652	66 745	66 839	66 932	67 025	67 117
47	67 210	67 302	67 394	67 486	67 578	67 669	67 761	67 852	67 943	68 034
48	68 124	68 215	68 305	68 395	68 485	68 574	68 664	68 753	68 842	68 931
49	69 020	69 108	69 197	69 285	69 373	69 461	69 548	69 636	69 723	69 810
50	69 897	69 984	70 070	70 157	70 243	70 329	70 415	70 501	70 586	70 672
N	L 0	1	2	3	4	5	6	7	8	9

Table A-1 (*continued*)

N	L 0	1	2	3	4	5	6	7	8	9
50	69 897	69 984	70 070	70 157	70 243	70 329	70 415	70 501	70 586	70 672
51	70 757	70 842	70 927	71 012	71 096	71 181	71 265	71 349	71 433	71 517
52	71 600	71 684	71 767	71 850	71 933	72 016	72 099	72 181	72 263	72 346
53	72 428	72 509	72 591	72 673	72 754	72 835	72 916	72 997	73 078	73 159
54	73 239	73 320	73 400	73 480	73 560	73 640	73 719	73 799	73 878	73 957
55	74 036	74 115	74 194	74 273	74 351	74 429	74 507	74 586	74 663	74 741
56	74 819	74 896	74 974	75 051	75 128	75 205	75 282	75 358	75 435	75 511
57	75 587	75 664	75 740	75 815	75 891	75 967	76 042	76 118	76 193	76 268
58	76 343	76 418	76 492	76 567	76 641	76 716	76 790	76 864	76 938	77 012
59	77 085	77 159	77 232	77 305	77 379	77 452	77 525	77 597	77 670	77 743
60	77 815	77 887	77 960	78 032	78 104	78 176	78 247	78 319	78 390	78 462
61	78 533	78 604	78 675	78 746	78 817	78 888	78 958	79 029	79 099	79 169
62	79 239	79 309	79 379	79 449	79 518	79 588	79 657	79 727	79 796	79 865
63	79 934	80 003	80 072	80 140	80 209	80 277	80 346	80 414	80 482	80 550
64	80 618	80 686	80 754	80 821	80 889	80 956	81 023	81 090	81 158	81 224
65	81 291	81 358	81 425	81 491	81 558	81 624	81 690	81 757	81 823	81 889
66	81 954	82 020	82 086	82 151	82 217	82 282	82 347	82 413	82 478	82 543
67	82 607	82 672	82 737	82 802	82 866	82 930	82 995	83 059	83 123	83 187
68	83 251	83 315	83 378	83 442	83 506	83 569	83 632	83 696	83 759	83 822
69	83 885	83 948	84 011	84 073	84 136	84 198	84 261	84 323	84 386	84 448
70	84 510	84 572	84 634	84 696	84 757	84 819	84 880	84 942	85 003	85 065
71	85 126	85 187	85 248	85 309	85 370	85 431	85 491	85 552	85 612	85 673
72	85 733	85 794	85 854	85 914	85 974	86 034	86 094	86 153	86 213	86 273
73	86 332	86 392	86 451	86 510	86 570	86 629	86 688	86 747	86 806	86 864
74	86 923	86 982	87 040	87 099	87 157	87 216	87 274	87 332	87 390	87 448
75	87 506	87 564	87 622	87 679	87 737	87 795	87 852	87 910	87 967	88 024
76	88 081	88 138	88 195	88 252	88 309	88 366	88 423	88 480	88 536	88 593
77	88 649	88 705	88 762	88 818	88 874	88 930	88 986	89 042	89 098	89 154
78	89 209	89 265	89 321	89 376	89 432	89 487	89 542	89 597	89 653	89 708
79	89 763	89 818	89 873	89 927	89 982	90 037	90 091	90 146	90 200	90 255
80	90 309	90 363	90 417	90 472	90 526	90 580	90 634	90 687	90 741	90 795
81	90 849	90 902	90 956	91 009	91 062	91 116	91 169	91 222	91 275	91 328
82	91 381	91 434	91 487	91 540	91 593	91 645	91 698	91 751	91 803	91 855
83	91 908	91 960	92 012	92 065	92 117	92 169	92 221	92 273	92 324	92 376
84	92 428	92 480	92 531	92 583	92 634	92 686	92 737	92 788	92 840	92 891
85	92 942	92 993	93 044	93 095	93 146	93 197	93 247	93 298	93 349	93 399
86	93 450	93 500	93 551	93 601	93 651	93 702	93 752	93 802	93 852	93 902
87	93 952	94 002	94 052	94 101	94 151	94 201	94 250	94 300	94 349	94 399
88	94 448	94 498	94 547	94 596	94 645	94 694	94 743	94 792	94 841	94 890
89	94 939	94 988	95 036	95 085	95 134	95 182	95 231	95 279	95 328	95 376
90	95 424	95 472	95 521	95 569	95 617	95 665	95 713	95 761	95 809	95 856
91	95 904	95 952	95 999	96 047	96 095	96 142	96 190	96 237	96 284	96 332
92	96 379	96 426	96 473	96 520	96 567	96 614	96 661	96 708	96 755	96 802
93	96 848	96 895	96 942	96 988	97 035	97 081	97 128	97 174	97 220	97 267
94	97 313	97 359	97 405	97 451	97 497	97 543	97 589	97 635	97 681	97 727
95	97 772	97 818	97 864	97 909	97 955	98 000	98 046	98 091	98 137	98 182
96	98 227	98 272	98 318	98 363	98 408	98 453	98 498	98 543	98 588	98 632
97	98 677	98 722	98 767	98 811	98 856	98 900	98 945	98 989	99 034	99 078
98	99 123	99 167	99 211	99 255	99 300	99 344	99 388	99 432	99 476	99 520
99	99 564	99 607	99 651	99 695	99 739	99 782	99 826	99 870	99 913	99 957
100	00 000	00 043	00 087	00 130	00 173	00 217	00 260	00 303	00 346	00 389
N	L 0	1	2	3	4	5	6	7	8	9

TABLE A-1 (*continued*)

N	L 0	1	2	3	4	5	6	7	8	9
100	00 000	043	087	130	173	217	260	303	346	389
101	432	475	518	561	604	647	689	732	775	817
102	860	903	945	988	*030	*072	*115	*157	*199	*242
103	01 284	326	368	410	452	494	536	578	620	662
104	703	745	787	828	870	912	953	995	*036	*078
105	02 119	160	202	243	284	325	366	407	449	490
106	531	572	612	653	694	735	776	816	857	898
107	938	979	*019	*060	*100	*141	*181	*222	*262	*302
108	03 342	383	423	463	503	543	583	623	663	703
109	743	782	822	862	902	941	981	*021	*060	*100
110	04 139	179	218	258	297	336	376	415	454	493
111	532	571	610	650	689	727	766	805	844	883
112	922	961	999	*038	*077	*115	*154	*192	*231	*269
113	05 308	346	385	423	461	500	538	576	614	652
114	690	729	767	805	843	881	918	956	994	*032
115	06 070	108	145	183	221	258	296	333	371	408
116	446	483	521	558	595	633	670	707	744	781
117	819	856	893	930	967	*004	*041	*078	*115	*151
118	07 188	225	262	298	335	372	408	445	482	518
119	555	591	628	664	700	737	773	809	846	882
120	918	954	990	*027	*063	*099	*135	*171	*207	*243
121	08 279	314	350	386	422	458	493	529	565	600
122	636	672	707	743	778	814	849	884	920	955
123	991	*026	*061	*096	*132	*167	*202	*237	*272	*307
124	09 342	377	412	447	482	517	552	587	621	656
125	691	726	760	795	830	864	899	934	968	*003
126	10 037	072	106	140	175	209	243	278	312	346
127	380	415	449	483	517	551	585	619	653	687
128	721	755	789	823	857	890	924	958	992	*025
129	11 059	093	126	160	193	227	261	294	327	361
130	394	428	461	494	528	561	594	628	661	694
131	727	760	793	826	860	893	926	959	992	*024
132	12 057	090	123	156	189	222	254	287	320	352
133	385	418	450	483	516	548	581	613	646	678
134	710	743	775	808	840	872	905	937	969	*001
135	13 033	066	098	130	162	194	226	258	290	322
136	354	386	418	450	481	513	545	577	609	640
137	672	704	735	767	799	830	862	893	925	956
138	988	*019	*051	*082	*114	*145	*176	*208	*239	*270
139	14 301	333	364	395	426	457	489	520	551	582
140	613	644	675	706	737	768	799	829	860	891
141	922	953	983	*014	*045	*076	*106	*137	*168	*198
142	15 229	259	290	320	351	381	412	442	473	503
143	534	564	594	625	655	685	715	746	776	806
144	836	866	897	927	957	987	*017	*047	*077	*107
145	16 137	167	197	227	256	286	316	346	376	406
146	435	465	495	524	554	584	613	643	673	702
147	732	761	791	820	850	879	909	938	967	997
148	17 026	056	085	114	143	173	202	231	260	289
149	319	348	377	406	435	464	493	522	551	580
150	17 609	638	667	696	725	754	782	811	840	869

P P

	44	43	42
1	4.4	4.3	4.2
2	8.8	8.6	8.4
3	13.2	12.9	12.6
4	17.6	17.2	16.8
5	22.0	21.5	21.0
6	26.4	25.8	25.2
7	30.8	30.1	29.4
8	35.2	34.4	33.6
9	39.6	38.7	37.8

	41	40	39
1	4.1	4.0	3.9
2	8.2	8.0	7.8
3	12.3	12.0	11.7
4	16.4	16.0	15.6
5	20.5	20.0	19.5
6	24.6	24.0	23.4
7	28.7	28.0	27.3
8	32.8	32.0	31.2
9	36.9	36.0	35.1

	38	37	36
1	3.8	3.7	3.6
2	7.6	7.4	7.2
3	11.4	11.1	10.8
4	15.2	14.8	14.4
5	19.0	18.5	18.0
6	22.8	22.2	21.6
7	26.6	25.9	25.2
8	30.4	29.6	28.8
9	34.2	33.3	32.4

	35	34	33
1	3.5	3.4	3.3
2	7.0	6.8	6.6
3	10.5	10.2	9.9
4	14.0	13.6	13.2
5	17.5	17.0	16.5
6	21.0	20.4	19.8
7	24.5	23.8	23.1
8	28.0	27.2	26.4
9	31.5	30.6	29.7

	32	31	30
1	3.2	3.1	3.0
2	6.4	6.2	6.0
3	9.6	9.3	9.0
4	12.8	12.4	12.0
5	16.0	15.5	15.0
6	19.2	18.6	18.0
7	22.4	21.7	21.0
8	25.6	24.8	24.0
9	28.8	27.9	27.0

N	L 0	1	2	3	4	5	6	7	8	9	P P

TABLE A-1 (*continued*)

N	L 0	1	2	3	4	5	6	7	8	9
150	17 609	638	667	696	725	754	782	811	840	869
151	898	926	955	984	*013	*041	*070	*099	*127	*156
152	18 184	213	241	270	298	327	355	384	412	441
153	469	498	526	554	583	611	639	667	696	724
154	752	780	808	837	865	893	921	949	977	*005
155	19 033	061	089	117	145	173	201	229	257	285
156	312	340	368	396	424	451	479	507	535	562
157	590	618	645	673	700	728	756	783	811	838
158	866	893	921	948	976	*003	*030	*058	*085	*112
159	20 140	167	194	222	249	276	303	330	358	385
160	412	439	466	493	520	548	575	602	629	656
161	683	710	737	763	790	817	844	871	898	925
162	952	978	*005	*032	*059	*085	*112	*139	*165	*192
163	21 219	245	272	299	325	352	378	405	431	458
164	484	511	537	564	590	617	643	669	696	722
165	748	775	801	827	854	880	906	932	958	985
166	22 011	037	063	089	115	141	167	194	220	246
167	272	298	324	350	376	401	427	453	479	505
168	531	557	583	608	634	660	686	712	737	763
169	789	814	840	866	891	917	943	968	994	*019
170	23 045	070	096	121	147	172	198	223	249	274
171	300	325	350	376	401	426	452	477	502	528
172	553	578	603	629	654	679	704	729	754	779
173	805	830	855	880	905	930	955	980	*005	*030
174	24 055	080	105	130	155	180	204	229	254	279
175	304	329	353	378	403	428	452	477	502	527
176	551	576	601	625	650	674	699	724	748	773
177	797	822	846	871	895	920	944	969	993	*018
178	25 042	066	091	115	139	164	188	212	237	261
179	285	310	334	358	382	406	431	455	479	503
180	527	551	575	600	624	648	672	696	720	744
181	768	792	816	840	864	888	912	935	959	983
182	26 007	031	055	079	102	126	150	174	198	221
183	245	269	293	316	340	364	387	411	435	458
184	482	505	529	553	576	600	623	647	670	694
185	717	741	764	788	811	834	858	881	905	928
186	951	975	998	*021	*045	*068	*091	*114	*138	*161
187	27 184	207	231	254	277	300	323	346	370	393
188	416	439	462	485	508	531	554	577	600	623
189	646	669	692	715	738	761	784	807	830	852
190	875	898	921	944	967	989	*012	*035	*058	*081
191	28 103	126	149	171	194	217	240	262	285	307
192	330	353	375	398	421	443	466	488	511	533
193	556	578	601	623	646	668	691	713	735	758
194	780	803	825	847	870	892	914	937	959	981
195	29 003	026	048	070	092	115	137	159	181	203
196	226	248	270	292	314	336	358	380	403	425
197	447	469	491	513	535	557	579	601	623	645
198	667	688	710	732	754	776	798	820	842	863
199	885	907	929	951	973	994	*016	*038	*060	*081
200	30 103	125	146	168	190	211	233	255	276	298
N	L 0	1	2	3	4	5	6	7	8	9

P P

	29	28
1	2.9	2.8
2	5.8	5.6
3	8.7	8.4
4	11.6	11.2
5	14.5	14.0
6	17.4	16.8
7	20.3	19.6
8	23.2	22.4
9	26.1	25.2

	27	26
1	2.7	2.6
2	5.4	5.2
3	8.1	7.8
4	10.8	10.4
5	13.5	13.0
6	16.2	15.6
7	18.9	18.2
8	21.6	20.8
9	24.3	23.4

	25
1	2.5
2	5.0
3	7.5
4	10.0
5	12.5
6	15.0
7	17.5
8	20.0
9	22.5

	24	23
1	2.4	2.3
2	4.8	4.6
3	7.2	6.9
4	9.6	9.2
5	12.0	11.5
6	14.4	13.8
7	16.8	16.1
8	19.2	18.4
9	21.6	20.7

	22	21
1	2.2	2.1
2	4.4	4.2
3	6.6	6.3
4	8.8	8.4
5	11.0	10.5
6	13.2	12.6
7	15.4	14.7
8	17.6	16.8
9	19.8	18.9

P P

TABLE A-1 (*continued*)

N	L 0	1	2	3	4	5	6	7	8	9
200	30 103	125	146	168	190	211	233	255	276	298
201	320	341	363	384	406	428	449	471	492	514
202	535	557	578	600	621	643	664	685	707	728
203	750	771	792	814	835	856	878	899	920	942
204	963	984	*006	*027	*048	*069	*091	*112	*133	*154
205	31 175	197	218	239	260	281	302	323	345	366
206	387	408	429	450	471	492	513	534	555	576
207	597	618	639	660	681	702	723	744	765	785
208	806	827	848	869	890	911	931	952	973	994
209	32 015	035	056	077	098	118	139	160	181	201
210	222	243	263	284	305	325	346	366	387	408
211	428	449	469	490	510	531	552	572	593	613
212	634	654	675	695	715	736	756	777	797	818
213	838	858	879	899	919	940	960	980	*001	*021
214	33 041	062	082	102	122	143	163	183	203	224
215	244	264	284	304	325	345	365	385	405	425
216	445	465	486	506	526	546	566	586	606	626
217	646	666	686	706	726	746	766	786	806	826
218	846	866	885	905	925	945	965	985	*005	*025
219	34 044	064	084	104	124	143	163	183	203	223
220	242	262	282	301	321	341	361	380	400	420
221	439	459	479	498	518	537	557	577	596	616
222	635	655	674	694	713	733	753	772	792	811
223	830	850	869	889	908	928	947	967	986	*005
224	35 025	044	064	083	102	122	141	160	180	199
225	218	238	257	276	295	315	334	353	372	392
226	411	430	449	468	488	507	526	545	564	583
227	603	622	641	660	679	698	717	736	755	774
228	793	813	832	851	870	889	908	927	946	965
229	984	*003	*021	*040	*059	*078	*097	*116	*135	*154
230	36 173	192	211	229	248	267	286	305	324	342
231	361	380	399	418	436	455	474	493	511	530
232	549	568	586	605	624	642	661	680	698	717
233	736	754	773	791	810	829	847	866	884	903
234	922	940	959	977	996	*014	*033	*051	*070	*088
235	37 107	125	144	162	181	199	218	236	254	273
236	291	310	328	346	365	383	401	420	438	457
237	475	493	511	530	548	566	585	603	621	639
238	658	676	694	712	731	749	767	785	803	822
239	840	858	876	894	912	931	949	967	985	*003
240	38 021	039	057	075	093	112	130	148	166	184
241	202	220	238	256	274	292	310	328	346	364
242	382	399	417	435	453	471	489	507	525	543
243	561	578	596	614	632	650	668	686	703	721
244	739	757	775	792	810	828	846	863	881	899
245	917	934	952	970	987	*005	*023	*041	*058	*076
246	39 094	111	129	146	164	182	199	217	235	252
247	270	287	305	322	340	358	375	393	410	428
248	445	463	480	498	515	533	550	568	585	602
249	620	637	655	672	690	707	724	742	759	777
250	794	811	829	846	863	881	898	915	933	950

N	L 0	1	2	3	4	5	6	7	8	9

P P

	22	21
1	2.2	2.1
2	4.4	4.2
3	6.6	6.3
4	8.8	8.4
5	11.0	10.5
6	13.2	12.6
7	15.4	14.7
8	17.6	16.8
9	19.8	18.9

	20
1	2.0
2	4.0
3	6.0
4	8.0
5	10.0
6	12.0
7	14.0
8	16.0
9	18.0

	19
1	1.9
2	3.8
3	5.7
4	7.6
5	9.5
6	11.4
7	13.3
8	15.2
9	17.1

	18
1	1.8
2	3.6
3	5.4
4	7.2
5	9.0
6	10.8
7	12.6
8	14.4
9	16.2

	17
1	1.7
2	3.4
3	5.1
4	6.8
5	8.5
6	10.2
7	11.9
8	13.6
9	15.3

P P

TABLE A-1 (*continued*)

N	L 0	1	2	3	4	5	6	7	8	9	P P	
250	39 794	811	829	846	863	881	898	915	933	950		
											18	
251	967	985	*002	*019	*037	*054	*071	*088	*106	*123	1	1.8
252	40 140	157	175	192	209	226	243	261	278	295	2	3.6
253	312	329	346	364	381	398	415	432	449	466	3	5.4
254	483	500	518	535	552	569	586	603	620	637	4	7.2
255	654	671	688	705	722	739	756	773	790	807	5	9.0
256	824	841	858	875	892	909	926	943	960	976	6	10.8
257	993	*010	*027	*044	*061	*078	*095	*111	*128	*145	7	12.6
258	41 162	179	196	212	229	246	263	280	296	313	8	14.4
259	330	347	363	380	397	414	430	447	464	481	9	16.2
260	497	514	531	547	564	581	597	614	631	647		
											17	
261	664	681	697	714	731	747	764	780	797	814	1	1.7
262	830	847	863	880	896	913	929	946	963	979	2	3.4
263	996	*012	*029	*045	*062	*078	*095	*111	*127	*144	3	5.1
264	42 160	177	193	210	226	243	259	275	292	308	4	6 8
265	325	341	357	374	390	406	423	439	455	472	5	8.5
266	488	504	521	537	553	570	586	602	619	635	6	10.2
267	651	667	684	700	716	732	749	765	781	797	7	11.9
268	813	830	846	862	878	894	911	927	943	959	8	13.6
269	975	991	*008	*024	*040	*056	*072	*088	*104	*120	9	15.3
270	43 136	152	169	185	201	217	233	249	265	281		
											16	
271	297	313	329	345	361	377	393	409	425	441	1	1.6
272	457	473	489	505	521	537	553	569	584	600	2	3.2
273	616	632	648	664	680	696	712	727	743	759	3	4.8
274	775	791	807	823	838	854	870	886	902	917	4	6.4
275	933	949	965	981	996	*012	*028	*044	*059	*075	5	8.0
276	44 091	107	122	138	154	170	185	201	217	232	6	9.6
277	248	264	279	295	311	326	342	358	373	389	7	11.2
278	404	420	436	451	467	483	498	514	529	545	8	12.8
279	560	576	592	607	623	638	654	669	685	700	9	14.4
280	716	731	747	762	778	793	809	824	840	855		
											15	
281	871	886	902	917	932	948	963	979	994	*010	1	1.5
282	45 025	040	056	071	086	102	117	133	148	163	2	3.0
283	179	194	209	225	240	255	271	286	301	317	3	4.5
284	332	347	362	378	393	408	423	439	454	469	4	6.0
285	484	500	515	530	545	561	576	591	606	621	5	7.5
286	637	652	667	682	697	712	728	743	758	773	6	9.0
287	788	803	818	834	849	864	879	894	909	924	7	10.5
288	939	954	969	984	*000	*015	*030	*045	*060	*075	8	12.0
289	46 090	105	120	135	150	165	180	195	210	225	9	13.5
290	240	255	270	285	300	315	330	345	359	374		
											14	
291	389	404	419	434	449	464	479	494	509	523	1	1.4
292	538	553	568	583	598	613	627	642	657	672	2	2.8
293	687	702	716	731	746	761	776	790	805	820	3	4.2
294	835	850	864	879	894	909	923	938	953	967	4	5.6
295	982	997	*012	*026	*041	*056	*070	*085	*100	*114	5	7.0
296	47 129	144	159	173	188	202	217	232	246	261	6	8.4
297	276	290	305	319	334	349	363	378	392	407	7	9.8
298	422	436	451	465	480	494	509	524	538	553	8	11.2
299	567	582	596	611	625	640	654	669	683	698	9	12.6
300	712	727	741	756	770	784	799	813	828	842		

N	L 0	1	2	3	4	5	6	7	8	9	P P	

TABLE A-1 (*continued*)

N	L 0	1	2	3	4	5	6	7	8	9
300	47 712	727	741	756	770	784	799	813	828	842
301	857	871	885	900	914	929	943	958	972	986
302	48 001	015	029	044	058	073	087	101	116	130
303	144	159	173	187	202	216	230	244	259	273
304	287	302	316	330	344	359	373	387	401	416
305	430	444	458	473	487	501	515	530	544	558
306	572	586	601	615	629	643	657	671	686	700
307	714	728	742	756	770	785	799	813	827	841
308	855	869	883	897	911	926	940	954	968	982
309	996	*010	*024	*038	*052	*066	*080	*094	*108	*122
310	49 136	150	164	178	192	206	220	234	248	262
311	276	290	304	318	332	346	360	374	388	402
312	415	429	443	457	471	485	499	513	527	541
313	554	568	582	596	610	624	638	651	665	679
314	693	707	721	734	748	762	776	790	803	817
315	831	845	859	872	886	900	914	927	941	955
316	969	982	996	*010	*024	*037	*051	*065	*079	*092
317	50 106	120	133	147	161	174	188	202	215	229
318	243	256	270	284	297	311	325	338	352	365
319	379	393	406	420	433	447	461	474	488	501
320	515	529	542	556	569	583	596	610	623	637
321	651	664	678	691	705	718	732	745	759	772
322	786	799	813	826	840	853	866	880	893	907
323	920	934	947	961	974	987	*001	*014	*028	*041
324	51 055	068	081	095	108	121	135	148	162	175
325	188	202	215	228	242	255	268	282	295	308
326	322	335	348	362	375	388	402	415	428	441
327	455	468	481	495	508	521	534	548	561	574
328	587	601	614	627	640	654	667	680	693	706
329	720	733	746	759	772	786	799	812	825	838
330	851	865	878	891	904	917	930	943	957	970
331	983	996	*009	*022	*035	*048	*061	*075	*088	*101
332	52 114	127	140	153	166	179	192	205	218	231
333	244	257	270	284	297	310	323	336	349	362
334	375	388	401	414	427	440	453	466	479	492
335	504	517	530	543	556	569	582	595	608	621
336	634	647	660	673	686	699	711	724	737	750
337	763	776	789	802	815	827	840	853	866	879
338	892	905	917	930	943	956	969	982	994	*007
339	53 020	033	046	058	071	084	097	110	122	135
340	148	161	173	186	199	212	224	237	250	263
341	275	288	301	314	326	339	352	364	377	390
342	403	415	428	441	453	466	479	491	504	517
343	529	542	555	567	580	593	605	618	631	643
344	656	668	681	694	706	719	732	744	757	769
345	782	794	807	820	832	845	857	870	882	895
346	908	920	933	945	958	970	983	995	*008	*020
347	54 033	045	058	070	083	095	108	120	133	145
348	158	170	183	195	208	220	233	245	258	270
349	283	295	307	320	332	345	357	370	382	394
350	407	419	432	444	456	469	481	494	506	518

N	L 0	1	2	3	4	5	6	7	8	9

P P

15
1	1.5
2	3.0
3	4.5
4	6.0
5	7.5
6	9.0
7	10.5
8	12.0
9	13.5

14
1	1.4
2	2.8
3	4.2
4	5.6
5	7.0
6	8.4
7	9.8
8	11.2
9	12.6

13
1	1.3
2	2.6
3	3.9
4	5.2
5	6.5
6	7.8
7	9.1
8	10.4
9	11.7

12
1	1.2
2	2.4
3	3.6
4	4.8
5	6.0
6	7.2
7	8.4
8	9.6
9	10.8

TABLE A-1 (*continued*)

N	L 0	1	2	3	4	5	6	7	8	9
350	54 407	419	432	444	456	469	481	494	506	518
351	531	543	555	568	580	593	605	617	630	642
352	654	667	679	691	704	716	728	741	753	765
353	777	790	802	814	827	839	851	864	876	888
354	900	913	925	937	949	962	974	986	998	*011
355	55 023	035	047	060	072	084	096	108	121	133
356	145	157	169	182	194	206	218	230	242	255
357	267	279	291	303	315	328	340	352	364	376
358	388	400	413	425	437	449	461	473	485	497
359	509	522	534	546	558	570	582	594	606	618
360	630	642	654	666	678	691	703	715	727	739
361	751	763	775	787	799	811	823	835	847	859
362	871	883	895	907	919	931	943	955	967	979
363	991	*003	*015	*027	*038	*050	*062	*074	*086	*098
364	56 110	122	134	146	158	170	182	194	205	217
365	229	241	253	265	277	289	301	312	324	336
366	348	360	372	384	396	407	419	431	443	455
367	467	478	490	502	514	526	538	549	561	573
368	585	597	608	620	632	644	656	667	679	691
369	703	714	726	738	750	761	773	785	797	808
370	820	832	844	855	867	879	891	902	914	926
371	937	949	961	972	984	996	*008	*019	*031	*043
372	57 054	066	078	089	101	113	124	136	148	159
373	171	183	194	206	217	229	241	252	264	276
374	287	299	310	322	334	345	357	368	380	392
375	403	415	426	438	449	461	473	484	496	507
376	519	530	542	553	565	576	588	600	611	623
377	634	646	657	669	680	692	703	715	726	738
378	749	761	772	784	795	807	818	830	841	852
379	864	875	887	898	910	921	933	944	955	967
380	978	990	*001	*013	*024	*035	*047	*058	*070	*081
381	58 092	104	115	127	138	149	161	172	184	195
382	206	218	229	240	252	263	274	286	297	309
383	320	331	343	354	365	377	388	399	410	422
384	433	444	456	467	478	490	501	512	524	535
385	546	557	569	580	591	602	614	625	636	647
386	659	670	681	692	704	715	726	737	749	760
387	771	782	794	805	816	827	838	850	861	872
388	883	894	906	917	928	939	950	961	973	984
389	995	*006	*017	*028	*040	*051	*062	*073	*084	*095
390	59 106	118	129	140	151	162	173	184	195	207
391	218	229	240	251	262	273	284	295	306	318
392	329	340	351	362	373	384	395	406	417	428
393	439	450	461	472	483	494	506	517	528	539
394	550	561	572	583	594	605	616	627	638	649
395	660	671	682	693	704	715	726	737	748	759
396	770	780	791	802	813	824	835	846	857	868
397	879	890	901	912	923	934	945	956	966	977
398	988	999	*010	*021	*032	*043	*054	*065	*076	*086
399	60 097	108	119	130	141	152	163	173	184	195
400	206	217	228	239	249	260	271	282	293	304
N	L 0	1	2	3	4	5	6	7	8	9

P P

13	
1	1.3
2	2.6
3	3.9
4	5.2
5	6.5
6	7.8
7	9.1
8	10.4
9	11.7

12	
1	1.2
2	2.4
3	3.6
4	4.8
5	6.0
6	7.2
7	8.4
8	9.6
9	10.8

11	
1	1.1
2	2.2
3	3.3
4	4.4
5	5.5
6	6.6
7	7.7
8	8.8
9	9.9

10	
1	1.0
2	2.0
3	3.0
4	4.0
5	5.0
6	6.0
7	7.0
8	8.0
9	9.0

TABLE A-1 (*continued*)

N	L 0	1	2	3	4	5	6	7	8	9
400	60 206	217	228	239	249	260	271	282	293	304
401	314	325	336	347	358	369	379	390	401	412
402	423	433	444	455	466	477	487	498	509	520
403	531	541	552	563	574	584	595	606	617	627
404	638	649	660	670	681	692	703	713	724	735
405	746	756	767	778	788	799	810	821	831	842
406	853	863	874	885	895	906	917	927	938	949
407	959	970	981	991	*002	*013	*023	*034	*045	*055
408	61 066	077	087	098	109	119	130	140	151	162
409	172	183	194	204	215	225	236	247	257	268
410	278	289	300	310	321	331	342	352	363	374
411	384	395	405	416	426	437	448	458	469	479
412	490	500	511	521	532	542	553	563	574	584
413	595	606	616	627	637	648	658	669	679	690
414	700	711	721	731	742	752	763	773	784	794
415	805	815	826	836	847	857	868	878	888	899
416	909	920	930	941	951	962	972	982	993	*003
417	62 014	024	034	045	055	066	076	086	097	107
418	118	128	138	149	159	170	180	190	201	211
419	221	232	242	252	263	273	284	294	304	315
420	325	335	346	356	366	377	387	397	408	418
421	428	439	449	459	469	480	490	500	511	521
422	531	542	552	562	572	583	593	603	613	624
423	634	644	655	665	675	685	696	706	716	726
424	737	747	757	767	778	788	798	808	818	829
425	839	849	859	870	880	890	900	910	921	931
426	941	951	961	972	982	992	*002	*012	*022	*033
427	63 043	053	063	073	083	094	104	114	124	134
428	144	155	165	175	185	195	205	215	225	236
429	246	256	266	276	286	296	306	317	327	337
430	347	357	367	377	387	397	407	417	428	438
431	448	458	468	478	488	498	508	518	528	538
432	548	558	568	579	589	599	609	619	629	639
433	649	659	669	679	689	699	709	719	729	739
434	749	759	769	779	789	799	809	819	829	839
435	849	859	869	879	889	899	909	919	929	939
436	949	959	969	979	988	998	*008	*018	*028	*038
437	64 048	058	068	078	088	098	108	118	128	137
438	147	157	167	177	187	197	207	217	227	237
439	246	256	266	276	286	296	306	316	326	335
440	345	355	365	375	385	395	404	414	424	434
441	444	454	464	473	483	493	503	513	523	532
442	542	552	562	572	582	591	601	611	621	631
443	640	650	660	670	680	689	699	709	719	729
444	738	748	758	768	777	787	797	807	816	826
445	836	846	856	865	875	885	895	904	914	924
446	933	943	953	963	972	982	992	*002	*011	*021
447	65 031	040	050	060	070	079	089	099	108	118
448	128	137	147	157	167	176	186	196	205	215
449	225	234	244	254	263	273	283	292	302	312
450	321	331	341	350	360	369	379	389	398	408

| N | L 0 | 1 | 2 | 3 | 4 | 5 | 6 | 7 | 8 | 9 |

P P

11
1	1.1
2	2.2
3	3.3
4	4.4
5	5.5
6	6.6
7	7.7
8	8.8
9	9.9

10
1	1.0
2	2.0
3	3.0
4	4.0
5	5.0
6	6.0
7	7.0
8	8.0
9	9.0

9
1	0.9
2	1.8
3	2.7
4	3.6
5	4.5
6	5.4
7	6.3
8	7.2
9	8.1

Tᴀʙʟᴇ A-1 (*continued*)

N	L 0	1	2	3	4	5	6	7	8	9	P P
450	65 321	331	341	350	360	369	379	389	398	408	
451	418	427	437	447	456	466	475	485	495	504	
452	514	523	533	543	552	562	571	581	591	600	
453	610	619	629	639	648	658	667	677	686	696	
454	706	715	725	734	744	753	763	772	782	792	
455	801	811	820	830	839	849	858	868	877	887	
456	896	906	916	925	935	944	954	963	973	982	**10**
457	992	*001	*011	*020	*030	*039	*049	*058	*068	*077	1 | 1.0
458	66 087	096	106	115	124	134	143	153	162	172	2 | 2.0
459	181	191	200	210	219	229	238	247	257	266	3 | 3.0
											4 | 4.0
460	276	285	295	304	314	323	332	342	351	361	5 | 5.0
											6 | 6.0
461	370	380	389	398	408	417	427	436	445	455	7 | 7.0
462	464	474	483	492	502	511	521	530	539	549	8 | 8.0
463	558	567	577	586	596	605	614	624	633	642	9 | 9.0
464	652	661	671	680	689	699	708	717	727	736	
465	745	755	764	773	783	792	801	811	820	829	
466	839	848	857	867	876	885	894	904	913	922	
467	932	941	950	960	969	978	987	997	*006	*015	
468	67 025	034	043	052	062	071	080	089	099	108	
469	117	127	136	145	154	164	173	182	191	201	
470	210	219	228	237	247	256	265	274	284	293	
471	302	311	321	330	339	348	357	367	376	385	**9**
472	394	403	413	422	431	440	449	459	468	477	1 | 0.9
473	486	495	504	514	523	532	541	550	560	569	2 | 1.8
474	578	587	596	605	614	624	633	642	651	660	3 | 2.7
475	669	679	688	697	706	715	724	733	742	752	4 | 3.6
476	761	770	779	788	797	806	815	825	834	843	5 | 4.5
477	852	861	870	879	888	897	906	916	925	934	6 | 5.4
478	943	952	961	970	979	988	997	*006	*015	*024	7 | 6.3
479	68 034	043	052	061	070	079	088	097	106	115	8 | 7.2
											9 | 8.1
480	124	133	142	151	160	169	178	187	196	205	
481	215	224	233	242	251	260	269	278	287	296	
482	305	314	323	332	341	350	359	368	377	386	
483	395	404	413	422	431	440	449	458	467	476	
484	485	494	502	511	520	529	538	547	556	565	
485	574	583	592	601	610	619	628	637	646	655	
486	664	673	681	690	699	708	717	726	735	744	
487	753	762	771	780	789	797	806	815	824	833	
488	842	851	860	869	878	886	895	904	913	922	**8**
489	931	940	949	958	966	975	984	993	*002	*011	1 | 0.8
											2 | 1.6
490	69 020	028	037	046	055	064	073	082	090	099	3 | 2.4
											4 | 3.2
491	108	117	126	135	144	152	161	170	179	188	5 | 4.0
492	197	205	214	223	232	241	249	258	267	276	6 | 4.8
493	285	294	302	311	320	329	338	346	355	364	7 | 5.6
494	373	381	390	399	408	417	425	434	443	452	8 | 6.4
495	461	469	478	487	496	504	513	522	531	539	9 | 7.2
496	548	557	566	574	583	592	601	609	618	627	
497	636	644	653	662	671	679	688	697	705	714	
498	723	732	740	749	758	767	775	784	793	801	
499	810	819	827	836	845	854	862	871	880	888	
500	897	906	914	923	932	940	949	958	966	975	
N	L 0	1	2	3	4	5	6	7	8	9	P P

TABLE A-1 (*continued*)

N	L 0	1	2	3	4	5	6	7	8	9
500	69 897	906	914	923	932	940	949	958	966	975
501	984	992	*001	*010	*018	*027	*036	*044	*053	*062
502	70 070	079	088	096	105	114	122	131	140	148
503	157	165	174	183	191	200	209	217	226	234
504	243	252	260	269	278	286	295	303	312	321
505	329	338	346	355	364	372	381	389	398	406
506	415	424	432	441	449	458	467	475	484	492
507	501	509	518	526	535	544	552	561	569	578
508	586	595	603	612	621	629	638	646	655	663
509	672	680	689	697	706	714	723	731	740	749
510	757	766	774	783	791	800	808	817	825	834
511	842	851	859	868	876	885	893	902	910	919
512	927	935	944	952	961	969	978	986	995	*003
513	71 012	020	029	037	046	054	063	071	079	088
514	096	105	113	122	130	139	147	155	164	172
515	181	189	198	206	214	223	231	240	248	257
516	265	273	282	290	299	307	315	324	332	341
517	349	357	366	374	383	391	399	408	416	425
518	433	441	450	458	466	475	483	492	500	508
519	517	525	533	542	550	559	567	575	584	592
520	600	609	617	625	634	642	650	659	667	675
521	684	692	700	709	717	725	734	742	750	759
522	767	775	784	792	800	809	817	825	834	842
523	850	858	867	875	883	892	900	908	917	925
524	933	941	950	958	966	975	983	991	999	*008
525	72 016	024	032	041	049	057	066	074	082	090
526	099	107	115	123	132	140	148	156	165	173
527	181	189	198	206	214	222	230	239	247	255
528	263	272	280	288	296	304	313	321	329	337
529	346	354	362	370	378	387	395	403	411	419
530	428	436	444	452	460	469	477	485	493	501
531	509	518	526	534	542	550	558	567	575	583
532	591	509	607	616	624	632	640	648	656	665
533	673	681	689	697	705	713	722	730	738	746
534	754	762	770	779	787	795	803	811	819	827
535	835	843	852	860	868	876	884	892	900	908
536	916	925	933	941	949	957	965	973	981	989
537	997	*006	*014	*022	*030	*038	*046	*054	*062	*070
538	73 078	086	094	102	111	119	127	135	143	151
539	159	167	175	183	191	199	207	215	223	231
540	239	247	255	263	272	280	288	296	304	312
541	320	328	336	344	352	360	368	376	384	392
542	400	408	416	424	432	440	448	456	464	472
543	480	488	496	504	512	520	528	536	544	552
544	560	568	576	584	592	600	608	616	624	632
545	640	648	656	664	672	679	687	695	703	711
546	719	727	735	743	751	759	767	775	783	791
547	799	807	815	823	830	838	846	854	862	870
548	878	886	894	902	910	918	926	933	941	949
549	957	965	973	981	989	997	*005	*013	*020	*028
550	74 036	044	052	060	068	076	084	092	099	107
N	L 0	1	2	3	4	5	6	7	8	9

P P

9
1	0.9
2	1.8
3	2.7
4	3.6
5	4.5
6	5.4
7	6.3
8	7.2
9	8.1

8
1	0.8
2	1.6
3	2.4
4	3.2
5	4.0
6	4.8
7	5.6
8	6.4
9	7.2

7
1	0.7
2	1.4
3	2.1
4	2.8
5	3.5
6	4.2
7	4.9
8	5.6
9	6.3

TABLE A-1 (*continued*)

N	L 0	1	2	3	4	5	6	7	8	9	P P
550	74 036	044	052	060	068	076	084	092	099	107	
551	115	123	131	139	147	155	162	170	178	186	
552	194	202	210	218	225	233	241	249	257	265	
553	273	280	288	296	304	312	320	327	335	343	
554	351	359	367	374	382	390	398	406	414	421	
555	429	437	445	453	461	468	476	484	492	500	
556	507	515	523	531	539	547	554	562	570	578	
557	586	593	601	609	617	624	632	640	648	656	
558	663	671	679	687	695	702	710	718	726	733	
559	741	749	757	764	772	780	788	796	803	811	
560	819	827	834	842	850	858	865	873	881	889	
561	896	904	912	920	927	935	943	950	958	966	
562	974	981	989	997	*005	*012	*020	*028	*035	*043	
563	75 051	059	066	074	082	089	097	105	113	120	
564	128	136	143	151	159	166	174	182	189	197	
565	205	213	220	228	236	243	251	259	266	274	
566	282	289	297	305	312	320	328	335	343	351	
567	358	366	374	381	389	397	404	412	420	427	
568	435	442	450	458	465	473	481	488	496	504	
569	511	519	526	534	542	549	557	565	572	580	
570	587	595	603	610	618	626	633	641	648	656	
571	664	671	679	686	694	702	709	717	724	732	
572	740	747	755	762	770	778	785	793	800	808	
573	815	823	831	838	846	853	861	868	876	884	
574	891	899	906	914	921	929	937	944	952	959	
575	967	974	982	989	997	*005	*012	*020	*027	*035	
576	76 042	050	057	065	072	080	087	095	103	110	
577	118	125	133	140	148	155	163	170	178	185	
578	193	200	208	215	223	230	238	245	253	260	
579	268	275	283	290	298	305	313	320	328	335	
580	343	350	358	365	373	380	388	395	403	410	
581	418	425	433	440	448	455	462	470	477	485	
582	492	500	507	515	522	530	537	545	552	559	
583	567	574	582	589	597	604	612	619	626	634	
584	641	649	656	664	671	678	686	693	701	708	
585	716	723	730	738	745	753	760	768	775	782	
586	790	797	805	812	819	827	834	842	849	856	
587	864	871	879	886	893	901	908	916	923	930	
588	938	945	953	960	967	975	982	989	997	*004	
589	77 012	019	026	034	041	048	056	063	070	078	
590	085	093	100	107	115	122	129	137	144	151	
591	159	166	173	181	188	195	203	210	217	225	
592	232	240	247	254	262	269	276	283	291	298	
593	305	313	320	327	335	342	349	357	364	371	
594	379	386	393	401	408	415	422	430	437	444	
595	452	459	466	474	481	488	495	503	510	517	
596	525	532	539	546	554	561	568	576	583	590	
597	597	605	612	619	627	634	641	648	656	663	
598	670	677	685	692	699	706	714	721	728	735	
599	743	750	757	764	772	779	786	793	801	808	
600	815	822	830	837	844	851	859	866	873	880	
N	L 0	1	2	3	4	5	6	7	8	9	P P

8

1	0.8
2	1.6
3	2.4
4	3.2
5	4.0
6	4.8
7	5.6
8	6.4
9	7.2

7

1	0.7
2	1.4
3	2.1
4	2.8
5	3.5
6	4.2
7	4.9
8	5.6
9	6.3

TABLE A-1 (*continued*)

N	L 0	1	2	3	4	5	6	7	8	9	P P	
600	77 815	822	830	837	844	851	859	866	873	880		
601	887	895	902	909	916	924	931	938	945	952		
602	960	967	974	981	988	996	*003	*010	*017	*025		
603	78 032	039	046	053	061	068	075	082	089	097		
604	104	111	118	125	132	140	147	154	161	168		
605	176	183	190	197	204	211	219	226	233	240		
606	247	254	262	269	276	283	290	297	305	312		**8**
507	319	326	333	340	347	355	362	369	376	383	1	0.8
608	390	398	405	412	419	426	433	440	447	455	2	1.6
609	462	469	476	483	490	497	504	512	519	526	3	2.4
											4	3.2
610	533	540	547	554	561	569	576	583	590	597	5	4.0
											6	4.8
611	604	611	618	625	633	640	647	654	661	668	7	5.6
612	675	682	689	696	704	711	718	725	732	739	8	6.4
613	746	753	760	767	774	781	789	796	803	810	9	7.2
614	817	824	831	838	845	852	859	866	873	880		
615	888	895	902	909	916	923	930	937	944	951		
616	958	965	972	979	986	993	*000	*007	*014	*021		
617	79 029	036	043	050	057	064	071	078	085	092		
618	099	106	113	120	127	134	141	148	155	162		
619	169	176	183	190	197	204	211	218	225	232		
620	239	246	253	260	267	274	281	288	295	302		
621	309	316	323	330	337	344	351	358	365	372		**7**
622	379	386	393	400	407	414	421	428	435	442	1	0.7
623	449	456	463	470	477	484	491	498	505	511	2	1.4
624	518	525	532	539	546	553	560	567	574	581	3	2.1
625	588	595	602	609	616	623	630	637	644	650	4	2.8
626	657	664	671	678	685	692	699	706	713	720	5	3.5
627	727	734	741	748	754	761	768	775	782	789	6	4.2
628	796	803	810	817	824	831	837	844	851	858	7	4.9
629	865	872	879	886	893	900	906	913	920	927	8	5.6
											9	6.3
630	934	941	948	955	962	969	975	982	989	996		
631	80 003	010	017	024	030	037	044	051	058	065		
632	072	079	085	092	099	106	113	120	127	134		
633	140	147	154	161	168	175	182	188	195	202		
634	209	216	223	229	236	243	250	257	264	271		
635	277	284	291	298	305	312	318	325	332	339		
636	346	353	359	366	373	380	387	393	400	407		
637	414	421	428	434	441	448	455	462	468	475		
638	482	489	496	502	509	516	523	530	536	543		**6**
639	550	557	564	570	577	584	591	598	604	611	1	0.6
											2	1.2
640	618	625	632	638	645	652	659	665	672	679	3	1.8
											4	2.4
641	686	693	690	706	713	720	726	733	740	747	5	3.0
642	754	760	767	774	781	787	794	801	808	814	6	3.6
643	821	828	835	841	848	855	862	868	875	882	7	4.2
644	889	895	902	909	916	922	929	936	943	949	8	4.8
645	956	963	969	976	983	990	996	*003	*010	*017	9	5.4
646	81 023	030	037	043	050	057	064	070	077	084		
647	090	097	104	111	117	124	131	137	144	151		
648	158	164	171	178	184	191	198	204	211	218		
649	224	231	238	245	251	258	265	271	278	285		
650	291	298	305	311	318	325	331	338	345	351		

N	L 0	1	2	3	4	5	6	7	8	9	P P

TABLE A-1 (*continued*)

N	L 0	1	2	3	4	5	6	7	8	9	P P
650	81 291	298	305	311	318	325	331	338	345	351	
651	358	365	371	378	385	391	398	405	411	418	
652	425	431	438	445	451	458	465	471	478	485	
653	491	498	505	511	518	525	531	538	544	551	
654	558	564	571	578	584	591	598	604	611	617	
655	624	631	637	644	651	657	664	671	677	684	
656	690	697	704	710	717	723	730	737	743	750	
657	757	763	770	776	783	790	796	803	809	816	
658	823	829	836	842	849	856	862	869	875	882	
659	889	895	902	908	915	921	928	935	941	948	
660	954	961	968	974	981	987	994	*000	*007	*014	
661	82 020	027	033	040	046	053	060	066	073	079	
662	086	092	099	105	112	119	125	132	138	145	
663	151	158	164	171	178	184	191	197	204	210	
664	217	223	230	236	243	249	256	263	269	276	
665	282	289	295	302	308	315	321	328	334	341	
666	347	354	360	367	373	380	387	393	400	406	
667	413	419	426	432	439	445	452	458	465	471	
668	478	484	491	497	504	510	517	523	530	536	
669	543	549	556	562	569	575	582	588	595	601	
670	607	614	620	627	633	640	646	653	659	666	
671	672	679	685	692	698	705	711	718	724	730	
672	737	743	750	756	763	769	776	782	789	795	
673	802	808	814	821	827	834	840	847	853	860	
674	866	872	879	885	892	898	905	911	918	924	
675	930	937	943	950	956	963	969	975	982	988	
676	995	*001	*008	*014	*020	*027	*033	*040	*046	*052	
677	83 059	065	072	078	085	091	097	104	110	117	
678	123	129	136	142	149	155	161	168	174	181	
679	187	193	200	206	213	219	226	232	238	245	
680	251	257	264	270	276	283	289	296	302	308	
681	315	321	327	334	340	347	353	359	366	372	
682	378	385	391	398	404	410	417	423	429	436	
683	442	448	455	461	467	474	480	487	493	499	
684	506	512	518	525	531	537	544	550	556	563	
685	569	575	582	588	594	601	607	613	620	626	
686	632	639	645	651	658	664	670	677	683	689	
687	696	702	708	715	721	727	734	740	746	753	
688	759	765	771	778	784	790	797	803	809	816	
689	822	828	835	841	847	853	860	866	872	879	
690	885	891	897	904	910	916	923	929	935	942	
691	948	954	960	967	973	979	985	992	998	*004	
692	84 011	017	023	029	036	042	048	055	061	067	
693	073	080	086	092	098	105	111	117	123	130	
694	136	142	148	155	161	167	173	180	186	192	
695	198	205	211	217	223	230	236	242	248	255	
696	261	267	273	280	286	292	298	305	311	317	
697	323	330	336	342	348	354	361	367	373	379	
698	386	392	398	404	410	417	423	429	435	442	
699	448	454	460	466	473	479	485	491	497	504	
700	510	516	522	528	535	541	547	553	559	566	
N	L 0	1	2	3	4	5	6	7	8	9	P P

PP columns:

7
1	0.7
2	1.4
3	2.1
4	2.8
5	3.5
6	4.2
7	4.9
8	5.6
9	6.3

6
1	0.6
2	1.2
3	1.8
4	2.4
5	3.0
6	3.6
7	4.2
8	4.8
9	5.4

TABLE A-1 (*continued*)

N	L 0	1	2	3	4	5	6	7	8	9
700	84 510	516	522	528	535	541	547	553	559	566
701	572	578	584	590	597	603	609	615	621	628
702	634	640	646	652	658	665	671	677	683	689
703	696	702	708	714	720	726	733	739	745	751
704	757	763	770	776	782	788	794	800	807	813
705	819	825	831	837	844	850	856	862	868	874
706	880	887	893	899	905	911	917	924	930	936
707	942	948	954	960	967	973	979	985	991	997
708	85 003	009	016	022	028	034	040	046	052	058
709	065	071	077	083	089	095	101	107	114	120
710	126	132	138	144	150	156	163	169	175	181
711	187	193	199	205	211	217	224	230	236	242
712	248	254	260	266	272	278	285	291	297	303
713	309	315	321	327	333	339	345	352	358	364
714	370	376	382	388	394	400	406	412	418	425
715	431	437	443	449	455	461	467	473	479	485
716	491	497	503	509	516	522	528	534	540	546
717	552	558	564	570	576	582	588	594	600	606
718	612	618	625	631	637	643	649	655	661	667
719	673	679	685	691	697	703	709	715	721	727
720	733	739	745	751	757	763	769	775	781	788
721	794	800	806	812	818	824	830	836	842	848
722	854	860	866	872	878	884	890	896	902	908
723	914	920	926	932	938	944	950	056	062	968
724	974	980	986	992	998	*004	*010	*016	*022	*028
725	86 034	040	046	052	058	064	070	076	082	088
726	094	100	106	112	118	124	130	136	141	147
727	153	159	165	171	177	183	189	195	201	207
728	213	219	225	231	237	243	249	255	261	267
729	273	279	285	291	297	303	308	314	320	326
730	332	338	344	350	356	362	368	374	380	386
731	392	398	404	410	415	421	427	433	439	445
732	451	457	463	469	475	481	487	493	499	504
733	510	516	522	528	534	540	546	552	558	564
734	570	576	581	587	593	599	605	611	617	623
735	629	635	641	646	652	658	664	670	676	682
736	688	694	700	705	711	717	723	729	735	741
737	747	753	759	764	770	776	782	788	794	800
738	806	812	817	823	829	835	841	847	853	859
739	864	870	876	882	888	894	900	906	911	917
740	923	929	935	941	947	953	958	964	970	976
741	982	988	994	999	*005	*011	*017	*023	*029	*035
742	87 040	046	052	058	064	070	075	081	087	093
743	099	105	111	116	122	128	134	140	146	151
744	157	163	169	175	181	186	192	198	204	210
745	216	221	227	233	239	245	251	256	262	268
746	274	280	286	291	297	303	309	315	320	326
747	332	338	344	349	355	361	367	373	379	384
748	390	396	402	408	413	419	425	431	437	442
749	448	454	460	466	471	477	483	489	495	500
750	506	512	518	523	529	535	541	547	552	558

| N | L 0 | 1 | 2 | 3 | 4 | 5 | 6 | 7 | 8 | 9 | P P |

P P

7
1	0.7
2	1.4
3	2.1
4	2.8
5	3.5
6	4.2
7	4.9
8	5.6
9	6.3

6
1	0.6
2	1.2
3	1.8
4	2.4
5	3.0
6	3.6
7	4.2
8	4.8
9	5.4

5
1	0.5
2	1.0
3	1.5
4	2.0
5	2.5
6	3.0
7	3.5
8	4.0
9	4.5

Table A-1 (*continued*)

N	L 0	1	2	3	4	5	6	7	8	9		P P
750	87 506	512	518	523	529	535	541	547	552	558		
751	564	570	576	581	587	593	599	604	610	616		
752	622	628	633	639	645	651	656	662	668	674		
753	679	685	691	697	703	708	714	720	726	731		
754	737	743	749	754	760	766	772	777	783	789		
755	795	800	806	812	818	823	829	835	841	846		
756	852	858	864	869	875	881	887	892	898	904		
757	910	915	921	927	933	938	944	950	955	961		
758	967	973	978	984	990	996	*001	*007	*013	*018		
759	88 024	030	036	041	047	053	058	064	070	076		
760	081	087	093	098	104	110	116	121	127	133		
761	138	144	150	156	161	167	173	178	184	190		
762	195	201	207	213	218	224	230	235	241	247		**6**
763	252	258	264	270	275	281	287	292	298	304		1 | 0.6
764	309	315	321	326	332	338	343	349	355	360		2 | 1.2
765	366	372	377	383	389	395	400	406	412	417		3 | 1.8
766	423	429	434	440	446	451	457	463	468	474		4 | 2.4
767	480	485	491	497	502	508	513	519	525	530		5 | 3.0
768	536	542	547	553	559	564	570	576	581	587		6 | 3.6
769	593	598	604	610	615	621	627	632	638	643		7 | 4.2
												8 | 4.8
770	649	655	660	666	672	677	683	689	694	700		9 | 5.4
771	705	711	717	722	728	734	739	745	750	756		
772	762	767	773	779	784	790	795	801	807	812		
773	818	824	829	835	840	846	852	857	863	868		
774	874	880	885	891	897	902	908	913	919	925		
775	930	936	941	947	953	958	964	969	975	981		
776	986	992	997	*003	*009	*014	*020	*025	*031	*037		
777	89 042	048	053	059	064	070	076	081	087	092		
778	098	104	109	115	120	126	131	137	143	148		
779	154	159	165	170	176	182	187	193	198	204		
780	209	215	221	226	232	237	243	248	254	260		**5**
												1 | 0.5
781	265	271	276	282	287	293	298	304	310	315		2 | 1.0
782	321	326	332	337	343	348	354	360	365	371		3 | 1.5
783	376	382	387	393	398	404	409	415	421	426		4 | 2.0
784	432	437	443	448	454	459	465	470	476	481		5 | 2.5
785	487	492	498	504	509	515	520	526	531	537		6 | 3.0
786	542	548	553	559	564	570	575	581	586	592		7 | 3.5
787	597	603	609	614	620	625	631	636	642	647		8 | 4.0
788	653	658	664	669	675	680	686	691	697	702		9 | 4.5
789	708	713	719	724	730	735	741	746	752	757		
790	763	768	774	779	785	790	796	801	807	812		
791	818	823	829	834	840	845	851	856	862	867		
792	873	878	883	889	894	900	905	911	916	922		
793	927	933	938	944	949	955	960	966	971	977		
794	982	988	993	998	*004	*009	*015	*020	*026	*031		
795	90 037	042	048	053	059	064	069	075	080	086		
796	091	097	102	108	113	119	124	129	135	140		
797	146	151	157	162	168	173	179	184	189	195		
798	200	206	211	217	222	227	233	238	244	249		
799	255	260	266	271	276	282	287	293	298	304		
800	309	314	320	325	331	336	342	347	352	358		
N	L 0	1	2	3	4	5	6	7	8	7		P P

TABLE A-1 (*continued*)

N	L 0	1	2	3	4	5	6	7	8	9	P P
800	90 309	314	320	325	331	336	342	347	352	358	
801	363	369	374	380	385	390	396	401	407	412	
802	417	423	428	434	439	445	450	455	461	466	
803	472	477	482	488	493	499	504	509	515	520	
804	526	531	536	542	547	553	558	563	569	574	
805	580	585	590	596	601	607	612	617	623	628	
806	634	639	644	650	655	660	666	671	677	682	
807	687	693	698	703	709	714	720	725	730	736	
808	741	747	752	757	763	768	773	779	784	789	
809	795	800	806	811	816	822	827	832	838	843	
810	849	854	859	865	870	875	881	886	891	897	
811	902	907	913	918	924	929	934	940	945	950	
812	956	961	966	972	977	982	988	993	998	*004	
813	91 009	014	020	025	030	036	041	046	052	057	
814	062	068	073	078	084	089	094	100	105	110	
815	116	121	126	132	137	142	148	153	158	164	
816	169	174	180	185	190	196	201	206	212	217	
817	222	228	233	238	243	249	254	259	265	270	
818	275	281	286	291	297	302	307	312	318	323	
819	328	334	339	344	350	355	360	365	371	376	
820	381	387	392	397	403	408	413	418	424	429	

6

1	0.6
2	1.2
3	1.8
4	2.4
5	3.0
6	3.6
7	4.2
8	4.8
9	5.4

N	L 0	1	2	3	4	5	6	7	8	9
821	434	440	445	450	455	461	466	471	477	482
822	487	492	498	503	508	514	519	524	529	535
823	540	545	551	556	561	566	572	577	582	587
824	593	598	603	609	614	619	624	630	635	640
825	645	651	656	661	666	672	677	682	687	693
826	698	703	709	714	719	724	730	735	740	745
827	751	756	761	766	772	777	782	787	793	798
828	803	808	814	819	824	829	834	840	845	850
829	855	861	866	871	876	882	887	892	897	903
830	908	913	918	924	929	934	939	944	950	955
831	960	965	971	976	981	986	991	997	*002	*007
832	92 012	018	023	028	033	038	044	049	054	059
833	065	070	075	080	085	091	096	101	106	111
834	117	122	127	132	137	143	148	153	158	163
835	169	174	179	184	189	195	200	205	210	215
836	221	226	231	236	241	247	252	257	262	267
837	273	278	283	288	293	298	304	309	314	319
838	324	330	335	340	345	350	355	361	366	371
839	376	381	387	392	397	402	407	412	418	423
840	428	433	438	443	449	454	459	464	469	474

5

1	0.5
2	1.0
3	1.5
4	2.0
5	2.5
6	3.0
7	3.5
8	4.0
9	4.5

N	L 0	1	2	3	4	5	6	7	8	9
841	480	485	490	495	500	505	511	516	521	526
842	531	536	542	547	552	557	562	567	572	578
843	583	588	593	598	603	609	614	619	624	629
844	634	639	645	650	655	660	665	670	675	681
845	686	691	696	701	706	711	716	722	727	732
846	737	742	747	752	758	763	768	773	778	783
847	788	793	799	804	809	814	819	824	829	834
848	840	845	850	855	860	865	870	875	881	886
849	891	896	901	906	911	916	921	927	932	937
850	942	947	952	957	962	967	973	978	983	988

N	L 0	1	2	3	4	5	6	7	8	9	P P

TABLE A-1 *(continued)*

N	L 0	1	2	3	4	5	6	7	8	9	P P	
850	92 942	947	952	957	962	967	973	978	983	988		
851	993	998	*003	*008	*013	*018	*024	*029	*034	*039		
852	93 044	049	054	059	064	069	075	080	085	090		
853	095	100	105	110	115	120	125	131	136	141		
854	146	151	156	161	166	171	176	181	186	192		
855	197	202	207	212	217	222	227	232	237	242		
856	247	252	258	263	268	273	278	283	288	293		**6**
857	298	303	308	313	318	323	328	334	339	344	1	0.6
858	349	354	359	364	369	374	379	384	389	394	2	1.2
859	399	404	409	414	420	425	430	435	440	445	3	1.8
											4	2.4
860	450	455	460	465	470	475	480	485	490	495	5	3.0
											6	3.6
861	500	505	510	515	520	526	531	536	541	546	7	4.2
862	551	556	561	566	571	576	581	586	591	596	8	4.5
863	601	606	611	616	621	626	631	636	641	646	9	4.8
864	651	656	661	666	671	676	682	687	692	697		
865	702	707	712	717	722	727	732	737	742	747		
866	752	757	762	767	772	777	782	787	792	797		
867	802	807	812	817	822	827	832	837	842	847		
868	852	857	862	867	872	877	882	887	892	897		
869	902	907	912	917	922	927	932	937	942	947		
870	952	957	962	967	972	977	982	987	992	997		
871	94 002	007	012	017	022	027	032	037	042	047		**5**
872	052	057	062	067	072	077	082	086	091	096	1	0.5
873	101	106	111	116	121	126	131	136	141	146	2	1.0
874	151	156	161	166	171	176	181	186	191	196	3	1.5
875	201	206	211	216	221	226	231	236	240	245	4	2.0
876	250	255	260	265	270	275	280	285	290	295	5	2.5
877	300	305	310	315	320	325	330	335	340	345	6	3.0
878	349	354	359	364	369	374	379	384	389	394	7	3.5
879	399	404	409	414	419	424	429	433	438	443	8	4.0
											9	4.5
880	448	453	458	463	468	473	478	483	488	493		
881	498	503	507	512	517	522	527	532	537	542		
882	547	552	557	562	567	571	576	581	586	591		
883	596	601	606	611	616	621	626	630	635	640		
884	645	650	655	660	665	670	675	680	685	689		
885	694	699	704	709	714	719	724	729	734	738		
886	743	748	753	758	763	768	773	778	783	787		
887	792	797	802	807	812	817	822	827	832	836		
888	841	846	851	856	861	866	871	876	880	885		**4**
889	890	895	900	905	910	915	919	924	929	934	1	0.4
											2	0.8
890	939	944	949	954	959	963	968	973	978	983	3	1.2
											4	1.6
891	988	993	998	*002	*007	*012	*017	*022	*027	*032	5	2.0
892	95 036	041	046	051	056	061	066	071	075	080	6	2.4
893	085	090	095	100	105	109	114	119	124	129	7	2.8
894	134	139	143	148	153	158	163	168	173	177	8	3.2
895	182	187	192	197	202	207	211	216	221	226	9	3.6
896	231	236	240	245	250	255	260	265	270	274		
897	279	284	289	294	299	303	308	313	318	323		
898	328	332	337	342	347	352	357	361	366	371		
899	376	381	386	390	395	400	405	410	415	419		
900	424	429	434	439	444	448	453	458	463	468		

N	L 0	1	2	3	4	5	6	7	8	9	P P	

TABLE A-1 (*continued*)

N	L 0	1	2	3	4	5	6	7	8	9	P P
900	95 424	429	434	439	444	448	453	458	463	468	
901	472	477	482	487	492	497	501	506	511	516	
902	521	525	530	535	540	545	550	554	559	564	
903	569	574	578	583	588	593	598	602	607	612	
904	617	622	626	631	636	641	646	650	655	660	
905	665	670	674	679	684	689	694	698	703	708	
906	713	718	722	727	732	737	742	746	751	756	
907	761	766	770	775	780	785	789	794	799	804	
908	809	813	818	823	828	832	837	842	847	852	
909	856	861	866	871	875	880	885	890	895	899	
910	904	909	914	918	923	928	933	938	942	947	
911	952	957	961	966	971	976	980	985	990	995	
912	999	*004	*009	*014	*019	*023	*028	*033	*038	*042	**5**
913	96 047	052	057	061	066	071	076	080	085	090	1 | 0.5
914	095	099	104	109	114	118	123	128	133	137	2 | 1.0
915	142	147	152	156	161	166	171	175	180	185	3 | 1.5
916	190	194	199	204	209	213	218	223	227	232	4 | 2.0
917	237	242	246	251	256	261	265	270	275	280	5 | 2.5
918	284	289	294	298	303	308	313	317	322	327	6 | 3.0
919	332	336	341	346	350	355	360	365	369	374	7 | 3.5
920	379	384	388	393	398	402	407	412	417	421	8 | 4.0 9 | 4.5
921	426	431	435	440	445	450	454	459	464	468	
922	473	478	483	487	492	497	501	506	511	515	
923	520	525	530	534	539	544	548	553	558	562	
924	567	572	577	581	586	591	595	600	605	609	
925	614	619	624	628	633	638	642	647	652	656	
926	661	666	670	675	680	685	689	694	699	703	
927	708	713	717	722	727	731	736	741	745	750	
928	755	759	764	769	774	778	783	788	792	797	
929	802	806	811	816	820	825	830	834	839	844	
930	848	853	858	862	867	872	876	881	886	890	**4**
931	895	900	904	909	914	918	923	928	932	937	1 | 0.4
932	942	946	951	956	960	965	970	974	979	984	2 | 0.8
933	988	993	997	*002	*007	*011	*016	*021	*025	*030	3 | 1.2
934	97 035	039	044	049	053	058	063	067	072	077	4 | 1.6
935	081	086	090	095	100	104	109	114	118	123	5 | 2.0
936	128	132	137	142	146	151	155	160	165	169	6 | 2.4
937	174	179	183	188	192	197	202	206	211	216	7 | 2.8
938	220	225	230	234	239	243	248	253	257	262	8 | 3.2
939	267	271	276	280	285	290	294	299	304	308	9 | 3.6
940	313	317	322	327	331	336	340	345	350	354	
941	359	364	368	373	377	382	387	391	396	400	
942	405	410	414	419	424	428	433	437	442	447	
943	451	456	460	465	470	474	479	483	488	493	
944	497	502	506	511	516	520	525	529	534	539	
945	543	548	552	557	562	566	571	575	580	585	
946	589	594	598	603	607	612	617	621	626	630	
947	635	640	644	649	653	658	663	667	672	676	
948	681	685	690	695	699	704	708	713	717	722	
949	727	731	736	740	745	749	754	759	763	768	
950	772	777	782	786	791	795	800	804	809	813	
N	L 0	1	2	3	4	5	6	7	8	9	P P

TABLE A-1 (*continued*)

N	L 0	1	2	3	4	5	6	7	8	9	P P	
950	97 772	777	782	786	791	795	800	804	809	813		
951	818	823	827	832	836	841	845	850	855	859		
952	864	868	873	877	882	886	891	896	900	905		
953	909	914	918	923	928	932	937	941	946	950		
954	955	959	964	968	973	978	982	987	991	996		
955	98 000	005	009	014	019	023	028	032	037	041		
956	046	050	055	059	064	068	073	078	082	087		
957	091	096	100	105	109	114	118	123	127	132		
958	137	141	146	150	155	159	164	168	173	177		
959	182	186	191	195	200	204	209	214	218	223		
960	227	232	236	241	245	250	254	259	263	268		**5**
961	272	277	281	286	290	295	299	304	308	313	1	0.5
962	318	322	327	331	336	340	345	349	354	358	2	1.0
963	363	367	372	376	381	385	390	394	399	403	3	1.5
964	408	412	417	421	426	430	435	439	444	448	4	2.0
965	453	457	462	466	471	475	480	484	489	493	5	2.5
966	498	502	507	511	516	520	525	529	534	538	6	3.0
967	543	547	552	556	561	565	570	574	579	583	7	3.5
968	588	592	597	601	605	610	614	619	623	628	8	4.0
969	632	637	641	646	650	655	659	664	668	673	9	4.5
970	677	682	686	691	695	700	704	709	713	717		
971	722	726	731	735	740	744	749	753	758	762		
972	767	771	776	780	784	789	793	798	802	807		
973	811	816	820	825	829	834	838	843	847	851		
974	856	860	865	869	874	878	883	887	892	896		
975	900	905	909	914	918	923	927	932	936	941		
976	945	949	954	958	963	967	972	976	981	985		
977	989	994	998	*003	*007	*012	*016	*021	*025	*029		
978	99 034	038	043	047	052	056	061	065	069	074		
979	078	083	087	092	096	100	105	109	114	118		
980	123	127	131	136	140	145	149	154	158	162		**4**
981	167	171	176	180	185	189	193	198	202	207	1	0.4
982	211	216	220	224	229	233	238	242	247	251	2	0.8
983	255	260	264	269	273	277	282	286	291	295	3	1.2
984	300	304	308	313	317	322	326	330	335	339	4	1.6
985	344	348	352	357	361	366	370	374	379	383	5	2.0
986	388	392	396	401	405	410	414	419	423	427	6	2.4
987	432	436	441	445	449	454	458	463	467	471	7	2.8
988	476	480	484	489	493	498	502	506	511	515	8	3.2
989	520	524	528	533	537	542	546	550	555	559	9	3.6
990	564	568	572	577	581	585	590	594	599	603		
991	607	612	616	621	625	629	634	638	642	647		
992	651	656	660	664	669	673	677	682	686	691		
993	695	699	704	708	712	717	721	726	730	734		
994	739	743	747	752	756	760	765	769	774	778		
995	782	787	791	795	800	804	808	813	817	822		
996	826	830	835	839	843	848	852	856	861	865		
997	870	874	878	883	887	891	896	900	904	909		
998	913	917	922	926	930	935	939	944	948	952		
999	957	961	965	970	974	978	983	987	991	996		
1000	00 000	004	009	013	017	022	026	030	035	039		
N	L 0	1	2	3	4	5	6	7	8	9	P P	

Source: Table 5, pp. 84–103 in H. Arkin and R. Colton, *Tables for Statisticians*, New York: Barnes and Noble, Inc. 1968.

TABLE A-2 TABLE OF NATURAL LOGARITHMS

N	.0	.1	.2	.3	.4	.5	.6	.7	.8	.9
1	0.000	0.095	0.182	0.262	0.336	0.405	0.470	0.531	0.588	0.642
2	0.693	0.742	0.788	0.833	0.875	0.916	0.956	0.993	1.030	1.065
3	1.099	1.131	1.163	1.194	1.224	1.253	1.281	1.308	1.335	1.361
4	1.386	1.411	1.435	1.459	1.482	1.504	1.526	1.548	1.569	1.589
5	1.609	1.629	1.649	1.668	1.686	1.705	1.723	1.740	1.758	1.775
6	1.792	1.808	1.825	1.841	1.856	1.872	1.887	1.902	1.917	1.932
7	1.946	1.960	1.974	1.988	2.001	2.015	2.028	2.041	2.054	2.067
8	2.079	2.092	2.104	2.116	2.128	2.140	2.152	2.163	2.175	2.186
9	2.197	2.208	2.219	2.230	2.241	2.251	2.262	2.272	2.282	2.293
10	2.303	2.313	2.322	2.332	2.342	2.351	2.361	2.370	2.380	2.389

TABLE A-3 VALUES OF e^x AND e^{-x}

x	e^x	e^{-x}	x	e^x	e^{-x}
0.0	1.00	1.00	3.1	22.2	.045
0.1	1.11	.905	3.2	24.5	.041
0.2	1.22	.819	3.3	27.1	.037
0.3	1.35	.741	3.4	30.0	.033
0.4	1.49	.670	3.5	33.1	.030
0.5	1.65	.607	3.6	36.6	.027
0.6	1.82	.549	3.7	40.4	.025
0.7	2.01	.497	3.8	44.7	.022
0.8	2.23	.449	3.9	49.4	.020
0.9	2.46	.407	4.0	54.6	.018
1.0	2.72	.368	4.1	60.3	.017
1.1	3.00	.333	4.2	66.7	.015
1.2	3.32	.301	4.3	73.7	.014
1.3	3.67	.273	4.4	81.5	.012
1.4	4.06	.247	4.5	90.0	.011
1.5	4.48	.223	4.6	99.5	.010
1.6	4.95	.202	4.7	110	.0091
1.7	5.47	.183	4.8	122	.0082
1.8	6.05	.165	4.9	134	.0074
1.9	6.69	.150	5.0	148	.0067
2.0	7.39	.135	5.1	164	.0061
2.1	8.17	.122	5.2	181	.0055
2.2	9.02	.111	5.3	200	.0050
2.3	9.97	.100	5.4	221	.0045
2.4	11.0	.091	5.5	245	.0041
2.5	12.2	.082	5.6	270	.0037
2.6	13.5	.074	5.7	299	.0033
2.7	14.9	.067	5.8	330	.0030
2.8	16.4	.061	5.9	365	.0027
2.9	18.2	.055	6.0	403	.0025
3.0	20.1	.050			

Source: Table II and Table III on page 761 in R. E. Johnson, F. L. Kiokemeister, and E. S. Wolk, *Calculus with Analytic Geometry*, fifth ed., Boston: Allyn and Bacon, Inc., 1974.

Table A-4 Compound Interest of $1: $(1 + i)^n$

n	0.02	0.04	0.06	0.08	0.10	0.12	0.14	0.16	0.18	0.20
1	1.0200	1.0400	1.0600	1.0800	1.1000	1.1200	1.1400	1.1600	1.1800	1.2000
2	1.0404	1.0816	1.1236	1.1664	1.2100	1.2544	1.2996	1.3456	1.3924	1.4400
3	1.0612	1.1249	1.1910	1.2597	1.3310	1.4049	1.4815	1.5609	1.6430	1.7280
4	1.0824	1.1699	1.2625	1.3605	1.4641	1.5735	1.6890	1.8106	1.9388	2.0736
5	1.1041	1.2167	1.3382	1.4693	1.6105	1.7623	1.9254	2.1003	2.2878	2.4883
6	1.1262	1.2653	1.4185	1.5869	1.7716	1.9738	2.1950	2.4364	2.6996	2.9860
7	1.1487	1.3159	1.5036	1.7138	1.9487	2.2107	2.5023	2.8262	3.1855	3.5832
8	1.1717	1.3686	1.5938	1.8509	2.1436	2.4760	2.8526	3.2784	3.7589	4.2998
9	1.1951	1.4233	1.6895	1.9990	2.3579	2.7731	3.2519	3.8030	4.4355	5.1598
10	1.2190	1.4802	1.7908	2.1589	2.5937	3.1058	3.7072	4.4114	5.2338	6.1917
11	1.2434	1.5395	1.8983	2.3316	2.8531	3.4785	4.2262	5.1173	6.1759	7.4301
12	1.2682	1.6010	2.0122	2.5182	3.1384	3.8960	4.8179	5.9360	7.2876	8.9161
13	1.2936	1.6651	2.1329	2.7196	3.4523	4.3635	5.4924	6.8858	8.5994	10.6993
14	1.3195	1.7317	2.2609	2.9372	3.7975	4.8871	6.2613	7.9875	10.1472	12.8392
15	1.3459	1.8009	2.3966	3.1722	4.1772	5.4736	7.1379	9.2655	11.9737	15.4070
16	1.3728	1.8730	2.5404	3.4259	4.5950	6.1304	8.1372	10.7480	14.1290	18.4884
17	1.4002	1.9479	2.6928	3.7000	5.0545	6.8660	9.2765	12.4677	16.6722	22.1861
18	1.4282	2.0258	2.8543	3.9960	5.5599	7.6900	10.5752	14.4625	19.6733	26.6233
19	1.4568	2.1068	3.0256	4.3157	6.1159	8.6128	12.0557	16.7765	23.2144	31.9480
20	1.4859	2.1911	3.2071	4.6610	6.7275	9.6463	13.7435	19.4608	27.3930	38.3376
21	1.5157	2.2788	3.3996	5.0338	7.4002	10.8038	15.6676	22.5745	32.3238	46.0051
22	1.5460	2.3699	3.6035	5.4365	8.1403	12.1003	17.8610	26.1864	38.1421	55.2061
23	1.5769	2.4647	3.8197	5.8715	8.9543	13.5523	20.3616	30.3762	45.0076	66.2474
24	1.6084	2.5633	4.0489	6.3412	9.8497	15.1786	23.2122	35.2364	53.1090	79.4968
25	1.6406	2.6658	4.2919	6.8485	10.8347	17.0001	26.4619	40.8742	62.6686	95.3962

n	0.02	0.04	0.06	0.08	0.10	0.12	0.14	0.16	0.18	0.20
26	1.6734	2.7725	4.5494	7.3964	11.9182	19.0401	30.1666	47.4141	73.9490	114.4755
27	1.7069	2.8834	4.8223	7.9881	13.1100	21.3249	34.3899	55.0004	87.2598	137.3705
28	1.7410	2.9987	5.1117	8.6271	14.4210	23.8839	39.2045	63.8004	102.9666	164.8447
29	1.7758	3.1187	5.4184	9.3173	15.8631	26.7499	44.6931	74.0085	121.5005	197.8136
30	1.8114	3.2434	5.7435	10.0627	17.4494	29.9599	50.9502	85.8499	143.3706	237.3763
31	1.8476	3.3731	6.0881	10.8677	19.1943	33.5551	58.0832	99.5859	169.1774	284.8516
32	1.8845	3.5081	6.4534	11.7371	21.1138	37.5817	66.2148	115.5196	199.6293	341.8219
33	1.9222	3.6484	6.8406	12.6760	23.2252	42.0915	75.4849	134.0027	235.5625	410.1863
34	1.9607	3.7943	7.2510	13.6901	25.5477	47.1425	86.0528	155.4432	277.9638	492.2235
35	1.9999	3.9461	7.6861	14.7853	28.1024	52.7996	98.1002	180.3141	327.9973	590.6682
36	2.0399	4.1039	8.1473	15.9682	30.9127	59.1356	111.8342	209.1643	387.0368	708.8019
37	2.0807	4.2681	8.6361	17.2456	34.0039	66.2318	127.4910	242.6306	456.7034	850.5622
38	2.1223	4.4388	9.1543	18.6253	37.4043	74.1797	145.3397	281.4515	538.9100	1020.6747
39	2.1647	4.6164	9.7035	20.1153	41.1448	83.0812	165.6873	326.4837	635.9138	1224.8096
40	2.2080	4.8010	10.2857	21.7245	45.2593	93.0510	188.8835	378.7211	750.3783	1469.7715
41	2.2522	4.9931	10.9029	23.4625	49.7852	104.2171	215.3272	439.3165	885.4464	1763.7258
42	2.2972	5.1928	11.5570	25.3395	54.7637	116.7231	245.4730	509.6072	1044.8268	2116.4710
43	2.3432	5.4005	12.2505	27.3666	60.2401	130.7299	279.8392	591.1443	1232.8956	2539.7652
44	2.3901	5.6165	12.9855	29.5560	66.2641	146.4175	319.0167	685.7274	1454.8168	3047.7182
45	2.4379	5.8412	13.7646	31.9204	72.8905	163.9876	363.6791	795.4438	1716.6838	3657.2618
46	2.4866	6.0748	14.5905	34.4741	80.1795	183.6661	414.5941	922.7148	2025.6869	4388.7142
47	2.5363	6.3178	15.4659	37.2320	88.1975	205.7060	472.6373	1070.3492	2390.3106	5266.4570
48	2.5871	6.5705	16.3939	40.2106	97.0172	230.3908	538.8065	1241.6050	2820.5665	6319.7484
49	2.6388	6.8333	17.3775	43.4274	106.7190	258.0377	614.2395	1440.2618	3328.2684	7583.6981
50	2.6916	7.1067	18.4202	46.9016	117.3909	289.0022	700.2330	1670.7037	3927.3568	9100.4377

Table A-5 Present Value of $1: $(1 + i)^{-n}$

n	0.02	0.04	0.06	0.08	0.10	0.12	0.14	0.16	0.18	0.20
1	0.9804	0.9615	0.9434	0.9259	0.9091	0.8929	0.8772	0.8621	0.8475	0.8333
2	0.9612	0.9246	0.8900	0.8573	0.8264	0.7972	0.7695	0.7432	0.7182	0.6944
3	0.9423	0.8890	0.8396	0.7938	0.7513	0.7118	0.6750	0.6407	0.6086	0.5787
4	0.9238	0.8548	0.7921	0.7350	0.6830	0.6355	0.5921	0.5523	0.5158	0.4823
5	0.9057	0.8219	0.7473	0.6806	0.6209	0.5674	0.5194	0.4761	0.4371	0.4019
6	0.8880	0.7903	0.7050	0.6302	0.5645	0.5066	0.4556	0.4104	0.3704	0.3349
7	0.8706	0.7599	0.6651	0.5835	0.5132	0.4523	0.3996	0.3538	0.3139	0.2791
8	0.8535	0.7307	0.6274	0.5403	0.4665	0.4039	0.3506	0.3050	0.2660	0.2326
9	0.8368	0.7026	0.5919	0.5002	0.4241	0.3606	0.3075	0.2630	0.2255	0.1938
10	0.8203	0.6756	0.5584	0.4632	0.3855	0.3220	0.2697	0.2267	0.1911	0.1615
11	0.8043	0.6496	0.5268	0.4289	0.3505	0.2875	0.2366	0.1954	0.1619	0.1346
12	0.7885	0.6246	0.4970	0.3971	0.3186	0.2567	0.2076	0.1685	0.1372	0.1122
13	0.7730	0.6006	0.4688	0.3677	0.2897	0.2292	0.1821	0.1452	0.1163	0.0935
14	0.7579	0.5775	0.4423	0.3405	0.2633	0.2046	0.1597	0.1252	0.0985	0.0779
15	0.7430	0.5553	0.4173	0.3152	0.2394	0.1827	0.1401	0.1079	0.0835	0.0649
16	0.7284	0.5339	0.3936	0.2919	0.2176	0.1631	0.1229	0.0930	0.0708	0.0541
17	0.7142	0.5134	0.3714	0.2703	0.1978	0.1456	0.1078	0.0802	0.0600	0.0451
18	0.7002	0.4936	0.3503	0.2502	0.1799	0.1300	0.0946	0.0691	0.0508	0.0376
19	0.6864	0.4746	0.3305	0.2317	0.1635	0.1161	0.0829	0.0596	0.0431	0.0313
20	0.6730	0.4564	0.3118	0.2145	0.1486	0.1037	0.0728	0.0514	0.0365	0.0261
21	0.6598	0.4388	0.2942	0.1987	0.1351	0.0926	0.0638	0.0443	0.0309	0.0217
22	0.6468	0.4220	0.2775	0.1839	0.1228	0.0826	0.0560	0.0382	0.0262	0.0181
23	0.6342	0.4057	0.2618	0.1703	0.1117	0.0738	0.0491	0.0329	0.0222	0.0151
24	0.6217	0.3901	0.2470	0.1577	0.1015	0.0659	0.0431	0.0284	0.0188	0.0126
25	0.6095	0.3751	0.2330	0.1460	0.0923	0.0588	0.0378	0.0245	0.0160	0.0105

n	0.02	0.04	0.06	0.08	0.10	0.12	0.14	0.16	0.18	0.20
26	0.5976	0.3607	0.2198	0.1352	0.0839	0.0525	0.0331	0.0211	0.0135	0.0087
27	0.5859	0.3468	0.2074	0.1252	0.0763	0.0469	0.0291	0.0182	0.0115	0.0073
28	0.5744	0.3335	0.1956	0.1159	0.0693	0.0419	0.0255	0.0157	0.0097	0.0061
29	0.5631	0.3207	0.1846	0.1073	0.0630	0.0374	0.0224	0.0135	0.0082	0.0051
30	0.5521	0.3083	0.1741	0.0994	0.0573	0.0334	0.0196	0.0116	0.0070	0.0042
31	0.5412	0.2965	0.1643	0.0920	0.0521	0.0298	0.0172	0.0100	0.0059	0.0035
32	0.5306	0.2851	0.1550	0.0852	0.0474	0.0266	0.0151	0.0087	0.0050	0.0029
33	0.5202	0.2741	0.1462	0.0789	0.0431	0.0238	0.0132	0.0075	0.0042	0.0024
34	0.5100	0.2636	0.1379	0.0730	0.0391	0.0212	0.0116	0.0064	0.0036	0.0020
35	0.5000	0.2534	0.1301	0.0676	0.0356	0.0189	0.0102	0.0055	0.0030	0.0017
36	0.4902	0.2437	0.1227	0.0626	0.0323	0.0169	0.0089	0.0048	0.0026	0.0014
37	0.4806	0.2343	0.1158	0.0580	0.0294	0.0151	0.0078	0.0041	0.0022	0.0012
38	0.4712	0.2253	0.1092	0.0537	0.0267	0.0135	0.0069	0.0036	0.0019	0.0010
39	0.4619	0.2166	0.1031	0.0497	0.0243	0.0120	0.0060	0.0031	0.0016	0.0008
40	0.4529	0.2083	0.0972	0.0460	0.0221	0.0107	0.0053	0.0026	0.0013	0.0007
41	0.4440	0.2003	0.0917	0.0426	0.0201	0.0096	0.0046	0.0023	0.0011	0.0006
42	0.4353	0.1926	0.0865	0.0395	0.0183	0.0086	0.0041	0.0020	0.0010	0.0005
43	0.4268	0.1852	0.0816	0.0365	0.0166	0.0076	0.0036	0.0017	0.0008	0.0004
44	0.4184	0.1780	0.0770	0.0338	0.0151	0.0068	0.0031	0.0015	0.0007	0.0003
45	0.4102	0.1712	0.0727	0.0313	0.0137	0.0061	0.0027	0.0013	0.0006	0.0003
46	0.4022	0.1646	0.0685	0.0290	0.0125	0.0054	0.0024	0.0011	0.0005	0.0002
47	0.3943	0.1583	0.0647	0.0269	0.0113	0.0049	0.0021	0.0009	0.0004	0.0002
48	0.3865	0.1522	0.0610	0.0249	0.0103	0.0043	0.0019	0.0008	0.0004	0.0002
49	0.3790	0.1463	0.0575	0.0230	0.0094	0.0039	0.0016	0.0007	0.0003	0.0001
50	0.3715	0.1407	0.0543	0.0213	0.0085	0.0035	0.0014	0.0006	0.0003	0.0001
n	**0.02**	**0.04**	**0.06**	**0.08**	**0.10**	**0.12**	**0.14**	**0.16**	**0.18**	**0.20**

TABLE A-6 AMOUNT OF AN ANNUITY OF $1: $s_{\overline{n}|i} = \dfrac{(1+i)^n - 1}{i}$

n	0.02	0.04	0.06	0.08	0.10	0.12	0.14	0.16	0.18	0.20
1	1.0000	1.0000	1.0000	1.0000	1.0000	1.0000	1.0000	1.0000	1.0000	1.0000
2	2.0200	2.0400	2.0600	2.0800	2.1000	2.1200	2.1400	2.1600	2.1800	2.2000
3	3.0604	3.1216	3.1836	3.2464	3.3100	3.3744	3.4396	3.5056	3.5724	3.6400
4	4.1216	4.2465	4.3746	4.5061	4.6410	4.7793	4.9211	5.0665	5.2154	5.3680
5	5.2040	5.4163	5.6371	5.8666	6.1051	6.3528	6.6101	6.8771	7.1542	7.4416
6	6.3081	6.6330	6.9753	7.3359	7.7156	8.1152	8.5355	8.9775	9.4420	9.9299
7	7.4343	7.8983	8.3938	8.9228	9.4872	10.0890	10.7305	11.4139	12.1415	12.9159
8	8.5830	9.2142	9.8975	10.6366	11.4359	12.2328	13.2328	14.2401	15.3270	16.4991
9	9.7546	10.5828	11.4913	12.4876	13.5795	14.7757	16.0853	17.5185	19.0859	20.7989
10	10.9497	12.0061	13.1808	14.4866	15.9374	17.5487	19.3373	21.3215	23.5213	25.9587
11	12.1687	13.4864	14.9716	16.6455	18.5312	20.6546	23.0445	25.7329	28.7551	32.1504
12	13.4121	15.0258	16.8699	18.9771	21.3843	24.1331	27.2707	30.8502	34.9311	39.5805
13	14.6803	16.6268	18.8821	21.4953	24.5227	28.0291	32.0887	36.7862	42.2187	48.4966
14	15.9739	18.2919	21.0151	24.2149	27.9750	32.3926	37.5811	43.6720	50.8180	59.1959
15	17.2934	20.0236	23.2760	27.1521	31.7725	37.2797	43.8424	51.6595	60.9653	72.0351
16	18.6393	21.8245	25.6725	30.3243	35.9497	42.7533	50.9804	60.9250	72.9390	87.4421
17	20.0121	23.6975	28.2129	33.7502	40.5447	48.8837	59.1176	71.6730	87.0680	105.9306
18	21.4123	25.6454	30.9057	37.4502	45.5992	55.7497	68.3941	84.1407	103.7403	128.1167
19	22.8406	27.6712	33.7600	41.4463	51.1591	63.4397	78.9692	98.6032	123.4135	154.7400
20	24.2974	29.7781	36.7856	45.7620	57.2750	72.0524	91.0249	115.3797	146.6280	186.6880
21	25.7833	31.9692	39.9927	50.4229	64.0025	81.6987	104.7684	134.8405	174.0210	225.0256
22	27.2990	34.2480	43.3923	55.4568	71.4027	92.5026	120.4360	157.4150	206.3448	271.0307
23	28.8450	36.6179	46.9958	60.8933	79.5430	104.6029	138.2970	183.6014	244.4868	326.2369
24	30.4219	39.0826	50.8156	66.7648	88.4973	118.1552	158.6586	213.9776	289.4945	392.4842
25	32.0303	41.6459	54.8645	73.1059	98.3471	133.3339	181.8708	249.2140	342.6035	471.9811

n	0.02	0.04	0.06	0.08	0.10	0.12	0.14	0.16	0.18	0.20
26	33.6709	44.3117	59.1564	79.9544	109.1818	150.3339	208.3327	290.0883	405.2721	567.3773
27	35.3443	47.0842	63.7058	87.3508	121.0999	169.3740	238.4993	337.5024	479.2211	681.8527
28	37.0512	49.9676	68.5281	95.3388	134.2099	190.6989	272.8892	392.5028	566.4809	819.2233
29	38.7922	52.9663	73.6398	103.9659	148.6309	214.5827	312.0937	456.3032	669.4474	984.0679
30	40.5681	56.0849	79.0582	113.2832	164.4940	241.3327	356.7868	530.3117	790.9480	1181.8815
31	42.3794	59.3283	84.8017	123.3459	181.9434	271.2926	407.7370	616.1616	934.3186	1419.2578
32	44.2270	62.7015	90.8898	134.2135	201.1378	304.8477	465.8202	715.7474	1103.4960	1704.1094
33	46.1116	66.2095	97.3432	145.9506	222.2515	342.4294	532.0350	831.2670	1303.1252	2045.9313
34	48.0338	69.8579	104.1838	158.6267	245.4767	384.5210	607.5199	965.2698	1538.6878	2456.1175
35	49.9945	73.6522	111.4348	172.3168	271.0244	431.6635	693.5727	1120.7129	1816.6516	2948.3411
36	51.9944	77.5983	119.1209	187.1021	299.1268	484.4631	791.6729	1301.0270	2144.6489	3539.0093
37	54.0343	81.7022	127.2681	203.0703	330.0395	543.5987	903.5071	1510.1913	2531.6857	4247.8111
38	56.1149	85.9703	135.9042	220.3159	364.0434	609.8305	1030.9981	1752.8219	2988.3891	5098.3733
39	58.2372	90.4091	145.0585	238.9412	401.4478	684.0102	1176.3378	2034.2734	3527.2991	6119.0480
40	60.4020	95.0255	154.7620	259.0565	442.5925	767.0914	1342.0251	2360.7572	4163.2129	7343.8576
41	62.6100	99.8265	165.0477	280.7810	487.8518	860.1424	1530.9086	2739.4783	4913.5913	8813.6291
42	64.8622	104.8196	175.9505	304.2435	537.6370	964.3594	1746.2358	3178.7948	5799.0377	10577.3549
43	67.1595	110.0124	187.5076	329.5830	592.4007	1081.0826	1991.7088	3688.4020	6843.8645	12693.8259
44	69.5027	115.4129	199.7580	356.9496	652.6408	1211.8125	2271.5481	4279.5463	8076.7601	15233.5910
45	71.8927	121.0294	212.7435	386.5056	718.9048	1358.2300	2590.5648	4965.2737	9531.5769	18281.3092
46	74.3306	126.8706	226.5081	418.4261	791.7953	1522.2176	2954.2439	5760.7175	11248.2607	21938.5710
47	76.8172	132.9454	241.0986	452.9001	871.9748	1705.8837	3368.8380	6683.4323	13273.9477	26327.2852
48	79.3535	139.2632	256.5645	490.1321	960.1723	1911.5897	3841.4753	7753.7815	15664.2582	31593.7422
49	81.9406	145.8337	272.9584	530.3427	1057.1896	2141.9805	4380.2819	8995.3865	18484.8247	37913.4906
50	84.5794	152.6671	290.3359	573.7701	1163.9085	2400.0182	4994.5213	10435.6483	21813.0931	45497.1887

TABLE A-7 PRESENT VALUE OF AN ANNUITY OF $1: $a_{\overline{n}|i} = \dfrac{1-(1+i)^{-n}}{i}$

n	0.02	0.04	0.06	0.08	0.10	0.12	0.14	0.16	0.18	0.20
1	0.9804	0.9615	0.9434	0.9259	0.9091	0.8929	0.8772	0.8621	0.8475	0.8333
2	1.9416	1.8861	1.8334	1.7833	1.7355	1.6901	1.6467	1.6052	1.5656	1.5278
3	2.8839	2.7751	2.6730	2.5771	2.4869	2.4018	2.3216	2.2459	2.1743	2.1065
4	3.8077	3.6299	3.4651	3.3121	3.1699	3.0373	2.9137	2.7982	2.6901	2.5887
5	4.7135	4.4518	4.2124	3.9927	3.7908	3.6048	3.4331	3.2743	3.1272	2.9906
6	5.6014	5.2421	4.9173	4.6229	4.3553	4.1114	3.8887	3.6847	3.4976	3.3255
7	6.4720	6.0021	5.5824	5.2064	4.8684	4.5638	4.2883	4.0386	3.8115	3.6046
8	7.3255	6.7327	6.2098	5.7466	5.3349	4.9676	4.6389	4.3436	4.0776	3.8372
9	8.1622	7.4353	6.8017	6.2469	5.7590	5.3282	4.9464	4.6065	4.3030	4.0310
10	8.9826	8.1109	7.3601	6.7101	6.1446	5.6502	5.2161	4.8332	4.4941	4.1925
11	9.7868	8.7605	7.8869	7.1390	6.4951	5.9377	5.4527	5.0286	4.6560	4.3271
12	10.5753	9.3851	8.3838	7.5361	6.8137	6.1944	5.6603	5.1971	4.7932	4.4392
13	11.3484	9.9856	8.8527	7.9038	7.1034	6.4235	5.8424	5.3423	4.9095	4.5327
14	12.1062	10.5631	9.2950	8.2442	7.3667	6.6282	6.0021	5.4675	5.0081	4.6106
15	12.8493	11.1184	9.7122	8.5595	7.6061	6.8109	6.1422	5.5755	5.0916	4.6755
16	13.5777	11.6523	10.1059	8.8514	7.8237	6.9740	6.2651	5.6685	5.1624	4.7296
17	14.2919	12.1657	10.4773	9.1216	8.0216	7.1196	6.3729	5.7487	5.2223	4.7746
18	14.9920	12.6593	10.8276	9.3719	8.2014	7.2497	6.4674	5.8178	5.2732	4.8122
19	15.6785	13.1339	11.1581	9.6036	8.3649	7.3658	6.5504	5.8775	5.3162	4.8435
20	16.3514	13.5903	11.4699	9.8181	8.5136	7.4694	6.6231	5.9288	5.3527	4.8696
21	17.0112	14.0292	11.7641	10.0168	8.6487	7.5620	6.6870	5.9731	5.3837	4.8913
22	17.6580	14.4511	12.0416	10.2007	8.7715	7.6446	6.7429	6.0113	5.4099	4.9094
23	18.2922	14.8568	12.3034	10.3711	8.8832	7.7184	6.7921	6.0442	5.4321	4.9245
24	18.9139	15.2470	12.5504	10.5288	8.9847	7.7843	6.8351	6.0726	5.4509	4.9371
25	19.5235	15.6221	12.7834	10.6748	9.0770	7.8431	6.8729	6.0971	5.4669	4.9476

n	0.02	0.04	0.06	0.08	0.10	0.12	0.14	0.16	0.18	0.20
26	20.1210	15.9828	13.0032	10.8100	9.1609	7.8957	6.9061	6.1182	5.4804	4.9563
27	20.7069	16.3296	13.2105	10.9352	9.2372	7.9426	6.9352	6.1364	5.4919	4.9636
28	21.2813	16.6631	13.4062	11.0511	9.3066	7.9844	6.9607	6.1520	5.5016	4.9697
29	21.8444	16.9837	13.5907	11.1584	9.3696	8.0218	6.9830	6.1656	5.5098	4.9747
30	22.3965	17.2920	13.7648	11.2578	9.4269	8.0552	7.0027	6.1772	5.5168	4.9789
31	22.9377	17.5885	13.9291	11.3498	9.4790	8.0850	7.0199	6.1872	5.5227	4.9824
32	23.4683	17.8736	14.0840	11.4350	9.5264	8.1116	7.0350	6.1959	5.5277	4.9854
33	23.9886	18.1476	14.2302	11.5139	9.5694	8.1354	7.0482	6.2034	5.5320	4.9878
34	24.4986	18.4112	14.3681	11.5869	9.6086	8.1566	7.0599	6.2098	5.5356	4.9898
35	24.9986	18.6646	14.4982	11.6546	9.6442	8.1755	7.0700	6.2153	5.5386	4.9915
36	25.4888	18.9083	14.6210	11.7172	9.6765	8.1924	7.0790	6.2201	5.5412	4.9929
37	25.9695	19.1426	14.7368	11.7752	9.7059	8.2075	7.0868	6.2242	5.5434	4.9941
38	26.4406	19.3679	14.8460	11.8289	9.7327	8.2210	7.0937	6.2278	5.5452	4.9951
39	26.9026	19.5845	14.9491	11.8786	9.7570	8.2330	7.0997	6.2309	5.5468	4.9959
40	27.3555	19.7928	15.0463	11.9246	9.7791	8.2438	7.1050	6.2335	5.5482	4.9966
41	27.7995	19.9931	15.1380	11.9672	9.7991	8.2534	7.1097	6.2358	5.5493	4.9972
42	28.2348	20.1856	15.2245	12.0067	9.8174	8.2619	7.1138	6.2377	5.5502	4.9976
43	28.6616	20.3708	15.3062	12.0432	9.8340	8.2696	7.1173	6.2394	5.5510	4.9980
44	29.0800	20.5488	15.3832	12.0771	9.8491	8.2764	7.1205	6.2409	5.5517	4.9984
45	29.4902	20.7200	15.4558	12.1084	9.8628	8.2825	7.1232	6.2421	5.5523	4.9986
46	29.8923	20.8847	15.5244	12.1374	9.8753	8.2880	7.1256	6.2432	5.5528	4.9989
47	30.2866	21.0429	15.5890	12.1643	9.8866	8.2928	7.1277	6.2442	5.5532	4.9991
48	30.6731	21.1951	15.6500	12.1891	9.8969	8.2972	7.1296	6.2450	5.5536	4.9992
49	31.0521	21.3415	15.7076	12.2122	9.9063	8.3010	7.1312	6.2457	5.5539	4.9993
50	31.4236	21.4822	15.7619	12.2335	9.9148	8.3045	7.1327	6.2463	5.5541	4.9995

APPENDIX B

*Answers
to selected problems*

Answers
to selected problems

CHAPTER 1

Section 1-1
1. (a) integers (b) natural numbers (c) rational numbers
   (d) real numbers (e) rational numbers
3. (a) $\frac{1}{2}, \frac{1}{5}, -\frac{1}{3}$ (b) $2, 4, \frac{4}{3}$ (c) $\frac{3}{5}, \frac{1}{10}, \frac{1}{2}$
6. (b) $A = \frac{1}{4}, B = 1$ (c) No
9. $x = 7$

11. (a) $x = 3$ (b) $x = -4$ (c) $x = 5$ (d) $x = -4$ (e) $x = \dfrac{-a}{b}$

   (f) $x = -2$
14, 15. (a) $x = -2, 3$ (b) $x = -2, -2$ (c) $x = -3, -4$ (d) $x = 6, \frac{1}{2}$
   (e) $x = 0, -3$ (f) $x = -3, 3$ (g) $x = a, -2$

Section 1-2
1. (a) 1 (b) 1 (c) 16 (d) $h^2 + 6h + 9$
3. Domain: All real numbers between 4 and 9, inclusive.
   Range: All real numbers between 10 and 25, inclusive.
5. Domain: All real numbers between -1 and 2 inclusive.
   Range: All real numbers between -1 and 3, inclusive.
15. (a) $x = -2, 3$ (b) $x = -2, -2$ (c) $x = -3, -4$ (d) $x = 6, \frac{1}{2}$
   (e) $x = -3, 0$ (f) $x = -3, 3$

Section 1-3
1. Lines AB, AC, and AD all have slope -3.
2. (a) 2 (b) 3 (c) -2 (d) 2 (e) $\frac{1}{2}$
3. (a) $-\frac{3}{2}, 3$ (b) $1, -3$ (c) $\frac{5}{2}, 5$ (d) $-3, 6$ (e) $3, -\frac{3}{2}$
7. $y = -3x + 8$
8. (a) $y = 3x - 5$ (b) $y = 2x + 1$ (c) $y = -\frac{1}{2}x + 2$ (d) $y = 4x - 12$
   (e) $y = -5x + 3$ (f) $y = -x + 7$
9. (b) $y = 0.525x + 0.475$ (c) $y = 0.425x + 0.775$
   (f) Average the y's at $x = 1$ and the y's at $x = 5$. Then pass a line
   through the points $(1, 1.1)$ and $(5, 3)$. $y = 0.475x + 0.625$.

10. (a) $y = 5x + 10$ (b) $y = -2x - 2$
11. (a) parallel (b) perpendicular (c) neither (d) neither
    (e) perpendicular (f) parallel
13. (a) 5 (b) 5 (c) 5 (d) $\sqrt{37} = 6.0828$ (e) $\sqrt{52} = 7.211$
    (f) $\sqrt{a^2 + b^2}$
14. (c) yes (d) $\sqrt{200} = \sqrt{180 + 20}$
15. (b) no (c) $\sqrt{17} \neq \sqrt{2} + \sqrt{5}$

Section 1-4

3. (a) $(1, -1)$ (b) $(-1, 2)$ (c) $(\frac{3}{2}, \frac{5}{2})$ (d) no solution
5. (a) no solution (b) no solution (c) $(-\frac{1}{2}, 0)$ (d) $(\frac{5}{3}, -\frac{1}{18})$
7. $x = -1, y = 5, z = -2$
9. $x = 2, y = -1, z = 5$
10. (a) no solution (b) $x = 1, y = 3, z = 2$
11. $x = 2, y = 1, z = -3$ 12. $z = \frac{7}{2} - \frac{3}{2}x$

13. downsloping, i.e., slope is negative 14. (b) $y = -\dfrac{x}{2000} + 6$

15. upsloping, i.e., slope is positive 16. (b) $y = \dfrac{x}{2000}$

17. equilibrium price = \$3.00, equilibrium quantity = 6000 units

Section 1-5

1. (a) 14 (b) 66 3. $x_1 f(x_1) + x_2 f(x_2) + x_3 f(x_3)$
8. (a) 516 (b) 39 9. $\bar{x} = 79, s = 10.36$ 10. $\bar{x} = 1395$
11. $\bar{x} = 3.35$ 12. It would cause unequal weights.
13. $\bar{x} = 5, s = 3.81$ 17. $s = 3.81$
18. (a) $\bar{x} = 0.00, s = 2.16$ (b) $\bar{x} = 25.00, s = 14.72$
19. $CS = 4.17$ 20. 50, 69, 524, 730, 2500

Section 1-6

2. (a) \$150 (b) \$350 (c) \$3.00 (d) \$7.00
3. \$400 5. $R = 3.00 x$ and $C = 2.00 x + 300$
7. \$5900 9. (a) $R = 200 x_1 + 150 x_2$ and $C = 50 x_1 + 20 x_2$
    (b) \$1900
14. one lot of 200 shares, \$202.00; two lots of 100 shares, \$130.00;
    savings = \$72.00
15. one lot of 200 shares, \$58.00; two lots of 100 shares, \$76.00;
    loss = \$18.00
19. (b) Yes, they both cost \$14.40.

Section 1-7

1. $(\frac{3}{2}, 6)$ 3. 750 units 6. 4000 units, \$8,000
7. If you are using the car more than 2000 miles per month, choose Plan 1.
   Including the cost of gas has no effect on the indifference point.
8. (a) Option 2 (b) Use Option 1 if less than 33 copies are required.
   (c) Use Option 1 if less than 37 copies are required.

Section 1-8

1. $\hat{y} = 65 + 0.05x$ 2. 800
3. 380, larger, yes, because of the least-squares principle 4. yes, 300, 80
6. (a) $R = 0.98$ (b) yes, $b = 0.42, a = 2.3$ (c) $\hat{y} = 2.3 + 0.42x$
   (d) \$3.64 million
8. (b) $\hat{y} = 11.61 + 0.37x$

(c) Cost of this house increases, on the average, by $370 per year.

(d) $14,940

Section 1-9

2. (a) $h = 1$ (b) $h = 6$ (c) $h = 3$ (d) $h = 3$ **4.** $5 < 10$

6. (a) $-3 \leq x$ (b) $x \leq 1$ (c) $3 \leq x$ **8.** (a) $x \leq -\frac{5}{3}$ (b) $x < \frac{10}{3}$

(c) $x \leq -2$

9. Special case of Prob. 10. See graph.

10. $a = 0.375, b = 0.125, c = 0.5$

15. (b) $f(x) = \begin{cases} 1926x, \ 2 \leq x \leq 10 \\ 1712x, \ 11 \leq x \leq 20 \\ 1498x, \ 21 \leq x \leq 30 \\ 1284x, \ 31 \leq x \end{cases}$

Section 1-10

5. The entire first quadrant   **7.** The corners of the solution space are

$(-\frac{24}{5}, \frac{18}{5})$, $(\frac{6}{7}, \frac{12}{7})$, and $(4, -3)$.

8. The corners of the solution space are $(0, 0)$, $(0, 3)$, $(2, 2)$, and $(4, 0)$.

11. $S \geq 1,000,000$ $CGS \leq 650,000$ $NI > 100,000$ $RR \geq 11\%$

13. $D \leq 20$ $S \geq 10,000$ $V \geq 2$

CHAPTER 2

Section 2-1

1. (a) equal (b) not equal; one is a row, the other is a column (c) not equal; different number of components (d) not equal; first components differ

2. (a) $(3, 7, 9)$ (b) one is a row, the other is a column (c) the numbers of components differ (d) (a, b, c)

5. The point corresponding to the sum is

(a) $(3, 8)$ (b) $(2, -2)$ (c) $(0, 3)$ (d) $(2, 5)$

7. An example is $(7, -2, 3, 1)$ and $\begin{pmatrix} a \\ b \\ c \\ d \\ e \end{pmatrix}$.

9. $(2, 1, 1)$

10. $\begin{pmatrix} 100,000 \\ 150,000 \\ 125,000 \end{pmatrix}$

11. $\begin{pmatrix} 1200 \\ 1000 \\ 800 \end{pmatrix}$

12. $\begin{pmatrix} 30 \\ 15 \\ 25 \\ 30 \end{pmatrix}$

Section 2-2

1. (a) $\begin{pmatrix} 2 \\ 3 \\ 1 \end{pmatrix}$ (b) $(12, 24, 21)$ (c) $\begin{pmatrix} x \\ 4x \\ 2x \end{pmatrix}$ (d) $\begin{pmatrix} 20 \\ 10 \\ 5 \end{pmatrix}$

2. (a) 17 (b) 58 (c) 57 (d) 107

6. $x\begin{pmatrix} 4 \\ 5 \\ 5 \end{pmatrix} + y\begin{pmatrix} 6 \\ 4 \\ 6 \end{pmatrix} + z\begin{pmatrix} 3 \\ 1 \\ 0 \end{pmatrix} = \begin{pmatrix} 2 \\ 1 \\ 4 \end{pmatrix}$

7. $4w + 2x + 3y = 4$
$9w + x + 2y = 9$
$3w + 2x + 4y = 3$

10. $(1, 2, 3, 4, 5)$, $(4, -2, 3, -6, 8)$, $(-1, -4, 3, 6, 10)$

11. *Hint:* Use closure under multiplication of real number system.

12. *Hint:* Use closure under addition of real number system.

13. **3a** (a) $(6, -9)$ (b) $(6, 3, -18)$ (c) $(-3, 6, -9, 12, -9)$
−b (a) $(1, -4)$ (b) $(-1, -3, -4)$ (c) $(-2, -4, -3, -6, -1)$
a + b (a) $(1, 1)$ (b) $(3, 4, -2)$ (c) $(1, 6, 0, 10, -2)$
a − b (a) $(3, -7)$ (b) $(1, -2, -10)$ (c) $(-3, -2, -6, -2, -4)$

14. (a) $\sqrt{58} = 7.616$ (b) $\sqrt{105} = 10.247$ (c) $\sqrt{69} = 8.307$

16. $s = \dfrac{d(x, y)}{\sqrt{n - 1}}$

Section 2-3

1. (a) not equal; $1 \neq 2$ (b) not equal; the sizes are not the same

3. (a) $\begin{pmatrix} 9 & 9 \\ 9 & 6 \end{pmatrix}$ (b) $\begin{pmatrix} 6 & 5 & 11 \\ 5 & 5 & 7 \end{pmatrix}$ (c) $\begin{pmatrix} 16 & 12 & 12 \\ 10 & 10 & 5 \\ 7 & 3 & 5 \end{pmatrix}$

5. $a = 3, b = 5$

8.

	W_1	W_2	W_3	W_4
R_1	5	7	9	16
R_2	10	5	11	10
R_3	8	7	4	8

9. (a) $C = \begin{pmatrix} 5 & 7 & 9 & 16 \\ 10 & 5 & 11 & 10 \\ 8 & 7 & 4 & 8 \end{pmatrix}$

(b) $c_{11} = 5$

(c) c_{21} corresponds to the route from Region 2 to Warehouse 1.
c_{12} corresponds to the route from Region 1 to Warehouse 2.

10. (a) $V = \begin{pmatrix} 20 & 10 \\ 15 & 5 \\ 10 & 3 \\ 5 & 2 \end{pmatrix}$

(b) v_{11} gives the material cost of model 1.
v_{32} gives the variable overhead for model 2.

(c) total variable cost for model 1.

11.

		buy	lease
Demand	low	10,000	12,000
	high	20,000	5,000

12. $P = \begin{pmatrix} 10,000 & 12,000 \\ 20,000 & 5,000 \end{pmatrix}$

13. $x = \frac{1}{5}, y = \frac{3}{5}$

Section 2-4

1. (a) $\begin{pmatrix} 48 & 72 \\ 16 & 8 \end{pmatrix}$ (b) $\begin{pmatrix} 6 & 3 & 12 \\ 15 & 18 & 24 \\ 21 & 9 & 6 \end{pmatrix}$ (c) (1.2, 2.4) (d) $\begin{pmatrix} 12.6 \\ 2.8 \\ 1.4 \end{pmatrix}$

2. (a) $\begin{pmatrix} 20 & 11 \\ 48 & 29 \end{pmatrix}$ (b) $\begin{pmatrix} 31 & 23 \\ 70 & 56 \end{pmatrix}$ (c) 43 (d) $\begin{pmatrix} 56 & 68 & 36 \\ 28 & 22 & 30 \\ 34 & 54 & 22 \end{pmatrix}$

5. (a) $\begin{pmatrix} -4 & -3 \\ 0 & -13 \end{pmatrix}$ (b) $\begin{pmatrix} 60 & 50 \\ 66 & 70 \end{pmatrix}$ (c) not defined

   (d) $\begin{pmatrix} 126 & 68 & 40 \\ 118 & 81 & 49 \\ 85 & 56 & 46 \end{pmatrix}$ (e) $\begin{pmatrix} 7 & 20 & 18 & 13 & 12 \\ 17 & 42 & 38 & 27 & 28 \end{pmatrix}$

Section 2-5

1. $\begin{pmatrix} 1 & -2 & 1 \\ 2 & 1 & -2 \\ 1 & 1 & 3 \end{pmatrix} \begin{pmatrix} x \\ y \\ z \end{pmatrix} = \begin{pmatrix} 9 \\ -1 \\ 2 \end{pmatrix}$

4. $4x_1 + 2x_2 + 6x_3 = 4$
   $9x_1 + x_2 \quad\quad = 9$
   $3x_1 + 2x_2 + 4x_3 = 3$

Section 2-6

3. \$56.75 6. (25, 52); 25 units of A and 52 units of B are required

8. \$206

9. $\begin{array}{c} \\ P_1 \\ P_2 \end{array} \begin{array}{ccc} \text{I} & \text{II} & \text{III} \\ \begin{pmatrix} 4 & 2 & 3 \\ 2 & 0 & 1 \end{pmatrix} \end{array}$

11. $\begin{array}{c} \\ P_1 \\ P_2 \end{array} \begin{array}{cc} 061 & 072 \\ \begin{pmatrix} 22 & 31 \\ 8 & 11 \end{pmatrix} \end{array}$

13. \$822 15. Three hundred units of part a are needed to fill the order.

CHAPTER 3

Section 3-1

1. $\begin{pmatrix} 0 & 0 \\ 0 & 0 \end{pmatrix}, \begin{pmatrix} 1 & 0 \\ 0 & 1 \end{pmatrix}$

2. $AB = \begin{pmatrix} 7 & 7 & 7 \\ 13 & 13 & 13 \\ 16 & 16 & 16 \end{pmatrix} \neq \begin{pmatrix} 4 & 2 & 1 \\ 6 & 3 & 4 \\ 8 & 7 & 1 \end{pmatrix} = A$

5. (a) $\begin{pmatrix} 0 & 0 & 0 & 0 \\ 0 & 0 & 0 & 0 \\ 0 & 0 & 0 & 0 \\ 0 & 0 & 0 & 0 \end{pmatrix}$ (b) $\begin{pmatrix} 0 & 0 \\ 0 & 0 \end{pmatrix}$

8. $\begin{pmatrix} 0 & 0 \\ 0 & 0 \end{pmatrix}$

Section 3-2

1. $(A + B) + C = A + (B + C)$
   $\begin{pmatrix} 14 & 20 \\ 10 & 7 \end{pmatrix} = \begin{pmatrix} 14 & 20 \\ 10 & 7 \end{pmatrix}$

3. $A(B + C) = AB + AC$

$$\begin{pmatrix} 2 & 4 \\ 6 & 3 \end{pmatrix}\begin{pmatrix} 12 & 16 \\ 4 & 4 \end{pmatrix} = \begin{pmatrix} 24 & 18 \\ 54 & 45 \end{pmatrix} + \begin{pmatrix} 16 & 30 \\ 30 & 63 \end{pmatrix}$$

$$\begin{pmatrix} 40 & 48 \\ 84 & 108 \end{pmatrix} = \begin{pmatrix} 40 & 48 \\ 84 & 108 \end{pmatrix}$$

5. $A + B = B + A$

$$\begin{pmatrix} 10 & 11 \\ 8 & 4 \end{pmatrix} = \begin{pmatrix} 10 & 11 \\ 8 & 4 \end{pmatrix}$$

7. $\begin{pmatrix} 15 & 8 & 9 \\ 17 & 8 & 10 \\ 13 & 8 & 8 \end{pmatrix}$

8. $\begin{pmatrix} 13 & 7 & 22 \\ 13 & 6 & 17 \\ 8 & 4 & 12 \end{pmatrix}$

Section 3-3

1. $AB = \begin{pmatrix} 19 & 13 \\ 30 & 22 \end{pmatrix}, BA = \begin{pmatrix} 13 & 42 \\ 8 & 28 \end{pmatrix}$

3. $\begin{pmatrix} 0 & 27 \\ -26 & 24 \end{pmatrix}$

5. $x = 1$

Section 3-4

1. (a) $\begin{pmatrix} -2 & -1 \\ -5 & -6 \end{pmatrix}$ (b) $\begin{pmatrix} -3 & -2 & -8 \\ -4 & -5 & -2 \\ -1 & -7 & -6 \end{pmatrix}$

2. $\begin{pmatrix} -\frac{1}{7} & +\frac{2}{7} \\ +\frac{6}{7} & -\frac{5}{7} \end{pmatrix}$

5. a, c, and d do not have a multiplicative inverse

9. $A^{-1} = \begin{pmatrix} 1/a & 0 & 0 \\ 0 & 1/b & 0 \\ 0 & 0 & 1/c \end{pmatrix}$ **10.** $A^{-1} = \begin{pmatrix} 1/2 & 0 & 0 \\ 0 & 1/3 & 0 \\ 0 & 0 & -1/4 \end{pmatrix}$

Section 3-5

1. (a) $\begin{pmatrix} 2 & 3 \\ 1 & -2 \end{pmatrix}\begin{pmatrix} x \\ y \end{pmatrix} = \begin{pmatrix} 4 \\ -5 \end{pmatrix}$

(b) $\begin{pmatrix} 2 & 3 \\ 1 & -2 \end{pmatrix}\begin{pmatrix} \frac{2}{7} & \frac{3}{7} \\ \frac{1}{7} & -\frac{2}{7} \end{pmatrix} = \begin{pmatrix} 1 & 0 \\ 0 & 1 \end{pmatrix}$

(c) $x = -1, y = 2$

3. (a) $\begin{pmatrix} 1 & 1 \\ 3 & -1 \end{pmatrix}\begin{pmatrix} x \\ y \end{pmatrix} = \begin{pmatrix} 4 \\ 2 \end{pmatrix}$

(b) $\begin{pmatrix} +\frac{1}{4} & +\frac{1}{4} \\ +\frac{3}{4} & -\frac{1}{4} \end{pmatrix}$

(c) $x = 1.5, y = 2.5$

5. (a) $\begin{pmatrix} 3 & 2 & 2 \\ 0 & 1 & 0 \\ 2 & 2 & 2 \end{pmatrix}\begin{pmatrix} x_1 \\ x_2 \\ x_3 \end{pmatrix} = \begin{pmatrix} 4 \\ 5 \\ 6 \end{pmatrix}$

(b) $\begin{pmatrix} 3 & 2 & 2 \\ 0 & 1 & 0 \\ 2 & 2 & 2 \end{pmatrix}\begin{pmatrix} 1 & 0 & -1 \\ 0 & 1 & 0 \\ -1 & -1 & \frac{3}{2} \end{pmatrix} = \begin{pmatrix} 1 & 0 & 0 \\ 0 & 1 & 0 \\ 0 & 0 & 1 \end{pmatrix}$

(c) $x_1 = -2, x_2 = 5, x_3 = 0$

6. $a = 6.2$, $b = 0.9$ **7.** $a = 2.3$, $b = 0.42$ **8.** $a = 10$, $b = -1.5$
11. *Hint:* Use $\mathbf{x} = I\mathbf{x}$.

Section 3-6

1. (a) $\begin{pmatrix} 2 & 0 & \vdots & 1 & 0 \\ 1 & 1 & \vdots & 0 & 1 \end{pmatrix}$ 　　　**(b)** $\begin{pmatrix} 1 & 0 & \vdots & 1 & 0 \\ 2 & 2 & \vdots & 0 & 1 \end{pmatrix}$

3. (a) $\begin{pmatrix} -\frac{1}{7} & \frac{2}{7} \\ \frac{6}{7} & -\frac{5}{7} \end{pmatrix}$ 　　　**(b)** $\begin{pmatrix} -\frac{2}{14} & +\frac{4}{14} \\ \frac{5}{14} & -\frac{3}{14} \end{pmatrix}$

5. (a) $\begin{pmatrix} \frac{2}{7} & \frac{3}{7} \\ \frac{1}{7} & -\frac{2}{7} \end{pmatrix}$ 　　　**(b)** $\begin{pmatrix} 1 & -3 & 7 \\ 0 & 1 & -2 \\ 0 & 0 & 0.5 \end{pmatrix}$

7. $\begin{pmatrix} 0 & \frac{1}{3} & 0 \\ 0.5 & -\frac{2}{3} & 0 \\ -0.5 & -1\frac{1}{3} & 1 \end{pmatrix}$

Section 3-7

4. $x_1 = 3230$, $x_2 = 3711$ **8.** $x_1 = 200$, $x_2 = 100$, $x_3 = 100$
9 $x_1 = 211.88$, $x_2 = 100.78$, $x_3 = 100.75$ **10.** $(I - A)^{-1} = \begin{pmatrix} \frac{3}{2} & \frac{2}{3} \\ \frac{1}{2} & \frac{4}{3} \end{pmatrix}$
11. $x_1 = 850$, $x_2 = 950$ **12.** $x_1 = 895$, $x_2 = 965$

CHAPTER 4

Section 4-1

1. (a) (4) (3), (1) (2) 　　　**(c)** (2) (6) (4), (3) (2) (1),
(b) $c_{11}c_{22}$, $c_{21}c_{22}$ 　　　　　　(4) (5) (7), (1) (6) (4),
　　　　　　　　　　　　　　　　　(7) (2) (2), (4) (5) (3)
　　　　　　　　　　　　　　(d) $x8$, $2y$
3. (a) 2 **(b)** 3 **(c)** 8 or some other even number **(d)** 1
6. odd **8. (a)** one **(b)** three **9.** minus, minus
11. (a) plus **(b)** minus **(c)** minus **(d)** minus
13. (a) 0 **(b)** -100

Section 4-2

1. -9 **3.** -110 **4.** 99 **7.** $x = 3$

Section 4-3

3. 8, -1, -10 **4.** $|A| = 3$ **5.** 25 **7. (a)** -18 **(b)** -9
11. 76 **12.** (a) 4 **(b)** -1

Section 4-4

1. (a) $x = 2.5$, $y = -1.5$ **3.** $x = 1$
5. $a = 2$, $b = -1$, $c = -3$

Section 4-5

1. (a) $A^{-1} = \begin{pmatrix} -\frac{1}{6} & \frac{2}{3} \\ \frac{1}{2} & -1 \end{pmatrix}$ 　　　**(b)** $A^{-1} = \begin{pmatrix} \frac{3}{19} & -\frac{2}{19} \\ -\frac{4}{19} & \frac{9}{19} \end{pmatrix}$

3. (a) $\begin{pmatrix} 6 & 2 & 6 \\ 5 & 3 & 8 \\ 4 & 1 & 9 \end{pmatrix}$ 　　　**(c)** $(2 \; 6 \; 1)$
　　　　　　　　　　(d) $\begin{pmatrix} 2 & 4 & 6 \\ 3 & 5 & 7 \end{pmatrix}$

(b) $\begin{pmatrix} c_{11} & c_{21} & c_{31} \\ c_{12} & c_{22} & c_{32} \end{pmatrix}$

5. **(a)** 8

(c) $\begin{pmatrix} 6 & -2 \\ -8 & 4 \end{pmatrix}$

(b) $\begin{pmatrix} 6 & -8 \\ -2 & 4 \end{pmatrix}$

(d) $B^{-1} = \begin{pmatrix} \frac{3}{4} & -\frac{1}{4} \\ -1 & \frac{1}{2} \end{pmatrix}$

7. **(a)** Determinant = 0 and inverse does not exist.

(b) $\begin{pmatrix} 0 & \frac{1}{3} & 0 \\ \frac{1}{2} & -\frac{2}{3} & 0 \\ -\frac{1}{2} & -\frac{4}{3} & 1 \end{pmatrix}$

13. Revenue = tr AB^t = 21,700   **14.** yes, $B^t = B$, $\therefore$ $AB^t = AB$

Section 4-6

1. $x = 3.5, y = -1.5$

3. $x = 3, y = -1, z = -1$

5. $x = 1, y = 2, z = -1$

7. $x_1 = 2, x_2 = -1, x_3 = -3$

CHAPTER 5

Section 5-1

1. $4x + y \le 36$ $P = 6x + 5y$
$2x + 4y \le 40$ $x \ge 0$
$y \ge 0$

2. $4x + y \le 36$ $P = 6x + 5y$
$2x + 4y \le 40$ $x \ge 0$
$2x + y \le 20$ $y \ge 0$

Section 5-2

1.   **4.**

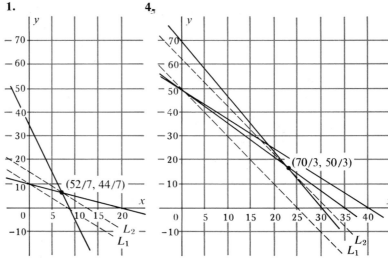

5. Corners: $(0, 0)$, $(0, 10)$, $(9, 0)$, $(\frac{52}{7}, \frac{44}{7})$
$P = 76$ at $(\frac{52}{7}, \frac{44}{7})$ or $P = 72$ at $(7, 6)$

7. Corners: $(0, 1)$, $(0, 8)$, $(7, 1)$
$P = 22$ at $(7, 1)$

Section 5-3

1. $\begin{pmatrix} 1 & 0 & 4 & 1 \\ 0 & 1 & 2 & 4 \end{pmatrix} \begin{pmatrix} w \\ z \\ x \\ y \end{pmatrix} = \begin{pmatrix} 36 \\ 40 \end{pmatrix}$

2. $\begin{pmatrix} 1 & 0 & 0 & 4 & 1 \\ 0 & 1 & 0 & 2 & 4 \\ 0 & 0 & 1 & 2 & 1 \end{pmatrix} \begin{pmatrix} w \\ z \\ t \\ x \\ y \end{pmatrix} = \begin{pmatrix} 36 \\ 40 \\ 20 \end{pmatrix}$

5.

	w	z	x	y	Constant
w	1	0	4	1	36
z	0	1	2	4	40
CTPPU	0	0	6	5	
DIOFPU			0	0	
NET			6	5	

6.

	w	z	t	x	y	Constant
w	1	0	0	4	1	36
z	0	1	0	2	4	40
t	0	0	1	2	1	20
CTPPU	0	0	0	6	5	
DIOFPU				0	0	
NET				6	5	

Section 5-4

1. TABLE 1

	w	z	x	y	Constant
w	1	0	4	1	36
z	0	1	2	4	40
CTPPU	0	0	6	5	
DIOFPU			0	0	
NET			6	5	

Table 2

	x	z	w	y	Constant
x	1	0	0.25	0.25	9
z	0	1	−0.5	3.5	22
CTPPU	6	0	0.0	5.0	
DIOFPU			1.5	1.5	
NET			−1.5	3.5	

Table 3

	x	y	w	z	Constant
x	1	0	$\frac{4}{14}$	$-\frac{1}{14}$	$52\frac{2}{7}$
y	0	1	$-\frac{2}{14}$	$\frac{4}{14}$	$44\frac{2}{7}$
CTPPU	6	5	0	0	
DIOFPU			1	1	
NET			−1	−1	

3. $A^{-1} = \dfrac{1}{|A|} B^t = \dfrac{1}{12} \begin{pmatrix} 5 & -3 \\ -1 & 3 \end{pmatrix} = \begin{pmatrix} \frac{5}{12} & -\frac{3}{12} \\ -\frac{1}{12} & \frac{3}{12} \end{pmatrix}$

5. $(4.00, 4.50) \begin{pmatrix} \frac{5}{12} \\ -\frac{1}{2} \end{pmatrix} = 1.2917$

$(4.00, 4.50) \begin{pmatrix} -\frac{3}{12} \\ \frac{3}{14} \end{pmatrix} = 0.125$

$0 - 1.2917 = -1.2917$

$0 - 0.125 = -0.125$

Section 5-5

1. $\begin{pmatrix} 3 & 3 & 1 & 0 & 0 \\ 1 & 5 & 0 & 1 & 0 \\ 4 & 4 & 0 & 0 & 1 \end{pmatrix} \begin{pmatrix} x \\ y \\ w \\ z \\ t \end{pmatrix} = \begin{pmatrix} 2400 \\ 1600 \\ 1600 \end{pmatrix}$

3. The NET row of Table 2 indicated that we could gain $3.10 for each x brought into the solution where each z brought into the solution would result in a loss of $0.90.

6. $(0, 4.50, 0) \begin{pmatrix} 2.4 \\ 0.2 \\ 3.2 \end{pmatrix} = 0.90$

$(0, 4.50, 0) \begin{pmatrix} -0.6 \\ 0.2 \\ -0.8 \end{pmatrix} = 0.90$

$4.00 - 0.90 = 3.10$

$0 - 0.90 = -0.90$

7. TABLE 1

	w	z	t	x	y	Constant
w	1	0	0	4	1	36
z	0	1	0	2	4	40
t	0	0	1	2	1	20
CTPPU				6	5	
DIOFPU				0	0	
NET				6	5	

TABLE 2

	x	z	t	w	y	Constant
x	1	0	0	$\frac{1}{4}$	$\frac{1}{4}$	9
z	0	1	0	$-\frac{1}{2}$	$\frac{7}{2}$	22
t	0	0	1	$-\frac{1}{2}$	$\frac{1}{2}$	2
CTPPU	6	0	0	0	5	
DIOFPU				$\frac{6}{4}$	$\frac{6}{4}$	
NET				$-\frac{1}{4}$	$\frac{7}{2}$	

TABLE 3

	x	z	y	w	t	Constant
x	1	0	0	$\frac{1}{2}$	$-\frac{1}{2}$	8
z	0	1	0	3	-7	8
y	0	0	1	-1	2	4
CTPPU	6	0	5	0	0	
DIOFPU				-2	7	
NET				$+2$	-7	

TABLE 4

	x	w	y	z	t	Constant
x	1	0	0	$-\frac{1}{6}$	$\frac{2}{3}$	$6\frac{2}{3}$
w	0	1	0	$\frac{1}{3}$	$-\frac{7}{3}$	$2\frac{2}{3}$
y	0	0	1	$\frac{1}{3}$	$-\frac{1}{3}$	$6\frac{2}{3}$
CTPPU	6	0	5	0	0	
DIOFPU				$\frac{2}{3}$	$2\frac{1}{3}$	
NET				$-\frac{2}{3}$	$-2\frac{1}{3}$	

9. Using x and y as your variables and w and z as slack variables the solution is $x = 12$, $y = 4$.

FINAL TABLE

	x	y	w	z	Constant
x	1	0	0.2	−0.25	12
y	0	1	−0.1	0.25	4
CTPPU	3	4	0	0	
DIOFPU			0.2	0.25	
NET			−0.2	−0.25	

10. One unit of x contributes $6 to profit rather than $3 (Problem 9); hence we should expect more x in the solution. Using x and y for your variables and w and z as slack variables, the solution is $x = 16$ and $z = 16$.

CHAPTER 6

Section 6-1

1. (a) $x^{1/2}$ (d) $x^2 y^2$
    (b) $x^{1/3}$ (e) $x^{3/2}$
    (c) $x^{3/2}$ (f) $(x + y)^{1/3}$
3. (a) 27   (c) $\frac{1}{8}$
    (b) x^3 (d) $\frac{1}{9}$
5. (a) $a(b + c)^2$ (c) $\frac{5}{7}$
    (b) $\frac{3}{4}$ (d) $\sqrt{\frac{13}{3}}$
7. (a) $x = 2$ (d) $x = -1$
    (b) $x = 0$ (e) $x = -2$
    (c) $x = 3$ (f) $x = 4$

Section 6-2

1. $2, 4, 3, 0, -1, -3, -2$
3. $2, -3, 5, \frac{1}{3}, \frac{1}{2}, \frac{1}{3}, \frac{1}{3}, \frac{2}{3}$
8. $\log_b x = 6$
9. (a) 3   (c) -1
    (b) 0   (d) $2 + \log_b (ab + 1)$
12. Common value is 2.   **13.** $\log_{10} (\frac{5}{3})$
14. (a) $\log_3 5$ (b) $\log_9 81 = 2$ **15.** $\log V_n = \log P + N \log (1 + i)$

Section 6-3

1. (a) 1 and 2   (e) 3 and 4
    (b) 1 and 2   (f) 3 and 4
    (c) 2 and 3   (g) -1 and 0
    (d) 2 and 3   (h) -3 and -2
3. (a) 4.82×10^2 (e) 3.52×10^6
    (b) 5.372×10^3 (f) 4.8×10^3
    (c) 4.3×10^{-2} (g) 5.73×10^5
    (d) 8.7×10^{-1} (h) 4.3×10^{-4}

5. (a) 3   (e) -2
     (b) 3   (f) -1
     (c) 1   (g) 5
     (d) 2   (h) -3
7. (a) 4.68320   (d) 3.92246
     (b) $0.92000 - 2$ (e) $0.09160 - 1$
     (c) 1.37495   (f) 5.86607
8. $b = 1.47403$

Section 6-4

1. (a) 10,000   (d) 468
     (b) 0.01   (e) 0.005133
     (c) 1   (f) 4.572
3. (a) 4   (c) 7.1138
     (b) 7.5595   (d) 0.3979
5. (a) 21.019   (c) 0.00066665
     (b) 0.047575   (d) 8.3094
7. (a) 3581.6   (b) 1.4693   (c) 2191.1   **9.** 2
10. (a) 2   (b) 125   (c) b (d) b^a

Section 6-5

1. (a)

x	y
1	0
2	1
4	2
8	3

(c)

x	y
1	0
2	1.386
e	2
4	2.772

(b)

x	y
1	0
4	1
8	1.5
16	2

(d)

x	y
1	0
$\sqrt{10}$	1
4	1.20412
10	2

4. $y = 2 \log x + 2$
6. $y = \log x + 5$
8. (a) Common value is 0.81291.   (b) Common value is 0.99123.

Section 6-6

1. (a)

x	y
-2	$\frac{1}{9}$
-1	$\frac{1}{3}$
0	1
1	3
2	9

(c)

x	y
-2	$\frac{3}{16}$
-1	$\frac{3}{4}$
0	3
1	12
2	48

(b)

x	y
-2	0.27
-1	0.736
0	2
1	5.44
2	14.78

(d)

x	y
-2	8
-1	4
0	2
1	1
2	$\frac{1}{2}$

403

3. $y = 3(2^x)$

5. (a)

x	y
−2	−8
−1	−1
0	0
1	1
2	8

(c)

x	y
0	0
1	½
4	16
9	121.5

(b)

x	y
0	0
1	3
2	4.24
4	6
9	9

(d)

x	y
−8	−4
−1	−2
0	0
1	2
8	4

7. $y = x$

8. (a) \$35,246,000 **(b)** \$49,520,000

9. (a)

x	1	2	3	4	5
y	1.100	1.2100	1.3310	1.4641	1.6105

(b) $y = 1,000,000(1.10)^x$

Section 6-7

1. x axis in log scale

(a)

x	y
1	2
2	2.602
5	3.397
10	4

(c)

x	y
1	0.301
5	1
10	1.301
50	2

(b)

x	y
1	2
2	2.903
5	4.094
10	5

(d)

x	y
1	3.301
5	4
10	4.301
50	5

3. $y = \log x + 5$ **5.** $y = 3(2^x)$

8. $y = x$ **9.** $y = 1(2^x)$

12. (a) exponential **(b)** $y = ab^x$ **(c)** semilog where y axis is logarithmic

13, 14. Data will plot as a straight line with $a = 1,000,000$ and $b = 1.10$.

15. exponential

16. $a = 160$, $\log b = (\log 180 - \log 160)/3 = 0.01705$, $b = 1.04$

CHAPTER 7

Section 7-1

1. (a) 6, 4, 3.333 . . . , 3, 2.8 **(b)** 1, 4, 9, 16, 25

(c) 1, 1.414 . . . , 1.732 . . . , 2, 2.236 . . .

(d) 0, 0.301, 0.477, 0.602, 0.699 **(e)** 0, 0.693, 1.099, 1.386, 1.609

(**f**)   2, 4, 8, 16, 32   (**g**) 2.718, 7.389, 20.086, 54.598, 148.413
(**h**)   0.368, 0.135, 0.050, 0.018, 0.007

4.   1, 2, 6, 24, 120   **5.** 1,1, 2, 6, 24   **6.**   2, 5, 8, 11, 14

7. $a, a + d, a + 2d, a + 3d, a + 4d$

8.   (**a**)   2, 7, 15, 26, 40   (**b**) $a, 2a + d, 3a + 3d, 4a + 6d, 5a + 10d$

11.   2, 6, 18, 54, 162 $a_5 = 2(3)^4 = 2(81) = 162$

15. $1, \dfrac{1}{1.06}, \dfrac{1}{1.06^2}$, i.e., 1, 0.943, 0.890

Section 7-2

1.   (**a**)   3   (**b**) $a_4 = 13, a_{10} = 31, a_{20} = 61$ (**c**) 650   **3.**   5050

4.   (**a**) $r = 3$ (**b**) $a_2 = 6, a_4 = 54, a_6 = 486$ (**c**) 728

5. $r = 2$ **6.**   255   **9.** $\frac{1}{2}(x_1 + x_n)$ **10.**   2

11.   (**a**)   1, 1.08, 1.1664, 1.2597   (**b**) $100, 100(1 + i), 100(1 + i)^2, 100(1 + i)^3$

12.   1, 0.9259, 0.8573, 0.7938   **13.**   4374.61

Section 7-3

1.   \$3650.10   **4.**   (**a**)   200   (**b**) 1.04   (**c**) 0.04

5.   \$5126.60   **9.**   \$1.0824

Section 7-4

1.   \$79.38   **4.**   (**a**)   1.0000   (**b**) 1.06   (**c**) 0.06   **5.**   \$7903

Section 7-5

2.   \$27,931.20   **3.**   \$758.68   **5.**   \$13,621.80

6.   \$2774.08   **7.**   \$34,211

CHAPTER 8

Section 8-2

1.   (**a**)   0   (**b**) -2 (**c**) -4 (**d**) -6

2. $y = -4x + 4$

6. $(n = 1)\ 3, (n = 2)\ \frac{5}{2}, (n = 3)\ \frac{7}{3}, (n = 4)\ \frac{9}{4}$

7. $2 + 1/n$

9. $R_f(A) = 2$

Section 8-3

1.   8.41, 8.9401, 8.994001

3. $x - 3$: 0.1, 0.01, 0.001 $f(x) - 9$: 0.61, 0.0601, 0.006001

5.

x	$f(x)$	$x - 1$	$f(x) - 3$
1.1	3.41	0.1	0.41
1.01	3.0401	0.01	0.0401
1.001	3.004001	0.001	0.004001

6.   The quantity $(x^2 + 2x) - 3$ gets closer and closer to zero as $x - 1$ gets close to zero.

10.   24   **11.**   3   **12.** $3a^2$

Section 8-4

1. $x_1 = 2, y_1 = 19$

x_2	Δx	y_2	Δy	$\Delta y/\Delta x$
3	1	32	13	13
2.4	0.4	23.72	4.72	11.8
2.02	0.02	19.2208	0.2208	11.04
2.001	0.001	19.011002	0.011002	11.002

3. $\Delta y/\Delta x$ simplifies to $2\Delta x + 11, f'(2) = 11$.
5. $g'(3) = 29$
7. (a) $h'(4) = 11$ (b) $h'(a) = 2a + 3$
9. The table in Problem 8 indicates 0.2485. (The true value is 0.25.)

Section 8-5

1. (a) 6 (b) 5 (c) 4.5 (d) 4.1
2. 4
5. (b) 6, 6, 6 (c) The slopes are all equal. (d) Whenever the given function is linear.
7. $R_f(A, B) = 5$; average rate of change between A and B equals slope of secant line between A and B.
8. $R_f(A) = 4$; the point rate of change at A equals the slope of the tangent line at A
9. (a) 20% (b) 10% (c) 2 (d) yes (e) yes, in choice of denominators

Section 8-6

1. (b) $2a + 3$ (c) 11
3. $y = 5x + 3$
5. (a) $2u$ (b) 1 (c) $2u + 2$ (d) $-2u$
7. $g'(u)$ and $\dfrac{dw}{du}$
9. $e_a = \dfrac{P}{x} f'(P)$ 10. Apply definition of derivative.   11. 2

Section 8-7

1. $y' = 6u - 2$
3. $y = f(u) + g(u)$ and $y' = f'(u) + g'(u)$, Theorem 7.2B
7. $\dfrac{dw}{dz} = kz^{k-1}$
9. (a) $24u^3$ (b) 5 (c) $8u - 8$ (d) $4u + 2 + \dfrac{1}{4u^{3/4}}$
10. (a) $8u^3$ (b) $3.51u^{1.7}$ (c) $1.12u^{-2.4}$

Section 8-8

1. (a) $\dfrac{1}{u} \log_3 (e)$ (b) $\dfrac{1}{u} \log_5 (e)$ (c) $2^u \ln 2$ (d) $10^u \ln 10$
4. (a) 2.25 (b) 2.5936 (c) 2.704 (d) 2.718 (based on 10-place table)
7. (a) $y' = 2^x \ln 2 + \dfrac{1}{x} \log_2 (e)$

(b) $y' = 3x^2 + 3^x \ln 3$ (c) $y' = -3x^{-4} + \dfrac{1}{x}$

(d) $y' = -5x^{-7/2} - 3/2x^{1/2} + 4^x \ln 4$
11. (a) $5.83(1.06)^u$ (b) $3.85(1 + 0.08)^u$ (c) $a \ln (1 + r)(1 + r)^u$

Section 8-9

1. $y = 12x - 18$
3. $y = x - 1$
5. $MC = 3x^2$, $MC = 48$ when $x = 4$
9. (1) $P = a - bx$ (2) $P = \dfrac{a}{x+b} - c$ (3) $P = a - bx^2$
10. Graph $P = 10 - x$ (1).

x	2	4	6	8	10
(1) P	8	6	4	2	0

11. (1) $R = ax - bx^2$ (2) $R = \dfrac{ax}{x+b} - cx$ (3) $R = ax - bx^3$
12. (1) $a - 2bx$ (2) $\dfrac{ab}{(x+b)^2} - c$
13. $c = x^3 - 3x^2 + 3x + 1$ (cubic cost function)
    $MC = 3x^2 - 6x + 3$ (quadratic marginal cost function)
14. (1) a (2) $2ax + b$ (3) $3ax^2 - 2bx + c$ 15. $\dfrac{bx - a}{bx}$

CHAPTER 9

Section 9-1

1. (a) 0.331 (b) 0.030301 (c) 0.003003001 (d) 0.000300030001
3. Yes, because $y = x^3$ is a nonlinear function
5. (a) e^x (b) e^{x^2} (c) $e^{x^2} + 4$ (d) e^{-x^2}

Section 9-2

1. (a) $12x^{11}$ (b) $30x^{29}$ (c) $3x^2$ (d) $3x^2$
3. (a) $2e^{2x}$ (b) $5e^{5x}$ (c) $4(2^{4x}) \ln 2$ (d) $5(3)^{5x} \ln 3$
5. (a) $2xe^{x^2}$ (b) $-2xe^{-x^2}$ (c) $3x^2(3)^{x^3} \ln 3$ (d) $\dfrac{2^{\sqrt{x}} \ln 2}{2\sqrt{x}}$
7. (a) $(2x + 3)e^{x^2+3x}$ (c) $9x^2(x^3 + 2)^2$
   (b) $\dfrac{2x + 4}{x^2 + 4x + 7}$ (d) $3e^{3x} + \dfrac{x}{\sqrt{x^2 + 4}}$
9. (a) $\Delta x = 2$ (b) $\Delta u = 6.38906$ (c) $\Delta y = 53.59815$

Section 9-3

2. (a) $18x^2$ (b) $\dfrac{3}{x} \log e$ (c) $\dfrac{5}{x}$ (d) $6(2)^x \ln 2$ (e) $5e^x$ (f) $10(3)^x \ln 3$
3. (a) $2h(x)^{h-1}$ (b) $ch(x)^{h-1}$ (c) he^x (d) $c(a)^x \ln a$
5. (a) $18x^2$ (b) $x^2e^x(x + 3)$ (c) $60x$ (d) $1 + \ln x$
   (e) $x \log e + 2x \log x$ (f) $5^x x^4(x \ln 5 + 5)$
7. (a) $\dfrac{3x + 3}{2}$ (b) $\frac{1}{2}$ (c) $\frac{1}{4}e^x$ (d) $\dfrac{1 - \ln x}{3x^2}$
   (e) $\dfrac{\log e - 2 \log x}{x^3}$ (f) $\dfrac{5^x(x \ln 5 - 3)}{6x^4}$

Section 9-4

1. $2x + 6$
3. $3x^2$
5. $2xe^{x^2} + 4$
7. $3/x$
9. $\dfrac{2(6)^{\sqrt{2x^2+5}} \ln 6}{\sqrt{2x^2 + 5}}$

11. $24x^3 + 72x$ 12. $\dfrac{3e^{3x^2}(2x^2 - 1)}{5x^4}$ 13. $1/(1 + 2x)^2$

14. $\dfrac{x(x + 3)}{\sqrt{x^2 + 4}} + \sqrt{x^2 + 4}$ 15. $\dfrac{-5}{2(x - 3)^2}\left(\dfrac{x + 2}{x - 3}\right)^{-1/2}$

16. $an(ax + b)^{n-1}$ 17. $2ax + b$ 18. $\dfrac{3e^{3x} + 3e^{-3x}}{2}$

19. $2f(x)f'(x)$ 20. $f(x)e^{g(x)}g'(x) + e^{g(x)}f'(x)$

Section 9-5

1. $y = -x + 2$
3. $MC = 0.122$ at $x = 60$ and $MC = 0.244$ at $x = 80$
5. $MC = e^x + \dfrac{1}{x}$
7. $x = 2.5$
9. $P = 0.21$ at $x = 2.3$, $P = 0.25$ at $x = 2.5$ and $P = 0.24$ at $x = 2.6$
11. $R = ax - bx^2$ and $MR = a - 2bx$

Section 9-6

1. (a) 1.44 (b) 1.4
3. 0.2
5. $dw = g'(z)\,dz$, $\Delta w = g(z + \Delta z) - g(z)$, $dz = \Delta z$ and $\Delta z = z_2 - z_1$

6. (a) $dy = (2x + 3)\,dx$ (b) $dy = \dfrac{dx}{2\sqrt{x}}$ (c) $dy = 3e^{3x}\,dx$

   (d) $dy = \dfrac{dx}{x}$ (e) $dy = -\dfrac{1}{2}x^{-3/2}\,dx$ (f) $dy = 2xe^{x^2}\,dx$

CHAPTER 10

Section 10-1

1. (a) $x = \frac{3}{2}$ (b) $x = -\frac{3}{2}$ (c) $x = 0, -\frac{4}{3}$ (d) $x = \sqrt{2}, -\sqrt{2}$

   (e) $x = 2, -3$ (f) $x = \dfrac{-4 + \sqrt{52}}{6}, \dfrac{-4 - \sqrt{52}}{6}$

3. (b) $f'(-3) = -2, f'(-1) = 2$ (c) minimum

5. (a) minimum at $(-\frac{3}{2}, \frac{7}{4})$ (b) maximum at $x = \dfrac{-2 - 2\sqrt{28}}{3}$,

   minimum at $x = \dfrac{-2 + 2\sqrt{28}}{3}$ (c) minimum at $(0, 1)$

7. (a) yes (c) no; $f'(x)$ fails to be continuous at $x = 1$. $f(x)$ is not differentiable at $x = 1$. (d) maximum at $(1, 1)$, minimum at $(2, -2)$

Section 10-2

1. **(a)** $y'' = 2$ **(b)** $y'' = -\frac{1}{4}x^{-3/2} + \frac{5}{16}x^{-9/4}$ **(c)** $z'' = 6x$
   (d) $y'' = (-3 - 4\log e)/x^2$
3. y'' is negative at $x = -2, -1$; y'' is positive at $x = 0, 2$
6. minimum at $x = \sqrt[3]{0.25}$
7. **(a)** inflection point at $(0, 0)$ **(b)** inflection point at $(0, 0)$
   (c) inflection point at $(-1, 2)$ **(d)** no inflection point

Section 10-3

3. **(a)** maximum at $x = -\frac{2}{3} - \frac{4}{3}\sqrt{7}$
      minimum at $x = -\frac{2}{3} + \frac{4}{3}\sqrt{7}$
   (b) minimum at $(0, 1)$
5. minimum at $(e^{-1}, -e^{-1})$
7. maximum at $(3, 0)$, minimum at $(\frac{11}{3}, -\frac{4}{27})$

Section 10-4

1. maximum at $(0, 0)$
3. maximum at $x = 2 - (\frac{1}{3})\sqrt{30}$, minimum at $x = 2 + (\frac{1}{3})\sqrt{30}$, inflection point at $x = 2$
5. maximum at $x = -3$, minimum at $x = 2$, inflection point at $x = -\frac{1}{2}$

Section 10-5

1. $q = \frac{110}{32}$
3. maximum profit at $x = 50$, maximum loss at $x = \sqrt{10}$
4. $C = x/2 + 5000/x$
5. minimum cost $= 100$ at $x = 100$

CHAPTER 11

Section 11-1

1. **(a)** 2.04 **(b)** 2.64 **(c)** 2.33
3. 1.716
4. 0.6911
7. $\int_a^b f(x)\,dx = \lim_{n\to\infty} S_n$

Section 11-2

3. 1.04 and 1.64
5. 4.319 based on $t_1 = 1.2$, $t_2 = 1.8$, $t_3 = 2.2$, and $t_4 = 2.8$
8. $\frac{5}{16}$

Section 11-3

1. $x_0 = 4$, $x_1 = 4.5$, ..., $x_{12} = 10$
   $t_1 = 4\frac{1}{4}$, $t_2 = 4\frac{3}{4}$, ..., $t_{12} = 9\frac{3}{4}$
3. 6.99
5. 84

Section 11-4

1. **(a)** $x^3/3$ **(b)** $6\ln x$ **(c)** $e^{4x}/4$ **(d)** $5^x/\ln 5$
3. **(a)** $22\frac{2}{3}$ **(b)** -32 **(c)** 0.693 **(d)** 6.2 **(e)** 15 **(f)** 2
4. **(a)** 3.195 **(b)** $1/\ln 2$ **(c)** 5.79 **(d)** $8/\ln 3$
7. **(a)** 0 **(b)** -10.5

Section 11-5

1. 2.64

2. $\frac{8}{3}$

5. 18

7. $S_2 = 45.64$, $S_4 = 51.43$, the exact value is 53.6

9. $-\frac{1}{4}$

Section 11-6

1. 1, 0.607, and 0.135

3. 0.3989, 0.24213, and 0.05385

5. 0.39892

7. 0.1915

9. $\dfrac{0.2881}{0.3989}$

Section 11-7

1. (a) $\dfrac{x^4}{4} + x^2 + 4x + C$ (b) $\dfrac{e^{4x}}{4} + C$ (c) $\ln|x + 4| + C$

(d) $\ln|x - 3| - \dfrac{3}{x - 3} + C$

3. (a) 0 (b) 1.099 (c) 1.3 (d) 0.693

5. $p = 2 - 3x$

6. $p = \dfrac{ax}{2} + b$

CHAPTER 12

Section 12-1

2. Only the sets in (a) are equal.

3. (a) yes (b) yes (c) no (d) yes (e) yes (f) no

5. a, b, d, g, h are true.

Section 12-2

1. (a) $A \cap B = \{2, 4\}$ (b) $A \cup B = \{1, 2, 3, 4, 7, 9\}$

3. (a)   (b)

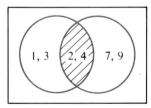 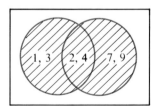

5. (a) A (b) B

7. (a) $\{3, 4, 6, 7, 8, 9, 10\}$ (c) $\{3, 9\}$

(b) $\{1, 2, 4, 6, 7, 8, 10\}$ (d) $\{1, 2, 4, 5, 6, 7, 8, 10\}$

Section 12-3

1. $\{HH, TT, HT, TH\}$ **3.** $\{A, B, C, D, F\}$

Section 12-4

1. $x_1 = \frac{1}{6}, x_2 = \frac{1}{6}, \ldots, x_6 = \frac{1}{6}$

6. (a) $\sum\limits_{i=1}^{3} x_i^2 f(x_i)$ **(b)** $\left(\sum\limits_{i=1}^{3} x_i f(x_i) \right)^2$

Section 12-5

2. *A* and *B*, *A* and *D*

3. (a) $\frac{1}{13}$ **(b)** $\frac{1}{13}$ **(c)** $\frac{3}{13}$

4. (a) 0 **(b)** $\frac{2}{13}$

Section 12-6

1.

$16	$61	$ 83	$125	$163
22	67	90	135	176
35	74	104	146	186
48	79	115	159	191

2–3.

Event	Balance	$f(E_i)$	$P(E_i)$
E_1	0– 49	4	0.20
E_2	50– 99	6	0.30
E_3	100–149	5	0.25
E_4	150–199	5	0.25
		20	1.00

Section 12-7

1. (a) 720 **(b)** 10 **(c)** 5040 **(d)** 21

3. (a) 10 **(b)** 1 **(c)** 4 **(d)** 16

5. 120

CHAPTER 13

Section 13-1

1. (a) $P(E_1) = 0.15$, $P(E_2) = 0.20$, $P(E_3) = 0.30$, $P(E_4) = 0.20$, $P(E_5) = 0.15$

(b) 0.20 **(c)** 0.35

(d) The probability that an employee chosen at random earns between $1.50 and $3.49 an hour.

4. (a)

Type of work Sex	Males	Females	
Production	6000	1000	7000
Sales	2000	1500	3500
	8000	2500	10,500

(b) 8000 **(c)** 2500 **(d)** 8500

5. (a)

	A_1	A_2	A_3	A_4	Total
B_1	30	40	60	70	200
B_2	270	210	190	130	800
Total	300	250	250	200	1000

(b) 300 **(c)** 800 **(d)** 1000 **(e)** 0.3 **(f)** 0.8

Section 13-2

1.

	D_1	D_2	D_3	D_4	D_5	Total
E_1	$9/52$	$1/52$	$1/52$	$1/52$	$1/52$	$13/52$
E_2	$9/52$	$1/52$	$1/52$	$1/52$	$1/52$	$13/52$
E_3	$9/52$	$1/52$	$1/52$	$1/52$	$1/52$	$13/52$
E_4	$9/52$	$1/52$	$1/52$	$1/52$	$1/52$	$13/52$
Total	$9/13$	$1/13$	$1/13$	$1/13$	$1/13$	1

3. (a)

	1	2	3	4	5	6	Total
H	$1/12$	$1/12$	$1/12$	$1/12$	$1/12$	$1/12$	$6/12$
T	$1/12$	$1/12$	$1/12$	$1/12$	$1/12$	$1/12$	$6/12$
Total	$1/6$	$1/6$	$1/6$	$1/6$	$1/6$	$1/6$	1

(b) $\frac{1}{12}$ **(c)** $\frac{1}{12}$ **(d)** $\frac{7}{12}$

5. (a) 0.5 **(b)** 0.4 **(c)** 0.06 **(d)** 0.93

7-8. (a) $P(B_1) = 0.1$ **(c)** $P(B_3 \cup A_1) = 0.75$

    (b) $P(A_1) = 0.5$ **(d)** $P(B_2 \cap A_1) = 0.1$

Section 13-3

1. (a) $\frac{1}{52}$ **(b)** $\frac{2}{13}$ **(c)** $\frac{1}{4}$ **(d)** $\frac{1}{4}$ **(e)** $\frac{1}{13}$

3. (a) joint **(c)** marginal **(d)** conditional **(e)** conditional

5.

	A_1	A_2	
B_1	0.28	0.22	0.5
B_2	0.42	0.08	0.5
	0.7	0.3	1

7. (a) 0.80 **(b)** 0.25 **(c)** 0.13 **(d)** 0.20 **(e)** 0.90 **(f)** 0.87

10. (a) 0.7 **(b)** 0.8 **(c)** 0.5 **(d)** 1 **(e)** 1/3

11. (a) 0.12 **(b)** 0.32 **(c)** 0.68 **(d)** 0.6 **(e)** 3/8

Section 13-4

1. y_1, x_1 and y_2, x_1 are independent events.

7.

	A_1	A_2	
B_1	0.12	0.18	0.30
B_2	0.28	0.42	0.70
	0.40	0.60	1

	A_1	A_2
B_1	0.3	0.3
B_2	0.7	0.7
	1	1

8. The variables A and B are not independent.
9. (a) $0.7^5 = 0.16807$ (b) $0.3^5 = 0.00243$ (c) $10(0.7)^2(0.3)^3 = 0.1323$
(d) $10(0.7)^3(0.3)^2 = 0.3087$ (e) 0.96922 (f) 0.83692
10. (a) 0.0156 (b) 0.3125 (c) 0.0156 (d) 0.65625
11. Note that the probability of x successes is equal to the number of possible ways x successes can occur multiplied by the probability of x successes.
12. See answers for Probs. 9 and 10.

Section 13-5

1. $P(B_1/A_1) = \frac{2}{3}$ $\quad P(B_2/A_1) = \frac{1}{3}$
$P(B_1/A_2) = \frac{3}{4}$ $\quad P(B_2/A_2) = \frac{1}{4}$
$P(B_1/A_3) = \frac{1}{3}$ $\quad P(B_2/A_3) = \frac{2}{3}$

3.

	x_1	x_2	
y_1	0.06	0.48	0.54
y_2	0.14	0.32	0.46
	0.20	0.80	1

	x_1	x_2
y_1	0.3	0.6
y_2	0.7	0.4
	1	1

7. $P(C/U) = 1/3$

Section 13-6

1. (a) and (d) are probability vectors.
3. (a) is a transition matrix.
5. $(0.592, 0.272, 0.136)$
7. $(0.38, 0.24, 0.38)$

Section 13-7

2. $\begin{pmatrix} 0.0003 & 0.4652 \\ -0.0003 & 0.5348 \end{pmatrix}$

5. EV (Act 1) $= \$14,000$ $\quad EV$ (Act 2) $= \$11,000$

6. (a)

	Demand low	Demand high
Option 1	61,446	122,892
Option 2	75,816	97,770

(b) $\begin{pmatrix} \text{Option 1} \\ \text{Option 2} \end{pmatrix} \begin{pmatrix} 11,446 & 72,892 \\ 25,816 & 47,770 \end{pmatrix} \begin{pmatrix} 0.5 \\ 0.5 \end{pmatrix} = \begin{pmatrix} 42,169 \\ 36,793 \end{pmatrix}$

Index